A New Atlas of the Kent Flora

Eric G. Philp

Published by the Kent Field Club

Published by the Kent Field Club, the natural history society of Kent.

The aims of the Kent Field Club are to promote an increased interest in natural history, to study and record the distribution and ecology of fauna and flora, and to promote nature conservation in association with the relevant organisations within the County of Kent.

First published 2010

Kent Field Club wishes to acknowledge the valuable assistance given by the Kent and Medway Biological Records Centre in the production of this book.

ISBN 978-0-9561926-2-2

Contents

Introduction

The first comprehensive flora of the county of Kent was the Flora of Kent by F.J. Hanbury and E.S. Marshall, published in 1899. The next publication covering the county was the Atlas of the Kent Flora by E.G. Philp in 1982. After that publication the author vowed never to become involved in another Flora. However, from the day that it was published, additional records were being made, either of plants that had been missed during the mapping, or of new plants extending their range. When the Atlas eventually sold out there was some pressure to publish a supplement, so a study was made of what would be involved.

The first thing that was done was to have a critical look at the procedures and records in the 1982 Atlas. For that Atlas, records were taken from volunteer recorders, mainly members of the Kent Field Club and the Botanical Society of the British Isles, many of whom were almost press-ganged into taking part. These volunteers ranged from really expert botanists down to people who had never identified a plant before. The recommended identification guide was that of Clapham, Tutin and Warburg (1962), but some of the older recorders were still using Bentham and Hooker (1924). With this mixture of botanical experience and skills there was some uneven coverage of the county, and although a check was made on all records that were submitted, it was inevitable that some errors of identification slipped through. However, the end result was very satisfactory, and for the first time since 1899 a very reasonable assessment of the distribution of the wild flowers of the county was available.

During the mapping for the 1982 Atlas there were no such aids as Global Positioning Systems (GPS) and on careful checking it soon became obvious that some of the rarer plants growing near the border of a tetrad had been recorded either in the wrong tetrad or in two tetrads by different recorders. It also became evident that some recorders had identification problems with some of the critical groups or were not prepared to tackle other groups such as grasses or true aquatic plants. Other recorders had included plants seen before the start date of the mapping whilst yet others had problems with the correct lettering of the tetrads. There also appear to be a few further examples of human error with that first Kent Atlas, but none of material significance in relation to the overall recorded distributions. So the author thought that it would be best to start from scratch and to map all the Kent flora again on a tetrads basis, but this time to see all the plants on the ground for himself, as this would eliminate any map reference or identification problems, and should result in an even coverage of the county. This he started in 1991, but just as a personal exercise and with no ambition to publish the end result.

Elmley Marshes © S. Poyser

The County

Kent is the county in the south-east corner of England. (See Map 1) It is bounded by the counties of Surrey and Sussex, the English Channel, the Thames with Essex on its north bank, and the Greater London Area. That part of former Kent which is now within the Greater London boundary has been excluded from this study as it has been adequately recorded in the Flora of the London Area by R.M. Burton (1983) and subsequent recording by the London Natural History Society. Although Medway Council is now an independent unitary authority its area is here still considered as part of Kent.

The recording units are based on the national grid as found on the Ordnance Survey maps. The county is first divided into 10 km squares. There are 58 of these, either wholly or partly falling within the county. Each 10 km square is then divided into 25 squares, called tetrads, each being 2 km square. (See Map 2)

These tetrads are then lettered vertically from A through to Z, (but not using the O), starting in the bottom left-hand corner and finishing in the top right-hand corner. There are 1043 whole or part tetrads covering the county.

Map 1: Location of Kent

Chalk grassland at Wye © A. Gay

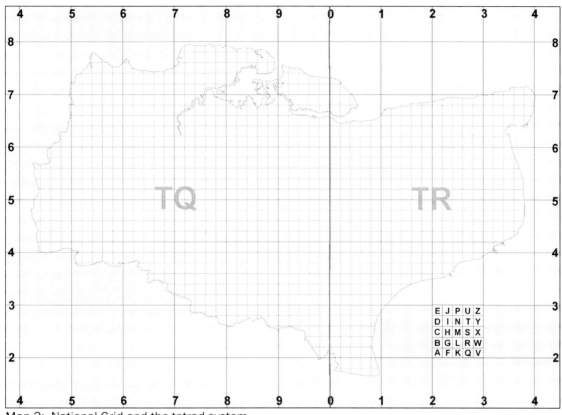

Map 2: National Grid and the tetrad system

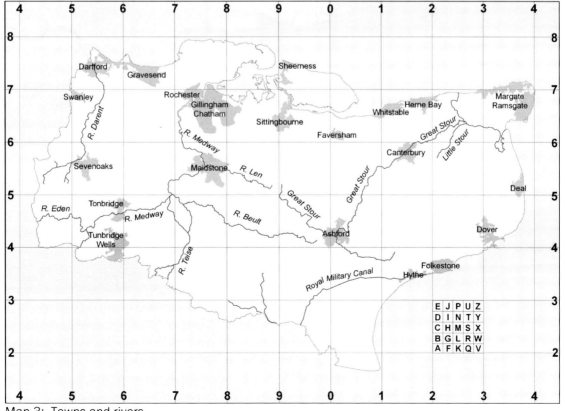

Map 3: Towns and rivers

Geology

The soil in which plants grow is derived in part from the underlying rocks. Weathering breaks down the rock into tiny particles forming the soil's basic structure and, at the same time, releasing minerals essential to plant growth. Generally speaking then, it can be said that different rocks produce different soils, and different soils support different plants. The exposed rocks of Kent are all sedimentary in origin, but they are very varied in type, and this is reflected in the flora. See Map 4.

One of the most well known and perhaps characteristic rocks of the county is the Chalk which is exposed in the cliffs around Dover and which forms the scarp slope of the North Downs. 'Downland' is in fact the uplands of the county, the highest point being the 252 metre summit of Westerham Hill, just inside the present boundary in tetrad TQ45I. The Chalk also outcrops regularly to the north, on the dip slope of the North Downs, and after down-warping beneath the more recent deposits of the Wantsum Channel, it reappears to form much of the Isle of Thanet.

Overlying the Chalk, particularly on the flatter areas, are found the superficial deposits called Clay-with-Flints. These tend to be much less alkaline than the Chalk and, in places, border on the acid. The London Clay is the major deposit in the north of the county where it also acts as the source rock for the mud of the fine salt-marshes in the Medway estuary, the Swale and the shores of the Thames. Deposits of Eocene Sands are also quite extensive in places. They are sandwiched between the Chalk and the London Clay and are exposed in the cliffs between Herne Bay and Reculver.

Underlying, and exposed immediately to the south of the Chalk is the Gault Clay which forms a fertile vale across the county. Although the soils derived from the Gault are heavily cultivated, the few remaining woods are very rich in a wide variety of plants. Many springs occur along the exposed junction between the Chalk and the Gault Clay which give rise to marshy areas and small streams.

Moving further south, the next outcrops are the Folkestone Beds. They consist for the most part of loosely consolidated sandstones and support a very different flora to that of the Gault. It is on these rocks that the few remaining scraps of Kentish heathland lie. Still further south are the Hythe Beds, a series of sandstones with irregular courses of hard gritty limestone known as Kentish rag or ragstone. The southern edge of this deposit forms another south facing scarp slope which, although quite shallow in places, is at times quite spectacular as in the area to the south of Maidstone.

The Weald Clay covers a large flat area in the centre of the county which is now heavily cultivated and contains very little woodland. As a result, the total number of plant species recorded in the Wealden Clay tetrads is below average for the county. Nevertheless, many interesting species are still to be found in and around the numerous ponds and streams as well as along some of the damp roadside verges. The oldest exposed rocks in Kent to be considered here, the Tunbridge Wells Sands, occur in the south (the Wadhurst Clay and Ashdown Beds are older, but cover only a small area). They are sandstones and give rise to a gently undulating countryside with rather acid and infertile soils. This lack of fertility, however, means there is much less pressure from modern methods of farming, and so this area retains a greater density of trees and woodland than elsewhere in Kent.

Romney Marsh is formed, for the most part, from recent deposits of alluvium, and at its southern end, around Dungeness, is to be found the greatest expanse of shingle in Europe. Further extensive shingle deposits can be seen on the coast south west of Hythe. The only sand-dunes of merit are those extending for some nine kilometres north from Deal through Sandwich Bay. Although these dunes are probably the richest and most famous locality in Kent from the botanical point of view, their area has been greatly reduced by the combined effects of sea-defences, golf courses and farming. There are also some remaining wind-blown sand-dunes along the east coast of Romney Marsh in the Greatstone - St. Mary's Bay area, and these too retain a very rich flora. In the north of the county, shell-sand beaches are to be found at several locations, in particular around the east end of the Swale such as at Shellness on Sheppey, and on the Isle of Grain in the mouth of the Medway. Shingle, blown sand and shell-sand are also shown.

Three main rivers, the Darent, the Medway and the Great Stour, have played a major role in the geological evolution of the county and they also have a great influence, both directly and indirectly, on the distribution of plants. For example, certain plants occur along one river system but not another (see maps for *Cardamine impatiens* and *Oenanthe fluviatilis*). Gravels that have been deposited along the river valleys have in recent years been extensively quarried; the resultant quarries are new geological environments, and plants which thrive in such places have quickly colonised them. This sort of change in the distribution of the flora in Kent will no doubt continue in the foreseeable future.

With such a geological mixture plus the fact that over half the edge of the county borders on tidal waters it is not surprising that Kent, the Garden of England, remains so rich in wild flowers. For a more detailed picture of the geology of the county and how the flora has been affected by land use over the years, see Green (2008).

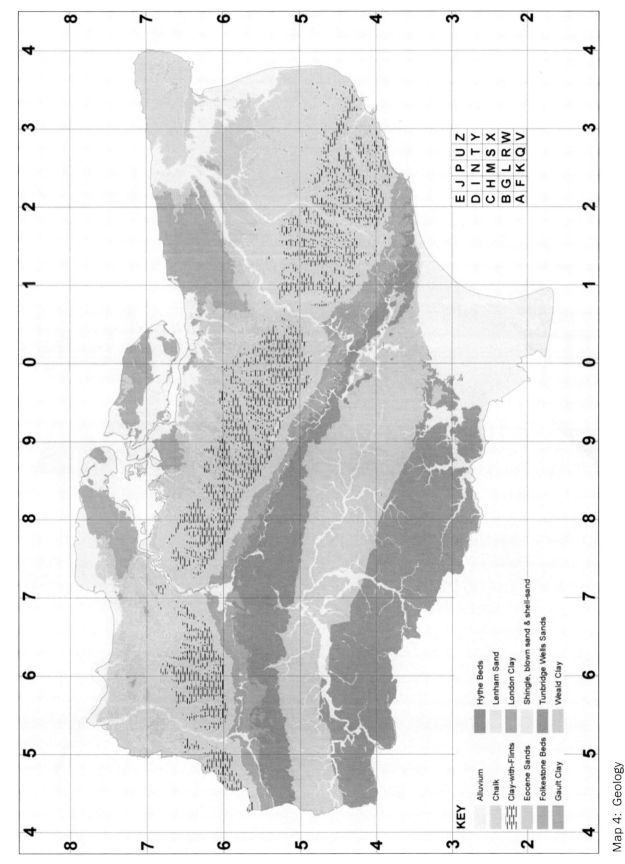

KEY

Alluvium		Hythe Beds
Chalk		Lenham Sand
Clay-with-Flints		London Clay
Eocene Sands		Shingle, blown sand & shell-sand
Folkestone Beds		Tunbridge Wells Sands
Gault Clay		Weald Clay

Map 4: Geology

Weather

Kent has generally a higher temperature in summer in comparison with the rest of the British Isles, and about average temperatures during the winter. There can be the occasional very cold spells during the winter months, but these have tended to become less frequent in recent years. With the rainfall at the lower end of the national average, the climate of Kent can be considered as warm, dry and moderately continental. This is probably the main reason why certain plants that occur regularly in the county, for example Lady Orchid and Late Spider Orchid, are not to be found in the colder and wetter areas to the north and west.

The following tables give some weather data for a few selected areas in the county. The data demonstrate a degree of variation, both between years and between localities. At all locations a maximum temperature was recorded for August 2003, when a UK record of 38.5°C was claimed for Faversham. Politicians and the media have been making a great issue of 'global warming' in recent years, but the weather has always been changing and, always will. Without doubt the overall earth temperatures have been rising in recent years. In the absence of any counter-balancing factors, they may be expected to continue to do so, irrespective of all the political exercises, if the world population continues to rise.

Rainfall in mm at Tunbridge Wells TQ54V

	Jan	Feb	Mar	Apr	May	Jun	Jul	Aug	Sep	Oct	Nov	Dec	Total
1991	94	43	37	60	18	121	82	9	52	27	103	21	667
1992	10	37	63	75	31	13	64	101	60	72	131	76	733
1993	91	6	24	87	58	38	52	31	109	127	48	138	809
1994	120	44	53	78	97	56	40	92	103	105	41	112	941
1995	168	97	59	10	18	16	38	1	163	22	33	108	733
1996	74	60	42	13	49	15	48	69	30	48	126	29	603
1997	18	98	12	9	43	126	23	52	19	83	130	95	708
1998	120	6	63	107	22	93	25	9	104	138	46	75	808
1999	114	31	36	48	16	34	27	85	107	63	33	144	738
2000	43	57	18	121	102	12	53	23	98	261	173	148	1109
2001	121	113	112	73	41	28	79	109	88	135	49	24	972
2002	85	99	43	46	88	59	58	46	47	86	154	142	953
2003	86	26	23	29	43	44	51	29	14	51	138	81	615
2004	111	28	40	69	60	29	54	83	26	120	27	53	700
2005	31	27	41	41	38	6	80	63	28	71	28	44	498
Av.	86	51	44	58	48	46	52	53	70	94	84	86	

Rainfall in mm at Sellindge TR13E

	Jan	Feb	Mar	Apr	May	Jun	Jul	Aug	Sep	Oct	Nov	Dec	Total
1991	85	33	28	59	22	128	106	4	40	31	129	30	695
1992	20	25	87	54	40	6	125	96	56	120	139	57	825
1993	73	16	8	70	25	47	71	38	75	144	57	148	772
1994	89	43	44	88	86	49	38	76	106	131	43	118	911
1995	131	101	48	16	18	25	27	6	117	23	39	86	637
1996	63	54	31	5	48	13	32	175	40	58	129	43	691
1997	20	77	11	7	51	127	35	83	3	96	126	134	770
1998	100	9	67	90	19	95	43	10	133	156	60	80	862
1999	86	29	43	54	30	71	11	101	128	79	54	126	812
2000	25	62	25	138	102	22	66	39	78	235	226	115	1133
2001	123	127	117	71	20	16	82	71	103	125	45	28	928
2002	79	81	37	37	87	62	63	24	83	70	148	56	827
2003	80	35	19	25	46	50	78	21	21	79	136	86	676
2004	125	34	33	64	70	37	84	134	30	113	31	68	823
2005	38	44	61	54	43	20	80	83	38	113	44	82	700
Av.	76	51	44	55	47	51	63	64	70	105	94	84	

Rainfall in mm at Elham TR14R

	Jan	Feb	Mar	Apr	May	Jun	Jul	Aug	Sep	Oct	Nov	Dec	Total
1999					33	68	12	88	128	63	37	106	535
2000	26	64	30	155	119	20	81	46	73	194	187	104	1099
2001	126	127	114	66	23	22	60	67	99	108	44	27	883
2002	60	66	37	36	80	70	74	50	84	64	134	137	892
2003	70	31	14	21	62	40	69	26	19	85	128	71	636
2004	112	31	26	57	54	41	76	125	29	115	31	61	758
2005	31	37	55	50	42	22	87	74	45	85	46	55	629
Av.	71	59	46	64	59	40	66	68	68	102	87	80	

Teasel © L. Manning

Maximum temperature in degrees Centigrade at Tunbridge Wells TQ54V

	Jan	Feb	Mar	Apr	May	Jun	Jul	Aug	Sep	Oct	Nov	Dec
1991	11.0	10.5	17.5	20.5	24.0	20.0	26.5	26.5	28.0	19.0	14.0	10.0
1992	11.0	12.5	14.5	19.0	16.0	29.0	29.0	28.0	24.0	17.5	15.0	11.5
1993	11.0	10.0	16.0	22.5	24.0	28.0	25.0	27.5	21.0	16.5	15.0	12.0
1994	11.0	11.0	16.0	20.0	21.0	27.0	32.0	29.0	21.0	18.0	17.0	13.0
1995	10.0	12.0	20.0	19.5	27.5	25.0	31.5	31.5	22.0	24.0	15.5	11.0
1996	10.0	10.0	15.0	23.0	25.0	31.0	30.0	30.0	22.0	20.0	15.0	10.0
1997	10.0	11.0	16.0	21.0	25.0	25.0	26.5	30.5	24.5	25.0	21.0	12.0
1998	10.0	16.0	17.0	21.0	23.0	19.0	25.0	30.0	24.0	17.0	14.0	12.0
1999	12.0	12.0	16.0	18.0	24.0	27.0	29.0	31.0	28.0	19.0	15.0	11.0
2000	11.0	12.0	15.0	19.0	27.0	29.0	25.0	26.0	26.0	18.0	13.0	12.0
2001	10.0	10.0	13.5	20.0	26.0	32.0	30.0	29.0	21.0	23.0	13.0	12.0
2002	11.0	13.0	16.5	22.0	24.0	28.0	31.0	29.0	23.0	19.0	14.0	11.0
2003	15.0	13.0	18.0	24.0	26.0	26.0	32.0	35.0	26.0	19.0	16.5	10.0
2004	10.0	15.0	17.5	20.0	24.0	29.0	27.5	28.5	26.0	16.0	12.5	11.5
2005	11.0	12.5	12.5	19.0	29.0	30.0	29.0	29.0	26.0	20.0	17.0	10.0
Mean	11.0	12.0	16.0	20.5	24.5	27.0	28.5	29.5	24.0	19.5	15.0	11.5

Minimum temperature in degrees Centigrade at Tunbridge Wells TQ54V

	Jan	Feb	Mar	Apr	May	Jun	Jul	Aug	Sep	Oct	Nov	Dec
1991	1.0	-3.5	-1.0	-2.0	0.0	2.5	10.5	8.0	5.0	-1.0	2.0	-6.5
1992	-6.0	-5.0	1.5	0.0	1.5	6.0	8.0	7.0	5.0	-2.5	-2.5	-6.5
1993	-8.0	-3.0	-3.0	1.0	1.0	6.5	6.0	5.0	4.5	-1.5	-6.0	-3.0
1994	-4.0	-7.0	-2.0	0.0	3.0	5.0	10.0	7.5	4.0	1.0	3.0	-5.0
1995	-5.0	0.0	-4.0	-3.0	0.5	6.0	10.0	8.0	5.0	2.0	-2.0	-6.0
1996	-5.5	-5.0	-5.0	-3.0	-1.0	6.0	6.0	7.0	5.0	2.0	-4.0	-6.0
1997	2.5	-3.0	0.0	-1.0	-2.0	11.0	9.0	9.0	5.5	4.0	5.0	3.0
1998	-3.0	-5.0	-2.0	-1.0	1.5	2.0	4.0	6.0	4.0	2.0	-3.0	-5.0
1999	-4.0	-3.0	-1.0	-5.0	4.0	5.0	9.0	8.0	5.0	3.0	-2.0	-6.0
2000	-4.0	-2.0	-2.0	-0.5	5.0	7.0	7.0	7.0	4.0	3.0	1.0	-5.0
2001	-6.0	-3.0	-5.0	0.0	6.0	3.0	10.0	8.5	9.0	6.0	-1.0	-3.0
2002	-5.0	0.0	0.0	0.0	3.0	7.0	8.5	8.0	5.0	5.0	0.5	-2.0
2003	-5.0	-5.0	-1.0	-2.5	2.0	7.0	11.0	6.0	1.0	-0.5	-1.5	-4.0
2004	-4.0	-5.0	-5.0	0.0	4.0	6.0	7.5	8.0	3.0	-3.0	-2.0	-5.0
2005	-2.0	-7.0	-6.0	-2.0	0.0	5.0	8.5	8.5	5.0	3.0	-7.5	-5.0
Mean	-3.9	-3.8	-2.4	-1.3	1.9	5.7	8.3	7.4	4.7	1.5	-1.3	-4.3

Maximum temperature in degrees Centigrade at Sellindge TR13E

	Jan	Feb	Mar	Apr	May	Jun	Jul	Aug	Sep	Oct	Nov	Dec
1991								28.0	27.0	20.0	14.5	14.0
1992	11.7	13.5	14.7	20.5	27.5	29.0	26.0	26.2	23.5	19.0	14.5	12.2
1993	11.7	10.5	17.0	22.0	22.5	29.0	26.7	25.0	21.0	18.0	17.0	12.5
1994	12.0	12.0	16.2	21.5	20.0	28.5	31.0	29.0	22.0	19.7	16.7	14.0
1995	11.2	14.5	16.2	21.2	15.7	30.0	31.5	33.5	22.0	22.2	16.2	13.5
1996	10.5	12.0	15.2	21.5	24.0	29.0	29.5	28.5	22.0	18.0	16.7	11.0
1997	12.7	13.2	18.0	20.7	25.7	24.5	25.5	30.0	24.5	26.0	14.7	13.0
1998	12.5	14.2	18.5	22.2	24.0	27.5	25.0	29.7	23.0	22.2	15.0	12.7
1999	12.7	13.5	18.5	19.0	24.5	24.7	29.2	30.2	27.5	19.0	16.0	12.5
2000	13.0	13.5	17.7	18.0	25.0	29.5	24.5	26.2	26.0	19.0	13.0	13.0
2001	10.5	12.0	14.5	19.0	26.7	30.2	29.2	30.2	22.0	23.5	16.5	12.5
2002	12.2	15.5	16.2	21.0	24.0	27.7	30.5	30.2	24.5	20.7	15.0	11.7
2003	18.5	14.0	18.2	25.5	26.2	25.5	30.7	35.2	26.5	20.5	15.5	12.2
2004	12.0	14.2	19.5	21.0	23.5	27.2	27.2	29.7	26.5	19.0	18.0	13.0
2005	11.5	13.2	18.5	22.5	29.0	31.0	29.2	30.2	27.0	22.0	16.7	12.2
Mean	12.3	13.3	17.1	21.1	24.2	28.1	28.3	29.5	24.3	20.6	15.8	12.7

Minimum temperature in degrees Centigrade at Sellindge TR13E

	Jan	Feb	Mar	Apr	May	Jun	Jul	Aug	Sept	Oct	Nov	Dec
1991	1.0	-3.5	-1.0	-2.0	0.0	2.5	10.5	8.0	5.0	-1.0	2.0	-6.5
1992	-6.0	-5.0	1.5	0.0	1.5	6.0	8.0	7.0	5.0	-2.5	-2.5	-6.5
1993	-8.0	-3.0	-3.0	1.0	1.0	6.5	6.0	5.0	4.5	-1.5	-6.0	-3.0
1994	-4.0	-7.0	-2.0	0.0	3.0	5.0	10.0	7.5	4.0	1.0	3.0	-5.0
1995	-5.0	0.0	-4.0	-3.0	0.5	6.0	10.0	8.0	5.0	2.0	-2.0	-6.0
1996	-5.5	-5.0	-5.0	-3.0	-1.0	6.0	6.0	7.0	5.0	2.0	-4.0	-6.0
1997	2.5	-3.0	0.0	-1.0	-2.0	11.0	9.0	9.0	5.5	4.0	5.0	3.0
1998	-3.0	-5.0	-2.0	-1.0	1.5	2.0	4.0	6.0	4.0	2.0	-3.0	-5.0
1999	-4.0	-3.0	-1.0	-5.0	4.0	5.0	9.0	8.0	5.0	3.0	-2.0	-6.0
2000	-4.0	-2.0	-2.0	-0.5	5.0	7.0	7.0	7.0	4.0	3.0	1.0	-5.0
2001	-6.0	-3.0	-5.0	0.0	6.0	3.0	10.0	8.5	9.0	6.0	-1.0	-3.0
2002	-5.0	0.0	0.0	0.0	3.0	7.0	8.5	8.0	5.0	5.0	0.5	-2.0
2003	-5.0	-5.0	-1.0	-2.5	2.0	7.0	11.0	6.0	1.0	-0.5	-1.5	-4.0
2004	-4.0	-5.0	-5.0	0.0	4.0	6.0	7.5	8.0	3.0	-3.0	-2.0	-5.0
2005	-2.0	-7.0	-6.0	-2.0	0.0	5.0	8.5	8.5	5.0	3.0	-7.5	-5.0
Mean	-3.9	-3.8	-2.4	-1.3	1.9	5.7	8.3	7.4	4.7	1.5	-1.3	-4.3

Maximum temperature in degrees Centigrade at Elham TR14R

	Jan	Feb	Mar	Apr	May	Jun	Jul	Aug	Sep	Oct	Nov	Dec
1999					26.0	27.0	32.0	34.0	30.0	19.0	16.0	12.0
2000	12.0	13.0	17.0	19.0	26.0	29.0	25.0	26.0	27.0	19.0	13.0	14.0
2001	10.0	11.0	14.0	19.0	27.0	31.0	30.0	31.0	21.0	24.0	15.0	13.0
2002	12.0	14.0	17.0	22.0	25.0	27.0	32.0	31.0	24.0	21.0	15.0	12.0
2003	16.0	13.0	18.0	25.0	27.0	26.0	31.0	36.0	27.0	19.0	15.0	12.0
2004	11.0	14.0	20.0	21.0	23.0	27.0	28.0	30.0	26.0	18.0	14.0	12.0
2005	12.0	13.0	20.0	23.0	30.0	31.0	27.0	30.0	27.0	22.0	16.0	12.0
Mean	12.0	13.0	18.0	21.0	26.0	28.0	29.0	31.0	26.0	20.0	15.0	12.0

Minimum temperature in degrees Centigrade at Elham TR14R

	Jan	Feb	Mar	Apr	May	Jun	Jul	Aug	Sep	Oct	Nov	Dec
1999					2.0	5.0	8.0	8.0	2.0	-2.0	-5.0	
2000	-5.0	-3.0	-2.0	-2.0	3.0	6.0	6.0	6.0	6.0	3.0	0.0	-6.0
2001	-6.0	-3.0	-5.0	-2.0	3.0	3.0	6.0	7.0	4.0	5.0	-2.0	-5.0
2002	-6.0	-1.0	-1.0	0.0	3.0	6.0	8.0	10.0	5.0	0.0	1.0	-2.0
2003	-5.0	-7.0	-2.0	-5.0	0.0	6.0	9.0	6.0	1.0	-2.0	-1.0	-3.0
2004	-5.0	-5.0	-5.0	-1.0	2.0	5.0	6.0	10.0	4.0	2.0	-2.0	-4.0
2005	-2.0	-4.0	-7.0	-1.0	1.0	3.0	9.0	8.0	7.0	5.0	-3.0	-6.0
Mean	-4.8	-3.8	-3.7	-1.8	2.0	4.9	7.4	7.9	4.1	1.6	-1.7	-4.3

Method of recording

A recording card containing a list, in abbreviated form, of all the plants most likely to occur, was prepared for each tetrad. All the species recorded in the first Atlas were marked with a red dot, all the extra species recorded between 1981 and 1990 with a blue dot, and any pre-1970 records were marked with a green dot. This meant that on arrival in any given tetrad there was a good clue as to which species should be present. Each tetrad was visited on as many occasions as possible in an attempt to get an even coverage throughout the seasons, and to seek all the species that had previously ever been recorded from that tetrad. The nomenclature and identification of the plants was to follow that of Stace (1997) although some updating of nomenclature has been undertaken in the following text.

The plan was to drive out and park at a suitable spot and then do a circular walk, either covering one or several tetrads. It was found that most habitats within a tetrad could be reached by public road or footpath, or public open space. On some of the narrow country lanes this meant at times clambering up the bank to allow passage of the occasional car, but the only problems came from cyclists who would often approach silently at great speeds which resulted in many near misses, several times being clipped, and on one occasion, a severe collision.

Members of the general public were often curious as to what was going on, and when informed they were always most interested, and on many occasions they would invite me (and a companion if present) to botanize over their garden or grounds. A few times it was necessary to ask permission from landowners or farmers to reach habitats that were not accessible from public rights of way and, except in two cases, this was always granted. The author is very grateful to all these people who I am afraid cannot be acknowledged by name.

The author either drove his own car, or was driven by Jim Bevan, Mervyn Brown, Doug Grant, Peter Heathcote or Brian Woodhams. Two people certainly make recording more efficient than by a single person as fewer plants are likely to be missed, and simple errors avoided when two people can check each identification. Without the help of these fellow botanists the cost of transport involved to reach every corner of the county at varying times of years would have not been viable. Public transport would not have been an alternative; apart from the prohibitive cost, the actual time involved would not have been practicable. The best times that could be arranged under public transport to reach some localities would have taken a day and a half to reach, whereas from a centrally situated position, any part of the county could be reached within the hour by car.

Over the period of the mapping the roads became more difficult as with a rising population there were more cars on the roads. At the same time there became less space on the roads as many were narrowed to make room for cycle or bus lanes, or restrictions were put in to allow the passage of only one vehicle through parts of the road. The biggest problem was usually in finding somewhere to park and often it has been necessary to drive right through a tetrad and then walk back as no parking area was available. Many lay-bys and other parking areas have recently been removed, not necessarily with any compelling reason on the part of the relevant local authorities.

Maidstone Museum Herbarium

Over the years a large collection of plants has been preserved and housed in the herbarium at Maidstone Museum (MNE). Specimens from all over the British Isles are represented, dated from the early 19th century through to the present. The herbarium is arranged in Stace (edition 2) order with two folders for each species, the first holding Kent specimens, and the second for British specimens from outside Kent. Incorporated are the Kent herbaria of Dr. Francis Rose, J.B. Marshall and Prof. C.A. Stace, a small collection of voucher material from Kent and Sussex by P.C. Hall, a large herbarium of hawkweeds from Dr. C. West, material from David McClintock including a collection from Buckingham Palace gardens and large numbers of alien plants, and a large British collection by Trudy Side. There is also voucher material from many other botanists to support records for this Atlas and the 1982 Atlas.

The author has also contributed a large amount of material, particularly for some of the critical species such as *Rubus*, and has also made attempts to make sure that there is voucher material for all the species recorded from Kent. The author has been responsible for validating the identification of all these specimens and these should be proofs, or otherwise, as to the correct identification of the records in this publication. The scientific and historical value of this herbarium cannot be over-estimated and it essential that it be maintained so that it may be consulted at all times in the future.

Results

Some plants have been recorded from every tetrad. It is considered that in general, maps have been compiled which represent a reasonable assessment of the present distribution. In no tetrad have all the plants previously recorded from there been found. On the other hand, on every occasion when mapping, right up until the final day, new tetrad records have been made on each visit. The conclusion is that it is 'mission impossible' to record every plant from every tetrad, and whilst an attempt has been made to try and achieve this, there is no doubt that any reader can go out and record plants in addition to the records found here.

Some plants show significant gains since the 1982 Atlas. *Conyza sumatrensis* is a recent arrival in the county and is still spreading, so this increase is obvious. Other plants such as *Cochlearia danica* have suddenly found another niche outside their previous few sea-sprayed localities on the coast and have extended their range along the main roads of the county. The increased number of records for the ferns is probably due to better recording, but the reason for the increase in records such as that for *Iris foetidissima* is more difficult to explain.

Other plants show losses in the number of records; some of these are quite significant. The reasons are varied and again all cannot always be explained. Wool-shoddy, (the waste from the woollen industry often containing seeds, particularly from Australia and South America) is no longer spread over fields where it was used to enrich the soil, particularly in hop-gardens. Practically all the wool-shoddy plants that used to occur in the county are no longer to be found. Changes in the regulations for the management of rubbish-tips have resulted in the rubbish now being continually covered by soil and the casual plants that used to be found are there no longer. Waste from the vegetable oil-milling industry (see Palmer, 1977) has produced a number of interesting plants in the past, but this is no longer deposited in the county.

The standards set for accepting plants from cultivation were interpreted in different ways by the various recorders for the 1982 Atlas; this time the standards have been a bit more rigorous and all set by the writer. With something like 70,000 species, hybrids and cultivars of plant now in cultivation in this country the chance of accidental escape or deliberate planting out is great. However, no plant that

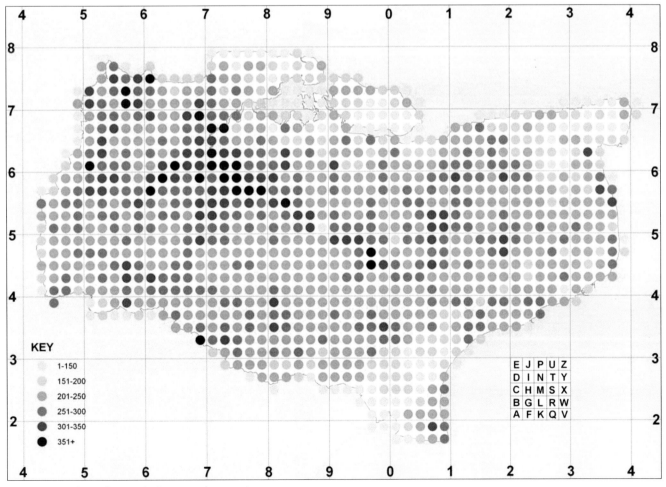

KEY

- 1-150
- 151-200
- 201-250
- 251-300
- 301-350
- 351+

E	J	P	U	Z
D	I	N	T	Y
C	H	M	S	X
B	G	L	R	W
A	F	K	Q	V

Map 5: Number of records from each tetrad

has *obviously* been planted has been recorded. Neither have any garden plants that set seeds in gardens or just outside gardens where the seed can drop. Relic plants from the previous year's crop or bedding-out have not been recorded either. Nor has the odd garden plant just still alive on a pile of dumped garden rubbish. However, plants such as *Lamiastrum galeobdolon* subsp. *argentatum* which might have originally arrived at a site with such rubbish, but are now well established and spreading, have been recorded.

However the main reason for the loss in numbers of records is due to loss of habitat Habitat change in Kent since the publication of the 1982 Flora has been the subject of two surveys. The first of these was carried out between 1990 and 1994 by the Kent Wildlife Habitat Survey Partnership led by Kent County Council (Kent Wildlife Habitat Survey County Report, 1995). This was a field-by-field survey which mapped all semi-natural habitats and included information on key plant species and habitat quality for each parcel of land. A second habitat survey of the County was carried out between 2001 and 2003 by the Kent Habitat Survey Partnership, again led by Kent County Council, using aerial photographs to re-map habitat boundaries, combined with targeted field surveys of Biodiversity Action Plan (BAP) priority habitats (Kent Habitat Survey Report, 2003). The writer's recording related primarily to the presence or absence of plants, rather than habitats, but throughout the fifteen years of mapping, each time the writer returned to an area there would be evidence of new houses, warehouses or other development, and so a gradual loss of habitat where wild flowers could grow. The reasons for this become a bit more obvious when one looks at the increased population which now averages out at more than 1600 per tetrad (or over 400 per 1 square kilometre).

Population in the administrative county of Kent (including Medway)

1901	806,486
1931	958,701
1951	1,091,153
1971	1,399,463
1981	1,463,055
1991	1,528,300
2005	1,621,000

The future for native wild flowers does not look very good. With the increasing population, then more houses and related infrastructure will continue to be built. Apart from large swathes of countryside such as the Swanscombe Marshes and the vast area around Ashford that have recently been, or are about to be destroyed, there is the continued loss of small areas. Large old houses are knocked down and replaced by a small estate, and likewise for old farm buildings. All these have provided many niches for wild flowers but are now replaced by dense buildings separated by brick or cement roads and a few 'garden areas' densely planted with a few alien shrubs and with any spare ground covered with bark chippings.

Another problem is the continued planting of alien bushes and trees and of sowing foreign seed, these particularly so along new roads and railways. The planners, aware of the need to try and preserve some countryside when an area has been 'developed', decide on areas for tree planting or seeding. Although native species, or at least genera, are listed it is practically always alien races or subspecies that get planted. However, it must be stressed that the official conservation bodies do go to great lengths to plant only native stock. Nevertheless, it is not always clear why tree planting schemes are promoted; in the author's garden there is a continual battle to remove wind-blown or bird-sown tree seedlings.

So with these constraints, the author has brought together records of all the plants that he has personally seen in Kent over the period 1991-2005 inclusive and these are now presented. These records would not have been possible without the help of many people who are acknowledged later.

Each species ever recorded in Kent is listed, the present status given plus a general comment on the habitat in which it is found. Also listed is the national rarity status, where appropriate, by reference to the Red List (Cheffings & Farrell (eds.), 2005), and finally a number which is the total, in bold, of the number of tetrads in which that species was recorded during the present survey. This is followed, in brackets, by the total number of records in the 1971-80 survey published in the 1982 Atlas (corrected where necessary) so that a comparison can be made in order to ascertain if the plant is on the increase or decrease. The assessment of present status, native or otherwise, is based on the following definitions. Native plants are species which have arrived in Kent without the help of man. Introduced species are listed as *archaeophytes*, which are those that were introduced before AD 1500, or as *neophytes*, which are plants introduced since AD 1500. Introduced plants that are not established are listed as casuals.

June 2008

Dungeness © J. Badmin

Key to layers used in species text

A number of different background layers have been used for the species maps to show interesting correlations or affinities for individual plants species. A key to the layers is given below.

Many species are influenced by geology. For example many species requiring calcareous conditions are found predominantly on the Chalk and Hythe Beds. Other species requiring damper conditions will be found mainly on clay (London Clay, Gault Clay and Weald Clay), while other species are restricted to sandy areas such as the Folkestone Beds and Eocene Sands. For a key to the geological layers please refer to Map 4 on page 5.

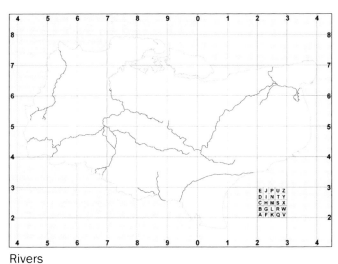

Rivers

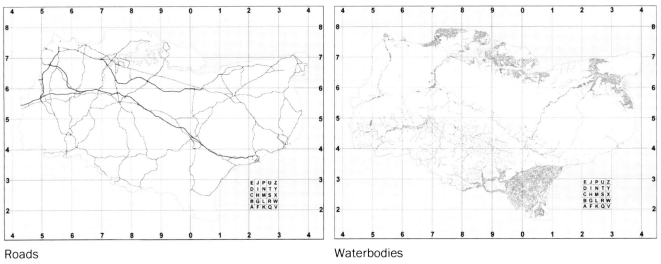

Roads

Waterbodies

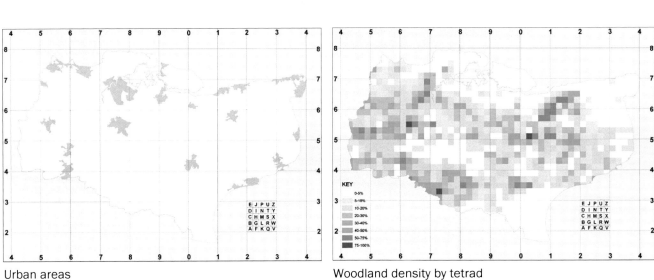

Urban areas

Woodland density by tetrad

KEY
0-5%
5-10%
10-20%
20-30%
30-40%
40-50%
50-75%
75-100%

The Vascular Plants of Kent

LYCOPODIACEAE

Lycopodiella inundata (L.) Holub   Marsh Clubmoss

Native, now extinct in the county. Last recorded at Hothfield before 1899 although a planted specimen existed there for a couple of years in the late 1950s. Last seen about 1930 at Keston Bog which is within the London area of Kent. **0** (0).

Lycopodium clavatum L.   Stag's-horn Clubmoss

Native of sandy heaths and woodland rides. Recorded at seven sites 1971-80, but there are no recent records and this plant now appears to be extinct in the county. **0** (7).

SELAGINELLACEAE

Selaginella kraussiana   Krauss's Clubmoss
(Kunze) A. Braun

Introduced. A casual plant of nurseries and damp shady places, recorded from West Kent in 1955, but there are no recent records. **0** (0).

Hothfield Common © A. Witts

13

EQUISETACEAE

Equisetum fluviatile L. Water Horsetail

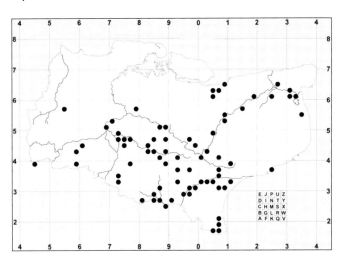

A native plant of ponds and ditches. Appears to have declined in recent years through loss of habitat. **75** (146).

Equisetum arvense L. Field Horsetail

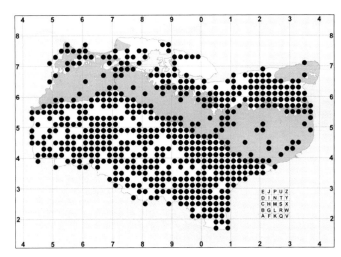

A native plant of river banks and fixed dune grassland, but now much associated with human activity and is frequent along roadsides and field edges. Being tolerant of herbicides it persists in gardens and in other developed areas. **582** (712).

Equisetum arvense x palustre
= *E.* x *rothmaleri* C.N. Page

Recorded in good quantity at the edge of Causton Wood TQ83I. **1** (0).

Equisetum sylvaticum L. Wood Horsetail

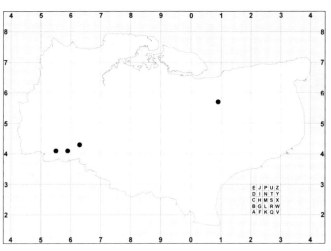

A native plant of damp woodland, or roadside verges kept permanently damp by flushing. A rare plant in Kent and the slight decline in localities, from six in the 1982 Atlas down to four, is in keeping with other losses in south-east England. **4** (6).

Great Horsetail *Equisetum telmateia* © L. Rooney

Equisetum palustre L. Marsh Horsetail

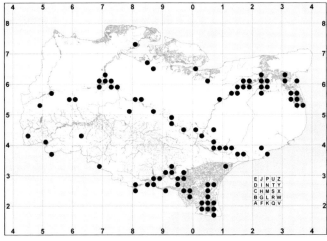

A native plant associated with marshes, damp pastures, ditches and dune-slacks. There appears to have been some decline in frequency, probably due to loss of habitat. **92** (155).

Equisetum telmateia Ehrh.　　　　　　Great Horsetail

A native plant of base-rich flushes and permanent seepages. It is particularly frequent along the spring-lines at the junction of the Chalk and Gault Clay and at the junction of the Hythe Beds and Weald Clay. The population appears stable as such habitats are less likely to be developed. **128** (141).

OSMUNDACEAE

Osmunda regalis L.　　　　　　　　　Royal Fern

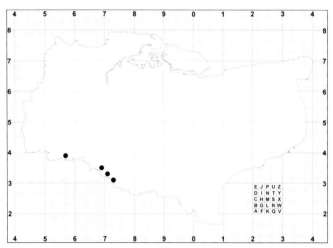

Native. A species of Western Britain, this fern is at the edge of its range in Kent and is only found in the area along the border with Sussex. It is open to debate as to whether these plants are truly native or are a result of being originally planted. **4** (7).

OPHIOGLOSSACEAE

Ophioglossum vulgatum L.　　　　　Adder's-tongue

A native fern of meadows, damp pastures and sand-dunes. It has been lost at some sites through intensive farming or development, but because it is an inconspicuous plant there will certainly be further unrecorded sites. **32** (40).

ADIANTACEAE

Adiantum capillus-veneris L.　　　　Maidenhair Fern

Introduced (neophyte). An escape from cultivation and found established at Sevenoaks TQ55H, Farningham TQ56N, Scotney Castle TQ63X and Wateringbury TQ65W. **4** (5).

PTERIDACEAE

Pteris cretica L.　　　　　　　　　　Ribbon Fern

Introduced (neophyte). Grown as a pot plant and occasionally found established on old walls. The only record during the present mapping was from a churchyard at Wateringbury TQ65W. **1** (3).

MARSILEACEAE

Botrychium lunaria (L.) Sw.　　　　　　Moonwort

Native, but now apparently extinct in the county. Last recorded in 1947. **0** (0).

Pilularia globulifera L.　　　　　　　　Pillwort

Native. Although recorded in the past, there is some doubt as to the authenticity of these records, and it probably should not be included as a Kent plant. **0** (0).

HYMENOPHYLLACEAE

Polypodium interjectum Shivas — Intermediate Polypody

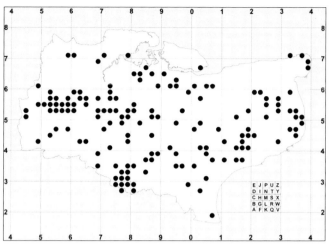

Hymenophyllum tunbrigense (L.) Sm. — Tunbridge Filmy-fern

Native, extinct. Recorded from the Tunbridge Wells area in the nineteenth century. It is still present in that area, but in Sussex, and some doubt exists as to whether it ever occurred within the boundaries of present day Kent. **0** (0).

Native. Found in a wide range of habitats and not so restricted to acidic soils as is *P. vulgare*. It is most frequently found on mortared stone walls such as are found at old churches, but does occur on roadside banks and on sand and shingle beaches. **152** (159).

POLYPODIACEAE

Polypodium vulgare L. — Polypody

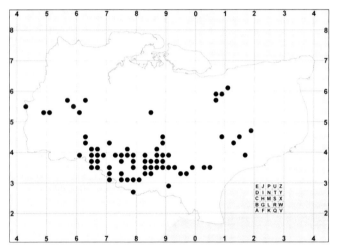

Polypodium cambricum L. — Southern Polypody

Native. Has not been re-found at the Penshurst site, or at any other locality in the county during the present survey. **0** (1).

A native fern found on natural sites such as on banks and on tree bases, usually on the more acidic soils. It is quite common in parts of the Weald and recorded more frequently than in the previous Atlas. All records of *Polypodium* have been checked by microscopic examination of the annulus. **72** (41).

DENNSTAEDTIACEAE

Polypodium vulgare x *interjectum*
= *P.* x *mantoniae* Rothm. & U. Schneid.

Pteridium aquilinum (L.) Kuhn — Bracken

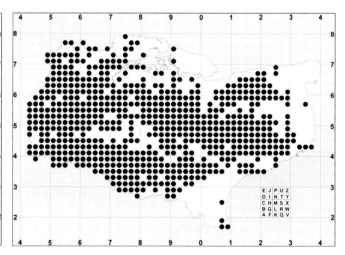

Recorded from roadside banks and hedgerows in seven sites, not always in the company of both parents. **7** (5).

Native. A common fern of heaths, woodland and hedgerows, particularly on sandy or acidic soils. At times it is also found on old walls, but is absent from most of the coastal marshes. Its status and distribution shows little change from the previous Atlas. **652** (706).

THELYPTERIDACEAE

ASPLENIACEAE

Thelypteris palustris Schott   Marsh Fern

Phyllitis scolopendrium (L.) Newman   Hart's-tongue

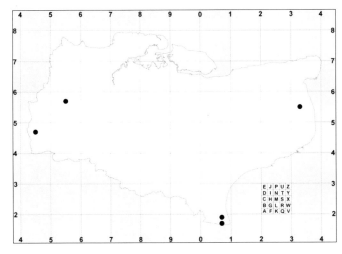

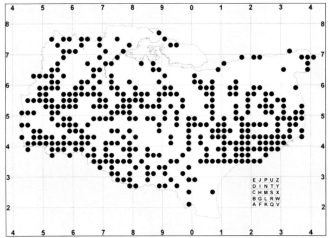

A native plant of open or partly wooded fen or open carr. It has always been a rare plant in Kent but still manages to survive in most of its long known localities. One new locality near Seal was completely unexpected, where it was found in good quantity. **5** (4).

Native. A frequent plant of damp woodlands, shaded roadside and stream banks on all but the most acidic soils. It is also found regularly on old walls, particularly those that are kept permanently damp. There appears to be little change in recent status and distribution. **393** (348).

Asplenium adiantum-nigrum L.   Black Spleenwort

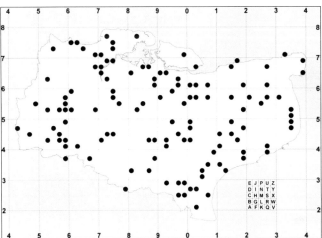

Oreopteris limbosperma
(All.) Holub   Lemon-scented Fern

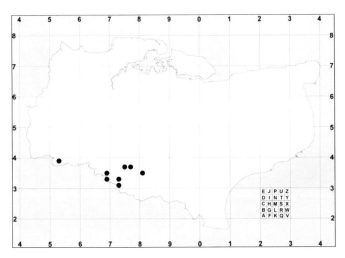

A native plant now almost confined to old man-made walls such as those of churches and railway bridges. Only rarely is this fern now found in natural habitats such as damp woodlands or roadside banks. There appears to be loss of some stations for this fern, probably through sites being destroyed or renovated. **123** (157).

A native fern of acidic or humus-rich soils where it is found in open woodland, alongside drainage ditches and by streamsides. A special effort has been made to record this plant, but it appears to be missing from a number of former localities, and although it might actually have been missed at some, it still shows a serious decline in the number of localities where it is still present. **8** (23).

Asplenium obovatum Viv.   Lanceolate Spleenwort

Native, extinct. Known from the Tunbridge Wells area of Kent until about 1855, but not recorded since. **0** (0).

Forked Spleenwort *Asplenium septentrionale* © S. Poyser

Asplenium ruta-muraria L.   Wall-rue

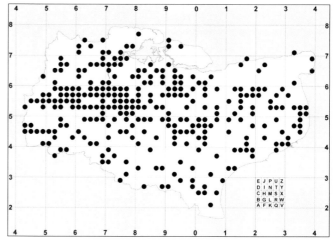

Native. Much the commonest of the 'wall-ferns' and found throughout the county where suitable habitat is present. This habitat is old mortared walls of brick, ragstone or other natural sandstones, and the plant is only rarely found on flint walls. **302** (342).

Asplenium septentrionale (L.) Hoffm.   Forked Spleenwort

Native. The plants on the old brick bridge near Brenzett TR02D were still present in 1981, but after a succession of hot dry summers, disappeared, and they could not be found on several visits in the 1990s and were considered now gone. However, in 2007 John Edgington re-discovered them at the original site, see Edgington (2007), and subsequent visits by the author have confirmed that this fern is now well established there. There is no chance that these plants had been introduced at this site and it is considered that this must be a natural expansion of range from spores blown in from the continent. **1** (1).

Asplenium marinum L.   Sea Spleenwort

Native, extinct. Recorded from on the cliffs at Dover in 1633, but not reported since. **0** (0).

Asplenium trichomanes L.   Maidenhair Spleenwort

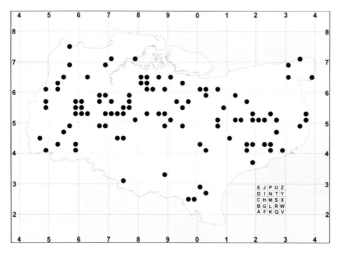

A native fern now restricted to mortared walls. It particularly favours walls built of ragstone, as found in many churchyards and older buildings and garden walls. There has been some loss of stations since the last Atlas, probably due to renovation, but it is still much more frequent than as recorded by Hanbury and Marshall toward the end of the nineteenth century. Our plant is subsp. *quadrivalvens* D.E. Mey. **104** (128).

Ceterach officinarum Willd.   Rustyback

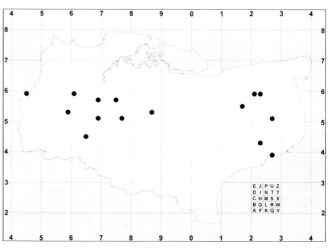

A native fern that occurs on old walls. A delightful plant that has always been scarce in the county and this remains so today. It has gone from some former sites through demolition or restoration work. **15** (22).

WOODSIACEAE

DRYOPTERIDACEAE

Athyrium filix-femina   Lady-fern
(L.) Roth

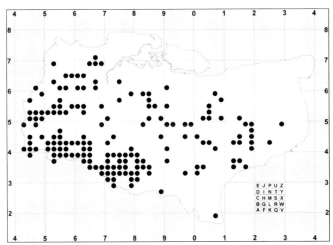

A native fern found in deciduous woodland, on roadside banks, and by streams. Frequent on some of the sandstones in the Weald, but can occur on slightly acidic clays overlaying the chalk. The distribution and status appear to be stable since the previous Atlas. **168** (166).

Polystichum setiferum   Soft Shield-fern
(Forssk.) T. Moore ex Woyn.

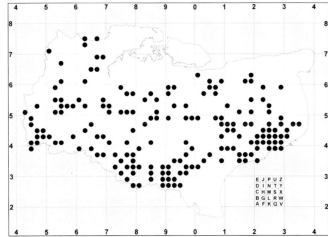

A native fern of deciduous woodlands, shaded roadside banks and streamsides. Generally distributed throughout the county, the apparent increase in records from the previous Atlas can be attributed to more efficient recording and not an increase in population. **180** (112).

Gymnocarpium dryopteris (L.) Newman   Oak Fern

Introduced (neophyte). Discovered, new to the county, in the Lyminge Forest TR14L in 1970, and still present there and with an additional site in TR14G during the 1971-80 Atlas recording. Another plant was discovered during 1981 in tetrad TR14M. All these plants were probably accidentally introduced during forestry work. The general area where these ferns occurred suffered badly in the Great Gale when many trees were blown down. The area then scrubbed up, but was eventually cleared and replanted. Since then there has been no sign of the Oak Fern in spite of several specific searches. **0** (2).

Polystichum aculeatum (L.) Roth   Hard Shield-fern

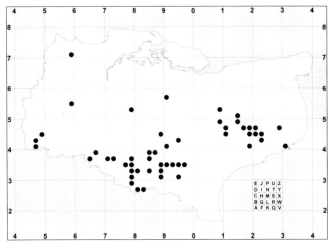

Cystopteris fragilis (L.) Bernh.   Brittle Bladder-fern

Introduced (neophyte). An escape from cultivation, the plants recorded in the 1982 Atlas could not be re-found and no new sites have come to light. However, this plant is likely to be found in the wild in the future as plants are now commonly offered for sale in supermarkets and garden centres. **0** (3).

A native plant of damp roadside banks and streamsides. It is much less frequent than the previous species both in localities and in the number of plants where it does occur, but the population does appear stable. **51** (53).

Cystopteris diaphana   Greenish Bladder-fern
(Bory) Blasdell

Two specimens labelled Harrison's Rocks, Tunbridge Wells, Kent, 1853-4 and 1855 have recently been discovered in the Thomas Moore Herbarium. There is some debate as to whether these were native plants or introduced. (see Rumsey, 2007). **0** (0).

Cyrtomium falcatum (L. f.) C. Presl   House Holly-fern

Introduced (neophyte). The only present record is of a small clump in a neglected wooded area in Mote Park, Maidstone TQ75X. **1** (1).

Dryopteris filix-mas Male-fern
(L.) Schott

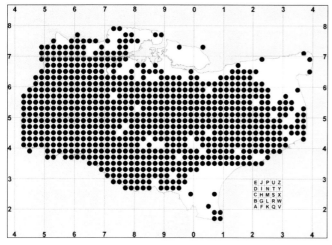

A common native fern found, with the exception of the coastal marsh areas, throughout most of the county. It occurs in woodland, hedgerows and streamsides in the countryside as well as on walls and wasteland in urban areas. **775** (762).

Dryopteris filix-mas x aemula

A sterile plant collected at Ashurst Park in 1857 and still in cultivation, appears to be this hybrid. There are no other records of this cross (see Rickard, 1994). **0** (0).

Dryopteris filix-mas x affinis
= *D.* x *complexa* Fraser-Jenk.

Recorded from Smokes Wood TQ85N, but would be expected to be found in a few other localities if carefully searched for. **1** (5).

Dryopteris affinis Scaly Male-fern
(Lowe) Fraser-Jenk.

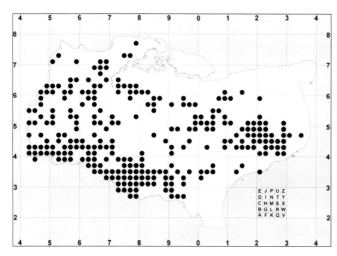

A native fern of deciduous woodland, shady banks and roadside verges, frequent in places, but absent from most coastal areas. There are more than double the number of records than from the previous Atlas, but this is probably due to a better understanding of the plant rather than an increase in the population. **269** (111).

Dryopteris aemula Hay-scented Buckler-fern
(Aiton) Kuntze

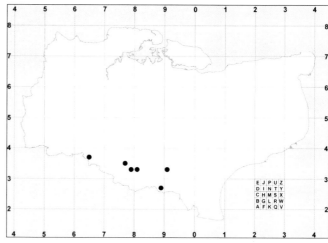

A rare native plant of steep-sided woodland gills. It persists at some of its traditional sites in the county but appears to have gone from one site near Bidborough TQ54L and has been discovered at a new site near Wittersham TQ82Y. **6** (8).

Dryopteris cristata (L.) A. Gray Crested Buckler-fern

Native. Recorded at Dungeness 1952-58, but not seen since in spite of many searches by numerous botanists and must be now considered extinct in the county. **0** (0).

Dryopteris carthusiana Narrow Buckler-fern
(Vill.) H.P. Fuchs

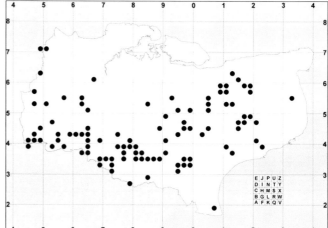

A native fern of wet woodland, heaths and fens. With scattered records through central Kent the population appears relatively stable. **101** (105).

Dryopteris carthusiana x *dilatata*
= *D.* x *deweveri* (J.T. Jansen) Jansen & Wacht.

Recorded, with both parents, from near Tenterden TQ83X, which is the only record, but should be expected to be found elsewhere if carefully looked for. **1** (9).

Blechnum spicant (L.) Roth   Hard-fern

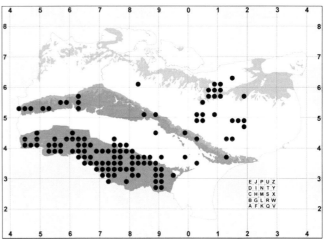

A native fern of woodland and heaths on the more acidic sandy soils in the county. It is usually found on banks or other well-drained areas and is frequent in such suitable habitats in the Weald. Elsewhere it is more local, but overall the population appears to be stable. **121** (124).

Dryopteris dilatata   Broad Buckler-fern
(Hoffm.) A. Gray

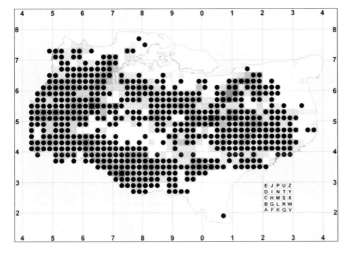

A common native plant of most woodlands throughout the county, but also occurs on roadside cuttings, hedgerows and occasionally in sallow carr, such as at Dungeness. **567** (474).

Azolla filiculoides Lam.   Water Fern

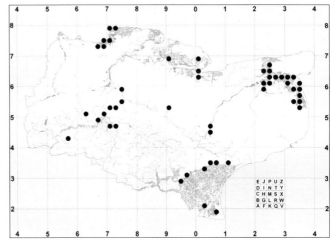

Introduced (neophyte). First recorded in Britain in 1883, this American fern is now well established in this country. A rather unpredictable plant, it will appear at times and completely cover a ditch or pond, and then disappear without trace. This makes the recording of its distribution a little difficult but there are obvious good populations on the Cliffe-Gravesend Marshes, at Sandwich and the Stour Valley, and on parts of the Romney Marsh. **50** (46).

Broad Buckler-fern *Dryopteris dilitata* © L. Manning

PINACEAE

Abies grandis (Douglas ex D. Don) Lindl. **Giant Fir**

Introduced (neophyte). Self-sown seedlings, and young trees, still to be found in the Bedgebury Pinetum and Forest area TQ73G. **1** (1).

Abies procera Rehder **Noble Fir**

Introduced (neophyte). Self-sown seedlings recorded from the Bedgebury area in the past, but not noted during the present survey. **0** (0).

Pseudotsuga menziesii (Mirb.) Franco **Douglas Fir**

Introduced (neophyte). First introduced into Britain in 1826 and now widely planted in forestry plots and occasionally in parks and gardens. Self-sown seedlings or young plants were noted in the Orlestone Forest area TQ93S, T, X & Y, Hoad's Wood TQ94L and Longbeech Wood TQ95V. The seeds appear to germinate easily and seedlings would be expected to occur in forestry plots elsewhere. **6** (2).

Tsuga heterophylla **Western Hemlock-spruce**
(Raf.) Sarg.

Introduced (neophyte). Planted in parks and small-scale forest plots from 1852 onwards, but not often used in recent years. Self-sown seedlings or young trees were recorded from Whitley Forest TQ55B, West Kingsdown TQ56W, Lamberhurst TQ63T, Bedgebury TQ73G, West Wood TR14L and Clowes Wood TR16G. **6** (2).

Picea sitchensis (Bong.) Carrière **Sitka Spruce**

Introduced (neophyte). Self-sown plants recorded from Bedgebury area in the past but not noted during the present survey. **0** (0).

Picea abies (L.) H. Karst. **Norway Spruce**

Neophyte. Introduced and widely planted in plantations, particularly for use as Christmas Trees. Only noted as self-sown at Upper Halling TQ66X, but would be expected to be found elsewhere. **1** (3).

Picea mariana **Black Spruce**
(Mill.) Britton, Sterns & Poggenb.

Introduced (neophyte). Self-sown plants of this Canadian tree have been recorded from the Bedgebury area in the past, but were not noted during the present survey. **0** (0).

Larix decidua Mill. **European Larch**

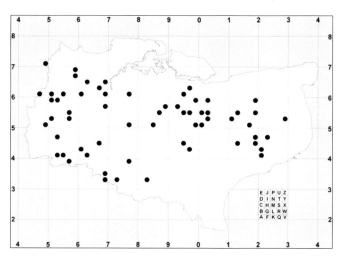

Introduced (neophyte). Commonly planted for forestry and ornament, and frequently self-sown. Now well naturalised in scattered localities in the county and often difficult to judge if self-sown or not. **61** (78).

Larix decidua x kaempferi **Hybrid Larch**
= L. x marschlinsii Coaz

This hybrid is now much planted in forestry plots and self-sown seedlings were noted in Joyden's Wood TQ57A. **1** (0).

Larix kaempferi (Lamb.) Carrière **Japanese Larch**

Introduced (neophyte). Much planted in forestry plots and self-sown seedlings or young trees have been noted at Bedgebury TQ73G, Little Chart TQ94N, Covert Wood TR14Z and Eggringe Wood TR15A. **4** (0).

Pinus sylvestris L. **Scots Pine**

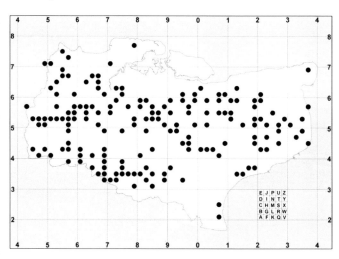

Introduced (neophyte). Not a native tree in Kent, but much planted for forestry and ornament and now widely established and self-seeding. It is particularly troublesome on some sites on the chalk where numerous seedlings are establishing themselves and likely to suppress the chalk flora. **173** (163).

Pinus nigra Austrian Pine, Corsican Pine
J.F. Arnold

Introduced (neophyte) to Britain in 1814 and widely planted for forestry, shelter-belts and for ornament. There are a few past records of self-sown plants but it was not recorded during the present survey. **0** (6).

Pinus contorta Lodgepole Pine
Douglas ex Loudon

Introduced (neophyte) and frequently planted in forestry plots. However, the only presumably self-sown plant noted during the present survey was at Dartford TQ57M. **1** (0).

Pinus pinaster Aiton Maritime Pine

Introduced (neophyte). Plants growing in the wild were noted at Sutton-at-Hone TQ57K and Thornden Wood TR16M. **2** (0).

Pinus radiata D. Don Monterey Pine

Introduced (neophyte). There are past records of self-sown seedlings from the Bedgebury Forest area, but it was not noted during the present survey. **0** (1).

Pinus strobus L. Weymouth Pine

Introduced (neophyte). There are past records of self-sown seedlings from the Bedgebury Forest area, but it was not noted during the present survey. **0** (1).

Sequoia sempervirens Coastal Redwood
(D. Don) Endl.

Introduced (neophyte). The occasional tree has been recorded in the past, but no wild growing trees were noted during the present mapping. **0** (0).

Sequoiadendron giganteum Wellingtonia
(Lindl.) Buchholz

Introduced (neophyte). A North American tree that is often planted in parks and large gardens. Wild, unattended trees were noted at Minching Wood TQ95E and Trenleypark Wood TR15Z. **2** (0).

CUPRESSACEAE

Cupressus macrocarpa Monterey Cypress
Hartw. ex Gordon

Introduced (neophyte). Often planted in parks and gardens. Although self-sown seedlings have been recorded in the past, none was found during the present survey. **0** (1).

Chamaecyparis lawsoniana Lawson's Cypress
(A. Murray bis) Parl.

Introduced (neophyte). A common tree in parks and gardens which frequently regenerates from seed. However, such seedlings were only noted at Bedgebury TQ73G and Bluebell Hill TQ76K during the present survey. **2** (8).

Chamaecyparis thyoides White Cypress
(L.) Britton, Sterns & Poggenb.

Introduced (neophyte). Self-sown plants reported from Bedgebury Pinetum in the past, but not recorded during the present survey. **0** (0).

TAXODIACEAE

Cryptomeria japonica Japanese Red-cedar
(L. f.) D. Don

Introduced (neophyte). Often planted in parks and gardens. A wild, but perhaps originally planted, tree in Trenleypark Wood TR15Z. **1** (3).

Thuja plicata Donn ex D. Don Western Red-cedar

Introduced (neophyte). First grown in Britain in 1853 and now widely planted in parks, graveyards and gardens. Self-sown plants were recorded from Mereworth Wood TQ65M, Maidstone TQ75T, Chart Sutton TQ75V, Orlestone Forest TQ93S and Eggringe Wood TR15A. **5** (1).

Juniperus communis L.   Common Juniper

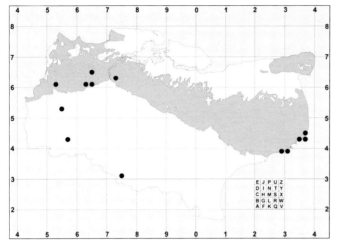

A native plant, particularly on the chalk, but now rare and declining. Some known shrubs have died as the result of a fungus infection, and others growing on the cliff tops in the east of the county have been lost through erosion. The plant in a hedgerow near Hawkhurst TQ73K might be introduced but all the other bushes appear to be genuine native plants. **13** (13).

ARAUCARIACEAE

Araucaria araucana (Molina) K. Koch   **Monkey-puzzle**

Introduced (neophyte). First introduced to Britain in 1795 and planted, usually as a specimen tree, in parks and large gardens. Trees in wild countryside that show no signs of care at Ditton TQ75I and Littlebourne TR25E might have some claim to be included in the Kent flora. **2** (0).

TAXACEAE

Taxus baccata L.   Yew

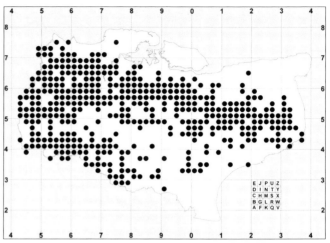

A native tree of woods and chalk downland. It seeds itself freely and seedlings or young trees are frequently found in gardens and hedgerows. It is regularly found in churchyards, often as fine old trees that must have been present there much longer than the church itself. **444** (468).

Yew tree *Taxus baccata* at Eastling © J. Church

LAURACEAE

Laurus nobilis L.   Bay

Introduced (neophyte). Occasionally planted in gardens for culinary use. Self-sown seedlings and young plants found established at Hawkhurst TQ72P, Appledore TQ92P and Selling TR05N, and a well grown tree in a hedgerow at Faversham TR06F. **4** (1).

Persea americana Mill.   Avocado

Introduced (neophyte). Occasional young plants have been found on rubbish-tips in the past, but none has been recorded during the present survey. **0** (3).

ARISTOLOCHIACEAE

Aristolochia clematitis L.   Birthwort

Introduced (neophyte). Formerly used medicinally and occasionally persisting on rough ground. Last recorded wild in the county in 1967. **0** (0).

Aristolochia rotunda L.   Smearwort

Introduced (neophyte) and occasionally naturalised, but in Kent last recorded on the chalk downs near Shoreham in 1901. **0** (0).

NYMPHAEACEAE

Nymphaea alba L.   White Water-lily

Native. Regularly planted in ornamental or fishing lakes, making it difficult, or impossible, to be sure if populations have been introduced or not. Only genuine wild-looking plants have been mapped. Frequent in the Weald and with scattered records elsewhere. **86** (79).

White Water-lily *Nymphaea alba* © D. Mills

Nuphar lutea (L.) Sm.   Yellow Water-lily

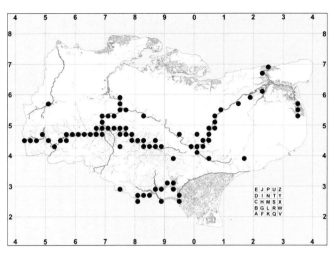

Native; in freshwater lakes, ponds, rivers and dykes. Particularly frequent along the rivers Beult, Medway and Great Stour. **81** (118).

CERATOPHYLLACEAE

Ceratophyllum demersum L.   Rigid Hornwort

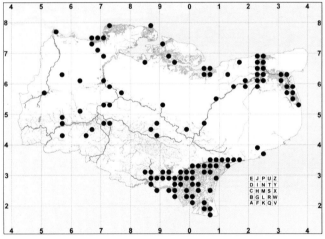

A native plant of ponds, ditches and slow-flowing rivers. Frequent in suitable habitats. **116** (109).

Marsh Marigold *Caltha palustris* © S. Poyser

Ceratophyllum submersum L.   Soft Hornwort

A native of ponds and ditches, now almost restricted to some of the coastal grazing marshes. It appears to have gone from some former sites, probably through changes in land management or actual loss of habitat. **23** (56).

RANUNCULACEAE

Caltha palustris L.   Marsh-marigold

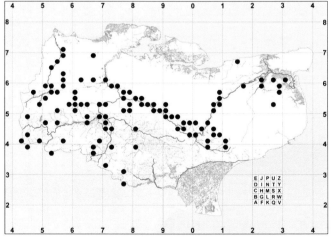

Native. A plant of marshes, streamsides and wet woods. There appears to be an increase in abundance at some sites, but in other places it has gone, mainly through loss of habitat. Note that the Marsh-marigold is one of the regularly planted species at newly created water-sites which could effect an apparent wider distribution in the future. **103** (123).

Helleborus foetidus L.   Stinking Hellebore

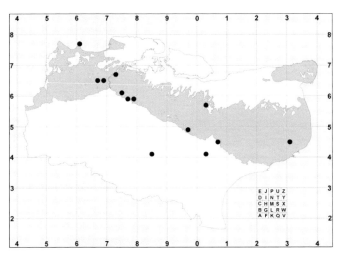

Native on the chalk downland around Halling TQ66S & X, Bluebell Hill TQ76K and Boxley TQ75U & Z. This plant is frequently grown in gardens where it readily sets seed and escapes. The other localities shown on the map are all of well established colonies growing in the wild, but all probably the result of such escapes. **13** (15).

Green Hellebore *Heleborus viridus* © S. Poyser

Helleborus viridis L.   Green Hellebore

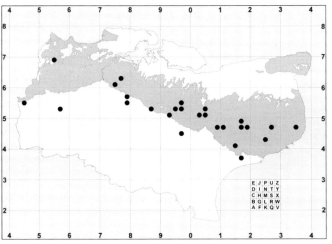

A native plant of woods and copses, usually on the chalk. There appears to be some decline in the number of populations as a result of destruction of habitat, or of woodland becoming scrubbed-up through the cessation of coppicing. **26** (37).

Eranthis hyemalis (L.) Salisb.   Winter Aconite

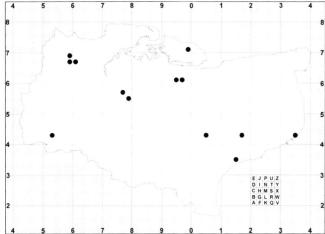

Introduced (neophyte). A garden plant present in Britain by 1596. It regularly becomes naturalised in gardens and formal parks, but only plants well in the wild and with no signs of recent cultivation have been mapped. **13** (9).

Nigella damascena L.   Love-in-a-mist

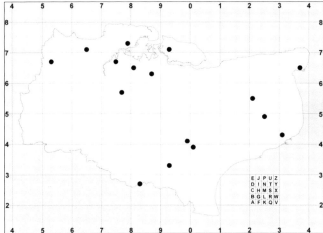

Introduced (neophyte). An annual garden plant that has been in cultivation in this country since at least 1570. It readily escapes and becomes temporarily established on waste ground, old walls or in pavement cracks. Only plants well away from gardens have been mapped. **16** (6).

Aconitum napellus L.   Monk's-hood

An introduced plant to Kent, but some doubt exists as to the true identity of past records as some, perhaps most, should be referred to the hybrid. The only record of the true species during this survey was of one plant in a damp copse by the river at Yalding TQ64Z. **1** (7).

Aconitum napellus x variegatum **Hybrid Monk's-hood**
= A. x cammarum L.

Introduced (neophyte). A garden plant that occasionally escapes, or might be deliberately planted, into the wild. Established plants were recorded at Maidstone TQ75T, Doddington TQ95I, near Eastling TQ94S and Larkeyvalley Wood near Canterbury TR15H. **4** (0).

Consolida ajacis (L.) Schur **Larkspur**

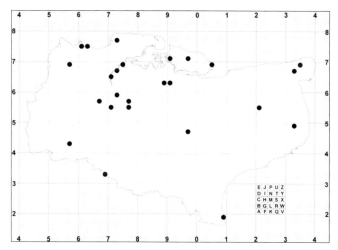

Introduced (neophyte). Grown in gardens since at least 1573 and first recorded in the wild in Kent in 1687. Formerly in cornfields and rubbish tips, but now a casual plant of cultivated ground and more frequently on disturbed roadside verges. **25** (49)

Anemone nemorosa L. **Wood Anemone**

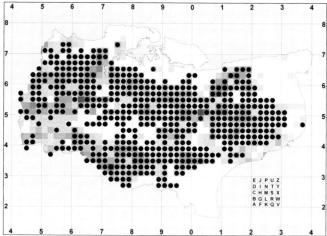

A native plant found in deciduous woods, copses and woodland-relic hedgerows. Common in suitable habitats. **512** (550).

Anemone apennina L. **Blue Anemone**

Introduced (neophyte). Often planted under trees in parkland and large gardens, and in churchyards. Recorded wild and established at Sevenoaks Weald TQ55F, Maidstone TQ75T, Boxley TQ75U, Canterbury TR15M and Folkestone TR23C. **5** (0).

Anemone ranunculoides L. **Yellow Anemone**

Introduced (neophyte). Recorded from Wrotham c. 1880, but has no real claim to the Kentish flora. **0** (0).

Wood Anemone *Anemone nemorosa* © S. Poyser

Anemone hupehensis x *vitifolia*   Japanese Anemone
= *A.* x *hybrida* Paxton

Introduced (neophyte). A garden hybrid that has been in cultivation since 1848. There have been a few casual records as a garden escape in the past, but it was not recorded during the present survey. **0** (4).

Clematis vitalba L.   Traveller's-joy

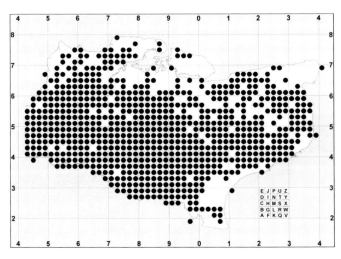

A native plant of hedgerows, thickets and open woodland on chalky or other calcareous soils. Sometimes found around old buildings or other constructions where concrete or cement has been used, in areas away from the chalk and ragstone. **625** (657).

Clematis flammula L.   Virgin's-bower

Introduced (neophyte). Still well naturalised on the sand-dunes at Sandwich Bay where it has been known since 1927. **1** (2).

Ranunculus acris L.   Meadow Buttercup

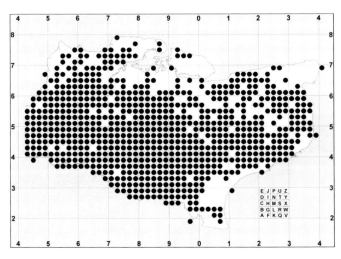

A native plant of pastures, damp meadows and grassy roadside verges. Although still a common plant, there appear to be some losses through the building on, or ploughing up, of former sites. **745** (849).

Ranunculus repens L.   Creeping Buttercup

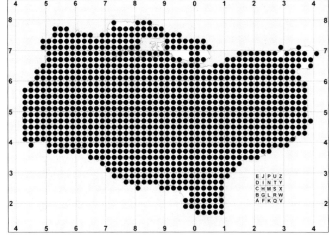

A native plant of cultivated and waste land, wet meadows and open woodland. A common plant, to be found throughout the county. **1003** (1017).

Ranunculus bulbosus L.   Bulbous Buttercup

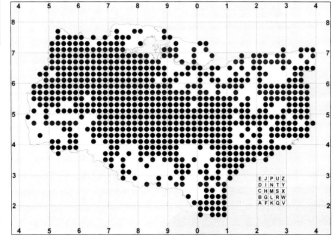

A native plant found in meadows, pastures, roadside verges and other well-drained grassland sites in all but the most acid areas. **735** (824).

Ranunculus sardous Crantz   Hairy Buttercup

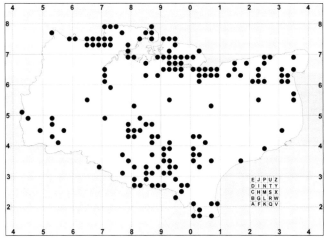

A native plant of coastal pastures, and in arable fields, damp pastures and roadside verges on clayey soils inland. **163** (123).

Ranunculus parviflorus L.   Small-flowered Buttercup

A native plant of dry fields or banks, particularly in areas disturbed by rabbits, apparently always a rare plant in the county, and still so. Recorded only from the edge of a field near Wouldham TQ76H; a field near Borstal TQ76I where it was in good quantity; a motorway bank near Ashford TR04K, and from scattered plants on small sandy banks over the shingle at Dungeness TR01T, Y and Z. **6** (4).

Ranunculus arvensis L.   Corn Buttercup

Introduced (archaeophyte). A cornfield weed known in the county since 1632. This species has shown a steady decline since the war due to the intensification of farming methods and during the present survey was only found at one site near Marden TQ74S; nationally, it is listed as 'Critically Endangered'. **1** (15).

Ranunculus auricomus L.   Goldilocks Buttercup

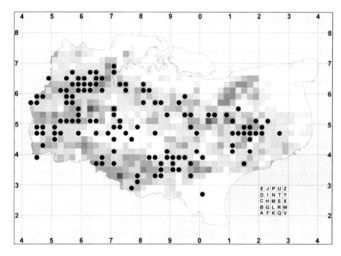

A native plant of deciduous woodland and sometimes found on roadsides or in scrub. It usually occurs in small thinly scattered numbers, and with a short flowering season, can be elusive to find and is perhaps a little under-recorded. However, there has been some loss through the destruction of woodland and scrub. **126** (236).

Ranunculus lingua L.   Greater Spearwort

A native plant that is found at the edge of ponds and ditches, and in marshes. It is sometimes introduced near habitation, but obvious freshly planted specimens have not been mapped. **18** (15).

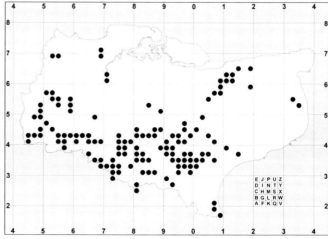

Goldilocks Buttercup *Ranunculus auricomus* © S. Poyser

Ranunculus sceleratus L.   Celery-leaved Buttercup

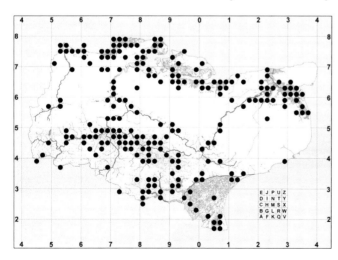

A native plant found in shallow water, or on mud at the edge of ponds, streams and ditches. It is particularly frequent in mud disturbed by drinking livestock, and on cattle grazed coastal marshes. **220** (317).

Ranunculus flammula L.   Lesser Spearwort

A plant photograph is shown here.

Native. A plant of wet habitats in woodlands and marshes, particularly on the more acid soils. **134** (174).

Ranunculus ficaria L. Lesser Celandine

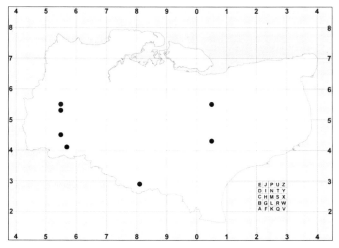

A common native plant, and one of the first of the herbaceous species to come into flower each year. It occurs in woodland, meadows, at the sides of roads and streams, and also in churchyards and gardens. Attempts were made to map the two subspecies separately but no difference in distribution within the county could be found, save that ssp. *ficaria* was more frequent in old and ancient woodlands and meadows and ssp. *bulbilifer* was more frequent in disturbed soils such as found in churchyards and gardens. However, there was some overlap and often the two subspecies could be found growing close together. **861** (805).

Ranunculus hederaceus L. Ivy-leaved Crowfoot

Native. A rather local and declining species found at the edge of ponds and streams, most often where disturbed by cattle. **7** (10).

Ranunculus omiophyllus Ten. Round-leaved Crowfoot

A native plant of Western Britain and recorded from the county at some time before 1899. There is a doubt as to whether these records were in error, but the species is in decline nationally and is not likely now to be found in Kent. **0** (0).

Ranunculus tripartitus DC. Three-lobed Crowfoot

A rare native plant of shallow pools and ditches. At times it can occur in pools that are flooded in winter but will dry out in summer, so that it can be rather ephemeral in its appearance. Recorded during the present survey from a pool in Combwell Wood TQ73C, a pool in coppiced woodland in Longrope Wood TQ93S, and in a flooded area from which scrub had been cleared on Hothfield Bog TQ94S. Noted in the Red List as Endangered. **3** (1).

Ranunculus baudotii Godr. Brackish Water-crowfoot

A native plant of coastal ditches and pools, usually, but not always, in brackish water. There appears to be some decline due to changes in farming practices, particularly where surrounding grazing marshes have been turned into arable, or with the drying-up or removal of ditches. **46** (79).

Ranunculus baudotii x trichophyllus
= R. x segretii A. Félix

This hybrid has been recorded from West Kent in the past, but was not noted during the present survey. **0** (0).

Brackish Water-crowfoot *Ranunculus baudotii* © L. Rooney

31

Ranunculus trichophyllus Thread-leaved Water-crowfoot
Chaix

Ranunculus peltatus Schrank   Pond Water-crowfoot

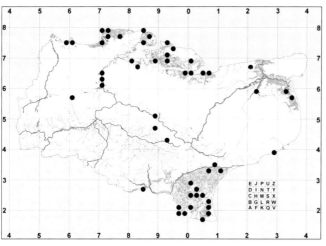

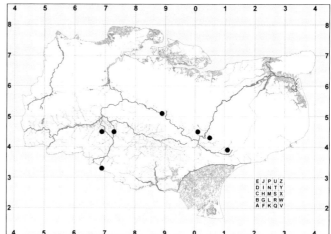

A native plant of ponds, ditches and slow-running streams. It is more frequent near the coast but there are some inland localities. All the water-crowfoots are difficult to determine and can only be so done when plants are found with both flowers and fruit. Not being able to get to all the localities at the correct time of year has probably resulted in some under-recording, but in many known localities it was searched for and not found, so there does appear to be some general loss. **51** (118).

A native plant of shallow lakes and ponds. This plant has been specifically searched for at a number of former localities and not found, and even allowing for where it has been missed, there appears to have been a serious loss in the number of sites still present in the county. **7** (36).

Ranunculus trichophyllus x aquatilis
= *R. x lutzii* A. Félix

This hybrid has been recorded from West Kent in the past, but was not found during the present survey. **0** (0).

Ranunculus penicillatus (Dumort.) Stream Water-crowfoot
Bab. **ssp. *pseudofluitans***
(Syme) S.D. Webster

Ranunculus aquatilis L.   Common Water-crowfoot

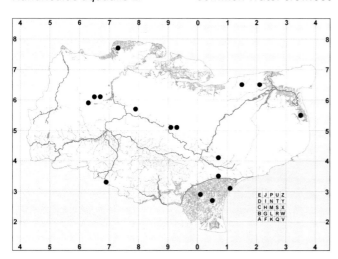

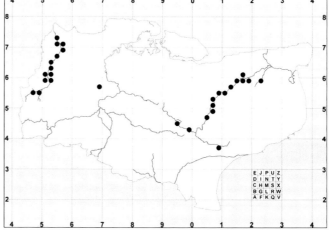

A native plant of shallow waters in ponds, ditches and slow-flowing streams. There are scattered records throughout the county, but nowhere can it live up to its English name. **16** (26).

A native plant of moderately or fast flowing rivers and streams. Although it is still widespread along the rivers Darent and Great Stour, there does appear to be a fall in the actual numbers of plants present. **29** (39).

Ranunculus circinatus Sibth. **Fan-leaved Water-crowfoot**

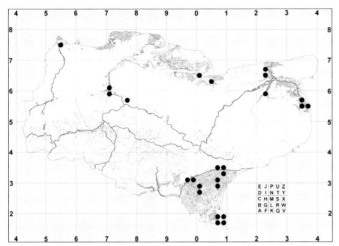

A native plant of lakes, flooded gravel-pits, canals and deeper marsh dykes and drains. Somewhat local and appears to be declining. **25** (48).

Adonis annua L. **Pheasant's-eye**

Introduced (archaeophyte). Historical records suggest that it was once a common plant in cornfields on the chalk, but started to decline in about 1880. This decline has continued and during the present survey it was only recorded at one site near Fawkham TQ56Z. Noted in the Red List as Endangered. **1** (4).

Myosurus minimus L. **Mousetail**

A native plant of damp arable ground. Formerly with scattered records over most of Kent, it has steadily declined over the last hundred years or so, and was last recorded in the county in 1975 and is now probably extinct. **0** (1).

Aquilegia vulgaris L. **Columbine**

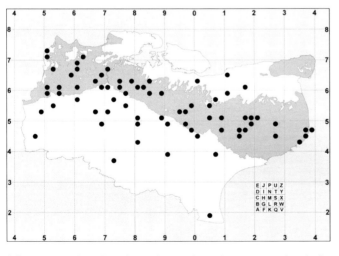

A frequent native plant found in woods and copses on the chalk. The Columbine is a common garden plant and wild plants away from the chalk are most likely to be escapes from cultivation. **72** (81).

Aquilegia olympica Boiss.

Introduced (neophyte). A garden escape was reported from chalky banks on Wrotham Hill in 1984; there are no subsequent records. **0** (0).

Thalictrum aquilegiifolium L. **French Meadow-rue**

Introduced (neophyte). A garden escape established on a railway bank near Tunbridge Wells from 1949 until at least the mid-1980s, but it was not noted during the present survey. **0** (1).

Thalictrum flavum L. **Common Meadow-rue**

A native plant of streamsides and wet meadows. This Meadow-rue was never a common plant in the county and most former sites were along the Medway and Stour valleys. Land drainage, agricultural intensification and building development have slowly eaten into the habitats of this plant and is now only known from a few plants on the east and west banks of the River Medway near Snodland TQ76A, and in good quantity in a small marsh by the river Great Stour at Wye TR04N. **2** (2).

Thalictrum minus L. **Lesser Meadow-rue**

Introduced (neophyte). A garden escape that has been recorded from a few scattered localities within the county in the past. The only records during the present survey were of a well established plant near Chatham TQ76S and a fine clump in a hedgerow, well away from any gardens, near St. Margaret's TR34S. **2** (3).

Thalictrum speciosissimum L.

Introduced (neophyte). Has been recorded as a relic from cultivation at Whetstead and Stone (both West Kent) in the past, but there are no subsequent records. **0** (0).

BERBERIDACEAE

Berberis vulgaris L. **Barberry**

Introduced (neophyte). In the past it was occasionally planted at the edges of woods and in hedgerows, where it could become well established. It was later found to be the host for the wheat rust *Puccinia graminis* and then actively eradicated by cereal growers. The odd plant might still linger on, but no wild plants were found during the present survey. **0** (5).

Berberis thunbergii DC. **Thunberg's Barberry**

Introduced (neophyte). A garden escape that has been reported from hedgerows and waste ground in the past, but was not encountered during the present survey. **0** (0).

Berberis x *hybrido-gagnepainii* Sur.

Introduced (neophyte). A garden plant that was recorded from a hedgerow near Halstead in the past (Clement & Foster, 1994), but with no other records. **0** (0).

Berberis *darwinii* Hook.   Darwin's Barberry

Introduced (neophyte). A common garden plant of which bird-sown seedlings have been reported from near Dartford in the past. There are no recent records. **0** (1).

Berberis x *stenophylla* Lindl.   Hedge Barberry

Introduced (neophyte). Suckers from a garden plant reported from a roadside near Westerham in the past, but with no subsequent records. **0** (1).

Berberis *manipurana* Ahrendt   Manipur Barberry

Introduced (neophyte). A large, bird-sown bush persisted from c. 1950 – c. 1990 on Tunbridge Wells Common. **0** (0).

Berberis x *ottawensis* C. K. Schneid.

Introduced (neophyte). A garden escape was recorded from West Kent in 1987 (Clement & Foster, 1994) **0** (0).

Mahonia *aquifolium* (Pursh) Nutt.   Oregon-grape

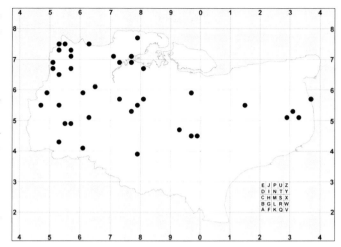

Introduced (neophyte). A North American shrub that is commonly planted for pheasant cover and for amenity purposes both in gardens and on roadside banks. Completely naturalised, or bird-sown plants, well away from gardens are to be found scattered throughout the county and only these have been mapped. **40** (63).

LARDIZABALACEAE

Akebia *quinata* (Houtt.) Decne.   Five-leaf Akebia

Introduced (neophyte). A relic from cultivation for which there is a past record from Sandling, near Hythe. (Clement & Foster, 1994). **0** (0).

Ranscombe Farm © S. Poyser

PAPAVERACEAE

Papaver pseudoorientale (Fedde) Medw.   Oriental Poppy

Introduced (neophyte). Commonly grown in gardens and occasionally found self-sown or naturalised on roadsides or other well-drained sites. Recorded from near Dunton Green TQ55E, Swanscombe TQ67B, Greet TQ95H and Sandwich Bay TR35T during the present survey. **4** (4).

Papaver atlanticum (Ball) Coss.   Atlas Poppy

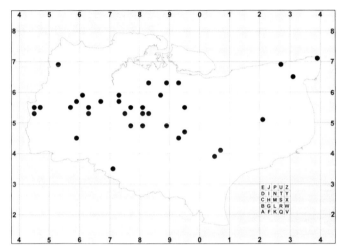

Introduced (neophyte). First taken into cultivation in this country in 1889 and recorded in the wild by 1928. It is now frequently found naturalised on waste ground, particularly in churchyards, and on old walls, especially those built of ragstone. **35** (14).

Papaver somniferum L.   Opium Poppy

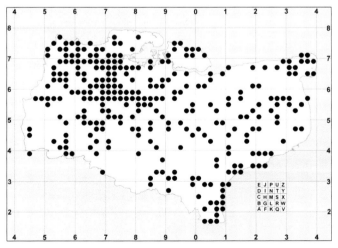

Introduced (archaeophyte). Much grown in gardens and frequently found as an escape on roadsides and waste ground. The pale lilac form is regularly found as an annual weed in cornfields and other arable crop fields where it behaves very much as a native plant. **296** (236).

Papaver rhoeas L.   Common Poppy

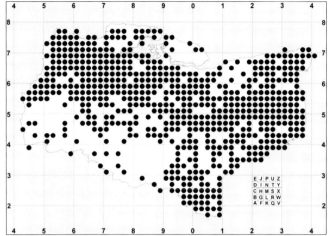

Introduced (archaeophyte). Long established, probably originally introduced as a contaminant in crop seed, eventually to become a common and regular plant in arable fields. It is still to be found commonly in cornfields on light calcareous soils. It also occurs on roadsides and other neglected ground, these occurrences sometimes as escapes from cultivation or as a result of the sowing of 'wild-flower' seed mixes. There appears to be some decline in the overall population due to more efficient farming methods. **644** (774).

Common Poppy *Papaver rhoeas* © S. Poyser

Papaver dubium L. ssp. dubium   Long-headed Poppy

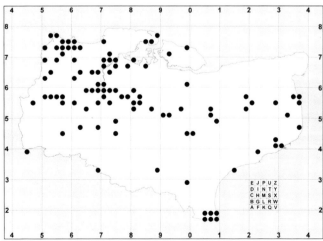

Introduced (archaeophyte). Found in cornfields or other disturbed ground, particularly on chalk or sandy soils. **102** (157).

Papaver dubium ssp. **lecoqii**
(Lamotte) Syme   Yellow-juiced Poppy

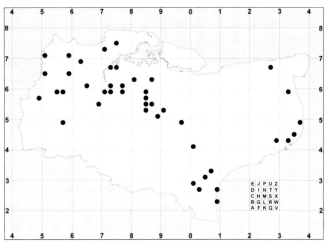

Introduced (archaeophyte). Found in arable fields, roadsides and gardens, particularly on the lighter soils. The apparent increase in records is probably due to more careful recording, and confirms the general pattern of distribution. **43** (24).

Papaver argemone L.   Prickly Poppy

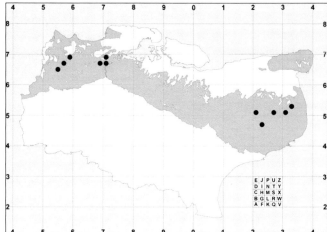

Introduced (archaeophyte). A plant of cornfields and unsprayed areas in other arable fields on light sandy or chalky soils. Like the previous species there has also been a serious decline in the population of this poppy and it is now listed in the Red List as Vulnerable. **11** (46).

Papaver nudicaule L.   Iceland Poppy

Introduced (neophyte). Recorded as an escape from cultivation in the Maidstone area in the past, but not noted during the present survey. **0** (1).

Papaver hybridum L   Rough Poppy

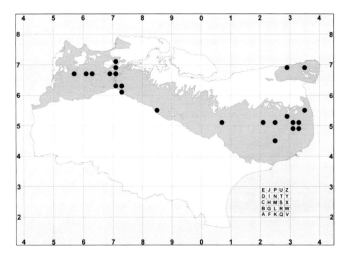

Introduced (archaeophyte). A long established annual that occurs in arable crops and in other disturbed habitats, usually on chalky soils. The long term decrease in this species continues and this is reflected in the 60% drop in the number of records since the 1971-80 survey. **23** (57).

Meconopsis cambrica (L.) Vig.   Welsh Poppy

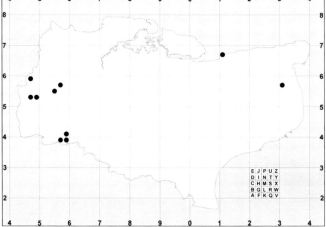

Introduced (neophyte). A garden escape that has become well naturalised on old walls and roadside banks, particularly in the west of the county. **10** (9).

Glaucium flavum Crantz   Yellow Horned-poppy

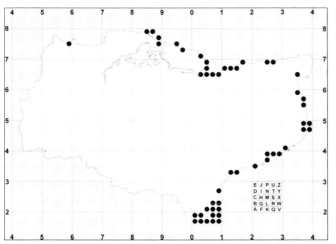

A native plant of shingle banks and stony beaches around the coast.   The present population appears to be relatively stable. **51** (49).

Glaucium corniculatum (L.) Rudolph   Red Horned-poppy

Introduced (neophyte). A garden outcast that has been recorded on a couple of occasions in the past, but was not seen during the present survey. **0** (0).

Chelidonium majus L.   Greater Celandine

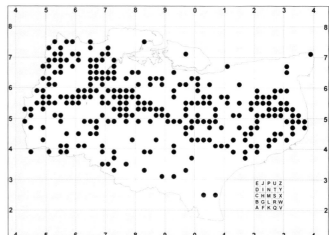

Introduced (archaeophyte) although fossil pollen has been found in Flandrian deposits in the county. A plant that was at one time cultivated for medicinal purposes and is now well naturalised on old walls and roadside banks, practically always near human habitation. **237** (309).

Yellow-horned Poppy *Glaucium flavum* © S. Poyser

Eschscholzia californica Cham. California Poppy

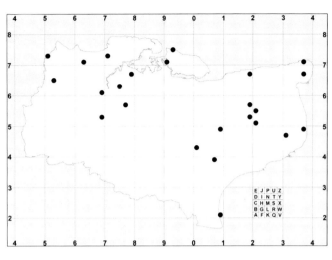

Introduced (neophyte). A commonly grown garden plant that frequently escapes, and at times persists, on roadsides, beaches and other waste ground. **24** (29).

Macleaya x **kewensis** Turrill Hybrid Plume-poppy

Introduced. A casual garden outcast recorded from waste ground near Dartford in the 1970s, but with no subsequent records. **0** (1).

FUMARIACEAE

Corydalis solida (L.) Clairv. Bird-in-a-bush

Introduced (neophyte). Well naturalised in Elham Park Wood TR14T where it has now been known for over fifty years. **1** (1).

Pseudofumaria lutea (L.) Borkh. Yellow Corydalis

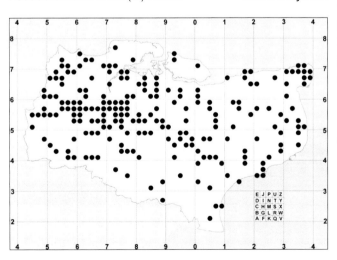

Introduced (neophyte). A garden plant first recorded growing wild in Britain in 1796. It is now widely distributed in Kent where it is found growing in crevices in old walls, pavement cracks and on old buildings, and on occasion on stony waste ground. **217** (236).

Ceratocapnos claviculata (L.) Lidén Climbing Corydalis

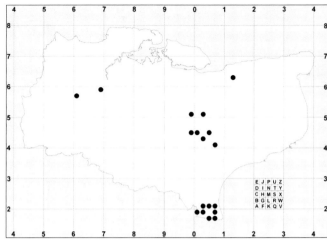

A native plant of sandy heathland or woodland, and on shingle beaches, usually growing in some sort of shade. It is frequent over the shingle in the Dungeness area but with only scattered records elsewhere on Eocene Sands or Folkestone Beds. **18** (21).

Fumaria capreolata L. White Ramping-fumitory

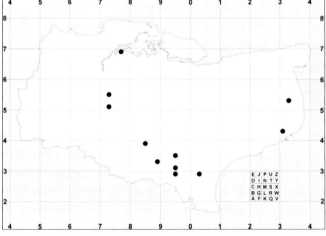

Native, although at some sites it might have originally been introduced. It occurs on roadsides, disturbed ground around buildings and in gardens. Although very local, it is usually quite frequent where it does occur. **11** (9).

Fumaria bastardii Boreau Tall Ramping-fumitory

Always rare and perhaps native to Kent, this plant was last recorded in the county in the 1950s. **0** (0).

Fumaria muralis
Sond. ex W.D.J.Koch

Common Ramping-fumitory

Fumaria densiflora DC.

Dense-flowered Fumitory

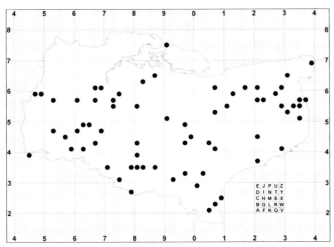

Native. A plant of hedgerows, arable fields, gardens and other disturbed soils. **68** (66).

A native plant of arable fields, particularly on the chalk, and found with both vegetable and cereal crops. Probably because of agricultural intensification this plant has declined greatly in recent years. **26** (60).

Fumaria officinalis L.

Common Fumitory

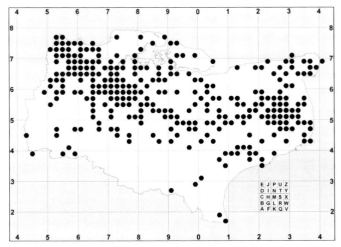

Native. A frequent plant of arable fields, gardens and disturbed waste ground. The impression is that this species has declined in recent years and this is backed up with a greatly reduced number of tetrad records. Ssp. *officinalis* is found throughout the county and ssp. *wirtgenii* occurs on the lighter soils, particularly on the chalk, but there is much overlap between the ranges and indeed between the two sub-species. **300** (496).

Dense-flowered Fumitory *Fumaria densiflora* © R. Moyse

Fumaria parviflora Lam.

Fine-leaved Fumitory

A native plant of arable fields on chalky soils. This has always been a rather scarce plant in the county and appears to have declined even further in recent years. During the present survey it was recorded from cornfields on the chalk near Cuxton in tetrads TQ76D & 76E, and from another cornfield on the chalk at Westwell TQ94E. In the Red List noted as 'Vulnerable'. **3** (10).

Fumaria vaillantii Loisel.

Few-flowered Fumitory

A rare native plant of arable fields on the chalk. The only records are from a cornfield at Horton Kirby TQ56T and from disturbed chalky soil near Snodland TQ76A. Its Red List category is 'Vulnerable'. **2** (1).

PLATANACEAE

Platanus x *hispanica*
Mill. ex Münchh.

London Plane

Introduced (neophyte). A frequently planted tree and considered naturalised and established at Penshurst TQ54H, East Malling TQ65Y, Aylesford TQ75J, Maidstone TQ75T, Bearsted TQ75X, Hollingbourne TQ85M and Oare TR06B. **7** (5).

ULMACEAE

Ulmus glabra Huds.

Wych Elm

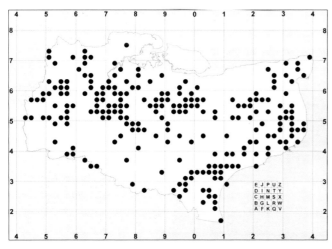

A native tree, but much planted and it is impossible to distinguish between truly native populations and those naturalised after planting. Frequent in woods and hedgerows throughout most of the county. **227** (361).

Ulmus glabra x *minor*
= *U.* x *vegeta* (Loudon) Ley

Huntingdon Elm

Well established trees and scrub fitting the description of this hybrid elm at Whitstable TR16D. **1** (0).

Ulmus x *hollandica* Mill.

Dutch Elm

Introduced (neophyte). The only records during this survey are of several trees at Five Oak Green TQ64M and of one tree on the banks of the River Bewl on the Scotney Castle Estate TQ63X. **2** (16).

Ulmus procera Salisb.

English Elm

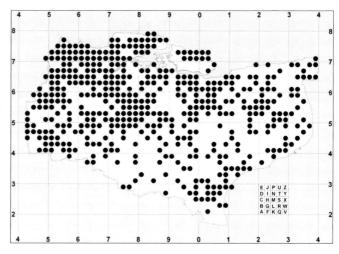

Native, although the status is a little confused because of much planting of this tree in the past. A large number of mature trees were lost during the outbreak of Dutch Elm Disease which started about 1965 and reached its height in the 1970s. Where the roots were not dug up or the hedgerows removed, the underground parts of the trees have thrown up suckers and matured so that trees and scrub of English Elm are still to be found commonly in hedgerows and small copses throughout most of the county. **485** (716).

Ulmus minor Mill.

Small-leaved Elm

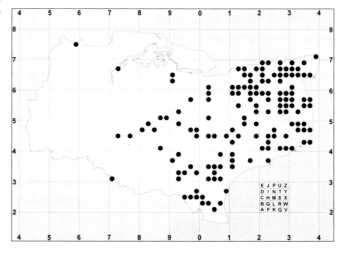

A native tree although much planted in the past, particularly in the east of the county. It suffered much the same fate with Dutch Elm Disease as the previous species, but likewise, the Small-leaved Elm has recovered and small trees and scrub are frequently encountered. Ssp. *minor* is the usual taxon encountered, but on the ragstone in the East Sutton area TQ84J some trees had affinities with ssp. *sarniensis*. **143** (249).

CANNABACEAE

MORACEAE

Cannabis sativa L.   Hemp

Ficus carica L.   Fig

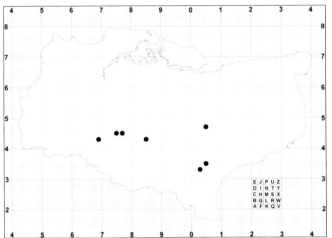

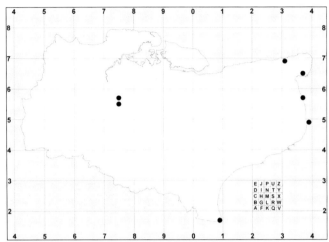

Introduced (neophyte). A casual plant on waste ground as a result of escape from cultivation or established from bird seed mixtures or fishing bait. During the 1971-80 survey it was commonly found on rubbish-tips but present management of such sites now prevents this. Plants that have obviously been planted and are being tended, as are often found on waste ground, have not been mapped. **7** (10).

Introduced (neophyte). Occasionally self-sown and naturalised on river banks and waste places. Some trees have been established for many years and regularly produce fruit. **7** (16).

URTICACEAE

Humulus lupulus L.   Hop

Urtica dioica L.   Common Nettle

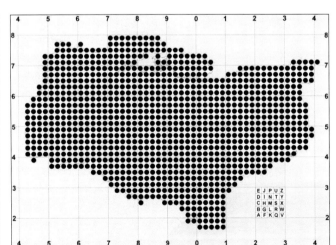

Native, although some plants might be relics from cultivation from when the Hop was widely grown in the county. Frequent in hedgerows, copses and thickets throughout most of the county. **559** (671).

Native. A common plant of woods, scrub, river banks, hedgerows, cultivated and waste ground, particularly on damp, nutrient-rich soils. A stingless form, sometimes known as *Urtica galeopsifolia*, has been noted at Hothfield TQ94S, near Chilham TR05W, Gibbin's Brook TR13E, West Wood TR14G and Northbourne TR35L. **1032** (1032).

41

Urtica urens L.   Small Nettle

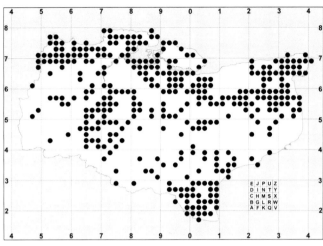

Introduced (archaeophyte). On arable fields with broad-leaved crops, gardens, allotments, farmyards and disturbed waste ground. **364** (541).

Urtica pilulifera L.   Roman Nettle

An introduced species first recorded in the county in 1640, but extinct before 1800 and not recorded since. **0** (0).

Parietaria judaica L.   Pellitory-of-the-wall

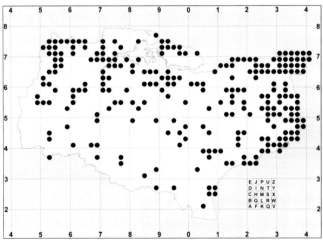

A native plant, although usually found near human habitation. In mortar crevices and cracks in brick and stone walls, on building rubble, but also in gardens, and on chalk cliffs and banks. **252** (227).

Soleirolia soleirolii   Mind-your-own-business
(Req.) Dandy

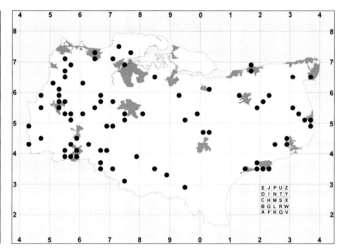

Introduced (neophyte). First cultivated in Britain in 1905 and escaping from gardens and greenhouses and first recorded in the wild in 1917. Now frequently found on old walls and damp banks in towns and around old country houses, and increasingly along river banks and other damp banks away from human habitation. **81** (41).

JUGLANDACEAE

Juglans regia L.   Walnut

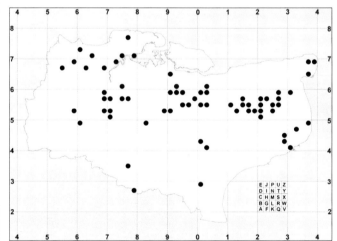

Introduced (neophyte). The Walnut has been in cultivation for over a thousand years and is still regularly planted out, particularly in open farmland. However it is often self-sown, or the seed is buried by grey squirrels or rooks, so that trees are regularly found in hedgerows, woodland and waste ground that can be termed genuinely wild. **68** (84).

MYRICACEAE

Myrica gale L.   Bog-myrtle

A native plant of raised bogs and wet heaths. Long lost from Tunbridge Wells and Willesborough Lees and now extinct in the county. A small colony on Keston Common in the London area of West Kent died out in 1957. **0** (0).

FAGACEAE

Castanea sativa Mill.   Sweet Chestnut

Fagus sylvatica L.   Beech

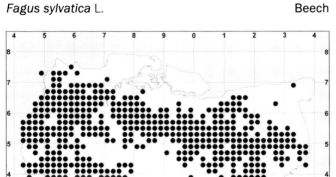

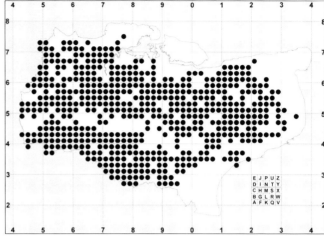

Introduced (neophyte). Formerly much planted for coppice woodland and as standard trees in parkland. Now well naturalised and frequently setting seed, and a common tree of 'Kentish' woodland. **567** (593).

A native tree, although frequently planted. In woods, copses and hedgerows on free-draining soils, but virtually absent from the coastal marshes and damp areas on the Weald Clay. **479** (579).

Beech trees at Ightham   © S. Poyser

43

Quercus cerris L.   Turkey Oak   *Quercus petraea* (Matt.) Liebl.   Sessile Oak

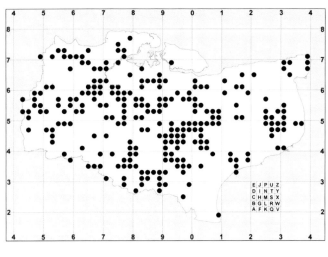 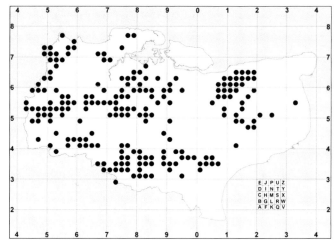

Introduced (neophyte). Commonly planted and now well naturalised and reproducing itself freely. In woods, copses and hedgerows, and at times in open scrub or wasteland, these latter probably due to the acorn having been buried by a Jay. **253** (262).

A native tree that is usually found on well drained acidic soils. Particularly frequent in the Blean Woods area around Canterbury, but the patchy distribution might be the result of introductions in the past. **207** (193).

Quercus cerris x *suber*   Lucombe Oak
= *Q.* x *crenata* Lam.

Introduced (neophyte). A naturalised tree on Dartford Heath TQ57G was the only one noted. **1** (0).

Quercus ilex L   Evergreen Oak   *Quercus petraea* x *robur* = *Q.* x *rosacea* Bechst.

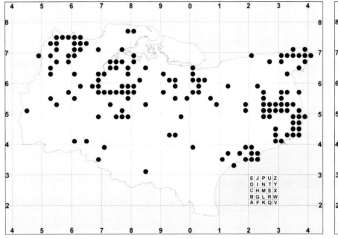 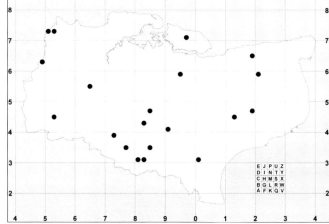

Neophyte. Introduced to this country in the 16th century, this tree was widely planted in parks and large gardens during the 18th century. Now, with many mature trees in parks and woodlands the resultant acorns are transported about by birds and squirrels, and seedlings are likely to occur almost anywhere in the county. In fact there are now many good trees or stands of trees in woods and hedgerows that are the result of this natural colonization. **155** (129).

There are scattered records from over the county, not always with one or both parents. This hybrid tree is easily missed and so probably under-recorded. **20** (5).

Quercus robur L.   Pedunculate Oak

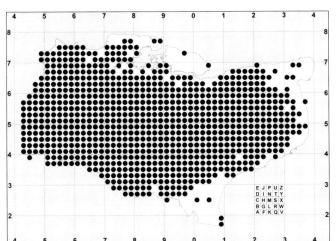

A common native tree found in woodland, parkland and hedgerows throughout most of the county. However, it is scarce or absent from Sheppey, Romney Marsh, and most other coastal marshes. **834** (839).

Betula pendula Roth   Silver Birch

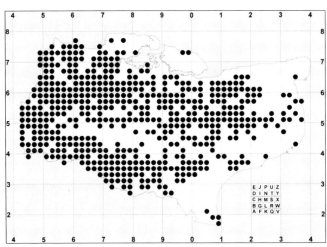

Native. Frequent in woods and heaths, but can occur on any well-drained, particularly acidic, soil. Any trees in coastal marshland areas are probably the result of introductions. **537** (650).

Quercus rubra L.   Red Oak

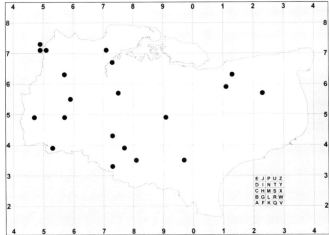

Introduced (neophyte). Frequently sown in forestry plots or for ornament in parks and large gardens. Self-sown saplings have been noted from scattered localities. **20** (0).

Quercus mas Thore

Introduced (neophyte). Self-sown seedlings have been reported from Stone and Bean (Clement & Foster, 1994). **0** (0).

Betula pendula x *pubescens*   Hybrid Birch
= *B.* x *aurata* Borkh.

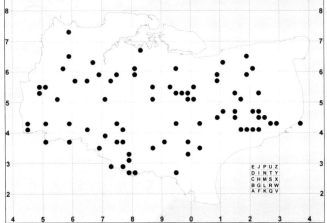

In similar habitats to its parents, one or both of which might be absent. It has a preference for disturbed soils and will readily colonize disused sand and gravel pits and other waste land. Many plantings from nursery stock sold as 'silver birch' when checked have proved to be this hybrid. Although great care has been taken with the identification of all birches this hybrid is almost certainly still very much under-recorded. **78** (0).

Betula pubescens Ehrh. Downy Birch

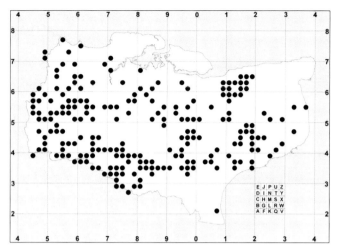

Native. Found in woods, heaths copses and hedgerows, particularly in wet, or at least damp areas. **219** (354).

Alnus glutinosa (L.) Gaertn. Alder

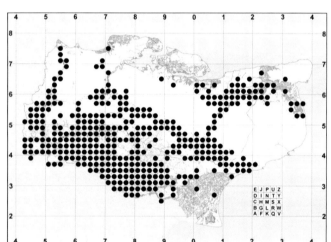

Native. In wet woods and by streams, ponds and on river banks. Frequent in suitable habitats throughout the county. **390** (434).

Alnus glutinosa x *incana*
= *A.* x *hybrida* A. Braun ex Rchb.

A planted tree was noted at a roadside near Brookland TQ92S. **1** (0).

Alnus incana (L.) Moench Grey Alder

Introduced (neophyte). A tree now much planted on roadsides and in shelter belts. Naturalised trees were noted near Maidstone at TQ75S & 75X, at Lenham Heath TQ94E and at Chartham TR15C. It is anticipated that this tree will be much more widely reported in the future as present plantings mature and set seed, or spread out by suckers. **4** (0).

Alnus cordata (Loisel.) Duby Italian Alder

Introduced (neophyte). Another Alder that is also much planted out for amenity purposes in parks and on roadsides, and again will be expected to be much more widely reported in the future. During the present survey naturalised plants were noted at Sundridge TQ45X, Dartford TQ57L, East Malling TQ75D, Rochester TQ76I & 76J, Little Chart TQ94N, near Conyer TQ96M and near Selling TR05T. **8** (0).

Carpinus betulus L. Hornbeam

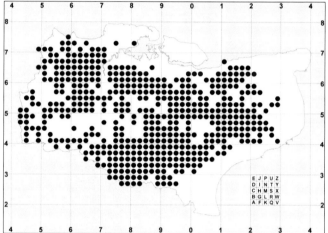

Native, although much planted in the past for charcoal and other uses. Now common in woods and hedgerows away from the coast. **511** (553).

Corylus avellana L. Hazel

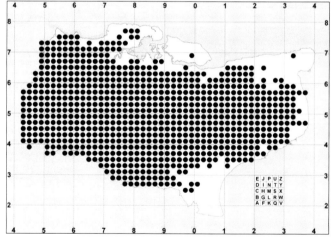

Native. In hedgerows, scrub and as understorey in woodland. Found throughout the county save for the coastal marshland areas. **787** (785).

Corylus maxima Mill. Kentish Cob or Filbert

Introduced (neophyte). Formerly much planted in the county, and many such plantations still remain. However, it has not been found growing wild during the present survey. **0** (0).

PHYTOLACCACEAE

Phytolacca acinosa Roxb. Indian Pokeweed

Introduced (neophyte). Found naturalised at Mersham TR03P. **1** (5).

AIZOACEAE

Aptenia cordifolia (L.f.) Schwantes Heart-leaf Ice-plant

Introduced. A garden plant that temporarily established itself on a rubbish-tip at Northfleet in the 1970s. **0** (1).

Disphyma crassifolium (L.) L. Bolus Purple Dewplant

Introduced (neophyte). Several long established clumps on the shingle at Sandgate TR23C. **1** (0).

Carpobrotus edulis (L.) N.E. Br. Hottentot-fig

Introduced (neophyte). Long established on the cliffs at Folkestone TR23I. **1** (1).

CHENOPODIACEAE

Chenopodium ambrosioides L. Mexican-tea

Introduced (neophyte). Was recorded as a casual on a rubbish-tip at Dartford in the 1970s. **0** (1).

Chenopodium pumilio R. Br. Clammy Goosefoot

Introduced. Recorded as a wool-alien in West Kent 1960-69, but not since. **0** (0).

Chenopodium carinatum R. Br. Keeled Goosefoot

Introduced (neophyte). Casual plants as a wool-alien at Birchington in 1961, but not seen since. **0** (0).

Chenopodium cristatum Crested Goosefoot
(F. Muell.) F. Muell.

Introduced. Recorded as a wool-alien in the 1950s, but not since. **0** (0).

Chenopodium capitatum (L.) Ambrosi Strawberry-bite

Introduced. Was recorded as a casual in an arable field at Patrixbourne in 1957, but there are no further sightings. **0** (0).

Chenopodium bonus-henricus L. Good-King-Henry

Introduced (archaeophyte). A casual plant found in disturbed soil around farmyards and other old buildings. It is no longer regularly grown as a salad plant and there has been a serious decline in records since the previous Atlas, reinforcing its national listing as 'Vulnerable'. During this survey it has been recorded from Brasted TQ45S, Romney Street TQ56K and Folkestone TR23D. **3** (25).

Chenopodium glaucum L. Oak-leaved Goosefoot

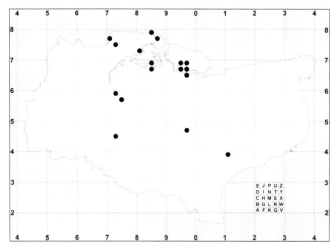

Introduced (archaeophyte). Long established around farm buildings, along tracks and on disturbed soils on the coast. Stable and regular populations are still to be found on and near the Thames, Medway and Swale. It has been introduced as a wool alien in the past and the inland records are probably casuals from such former introductions. A rare and declining plant and its Red List Category is 'Vulnerable'. **17** (5).

Chenopodium rubrum L. Red Goosefoot

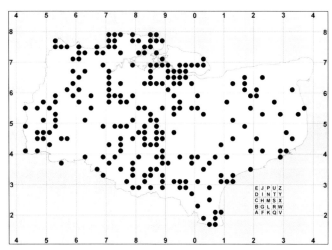

A native plant on nutrient-rich mud in ponds and ditches that are trampled by livestock, particularly those near the coast. It is also found in farmyards, on manure heaps and on cultivated ground. **233** (376).

47

Chenopodium chenopodioides   Saltmarsh Goosefoot
(L.) Aellen

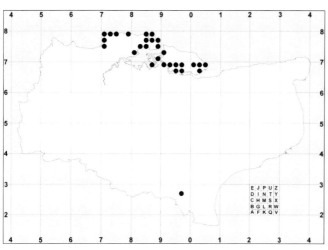

Native. On exposed mud at the edge of brackish dykes and creeks, and on cattle grazed salt-marshes. Nationally a rare plant that is restricted to south-east England, but which can at times be abundant, often mixed with the previous species, in some of the North Kent localities. **29** (21).

Chenopodium vulvaria L.   Stinking Goosefoot

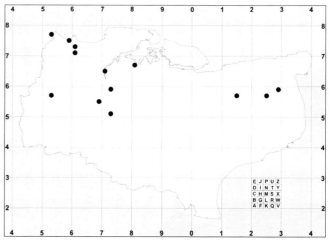

Introduced (archaeophyte). Long established, and looking native, on bare, or cattle trampled, soils on the coast. A rare and declining species with a Red List Category of 'Endangered'. **7** (1).

Chenopodium hybridum L.   Maple-leaved Goosefoot

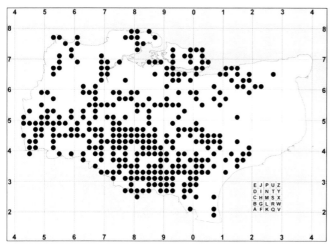

Introduced (archaeophyte). Known since before Roman times, this is a scarce but well-established plant of arable land, gardens and disturbed waste land. It has been a weed in the writer's garden for over forty years where it receives no special protection. **13** (17).

Chenopodium polyspermum L.   Many-seeded Goosefoot

Introduced (archaeophyte). Long established, and looking native. in damp woodland rides, arable fields and on disturbed waste land. Frequent, but scarce or absent from most areas on the chalk. **350** (392).

Maple-leaved Goosefoot *Chenopodium hybridum* © L. Rooney

Chenopodium urbicum L.　　　　　Upright Goosefoot

Introduced (archaeophyte). A plant of cultivated and waste ground. Always rare, it has not been recorded in the county since before 1930. **0** (0).

Chenopodium murale L.　　　Nettle-leaved Goosefoot

Introduced (archaeophyte). Long established but always rather local, and with many records in the past due to seed imported with wool shoddy. This practice has now stopped and during this survey this goosefoot was only found on a rubbish-tip at Dartford TQ57M and on some disturbed ground at Dungeness TR01U. It is listed nationally as 'Vulnerable'. **2** (12).

Chenopodium ficifolium Sm.　　　Fig-leaved Goosefoot

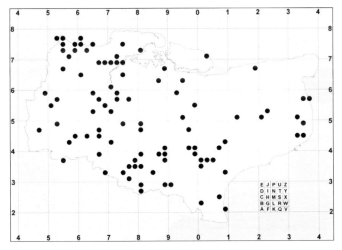

Introduced (archaeophyte), although looking native. In arable fields, gardens and disturbed waste ground, and usually found growing together with *Chenopodium album*. **95** (84).

Chenopodium hircinum Schrad.　　　Foetid Goosefoot

Introduced. Casual plants with wool shoddy at Birchington in 1961, but this goosefoot has not been found since. **0** (0).

Chenopodium missouriense　　Soya-bean Goosefoot
Aellen

Introduced. Was recorded as an oil-seed alien on three rubbish-tips in the Dartford area 1973-4, but has not been seen since. **0** (3).

Chenopodium opulifolium　　　　Grey Goosefoot
Schrad. ex W.D.J. Koch & Ziz

Introduced. A casual plant on two rubbish-tips at Dartford in the 1970s, probably introduced with oil-seed waste, but not recorded since. **0** (2).

Chenopodium album L.　　　　　　　　Fat-hen

Native. A common plant of cultivated and disturbed waste land throughout the county. **938** (985).

Chenopodium strictum Roth　　　Striped Goosefoot

Introduced (neophyte). Casual plants associated with oil-seed waste on two rubbish-tips in the Dartford area in the 1970s, but has not been recorded since. **0** (3).

Chenopodium probstii Aellen　　　Probst's Goosefoot

Introduced (neophyte). A casual plant of roadsides and waste places. Recorded during the present survey from Sevenoaks TQ55I, Sutton-at-Hone TQ57K, Cheeseman's Green TR03J and St. Nicholas at Wade TR26T. **4** (8).

Chenopodium giganteum D. Don　　　Tree Spinach

Introduced. Many plants on some fresh soil-heaps at Sutton-at-Hone TQ57K in 1992 constitute the only record. **1** (0).

Chenopodium quinoa Willd.　　　　　　Quinoa

Introduced (neophyte). Plants in arable fields at High Halstow and Godmersham TR05Q were almost certainly casual relics from cultivation. **2** (0).

Bassia scoparia (L.) Voss Summer-cypress

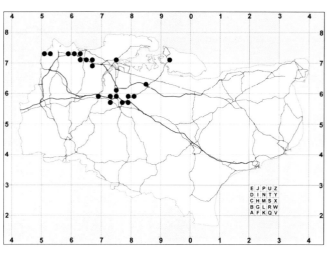

Introduced (neophyte). A recent colonist found growing along motorways and class A roads in West and Central Kent during 2005 and almost certain to spread further in the future. **21** (0).

Corispermum leptopterum (Asch.) Iljin Bugseed

Introduced (neophyte). Recorded on a rubbish-tip at Dene Valley, Margate in 1985, but not seen since. **0** (0).

Atriplex hortensis L. Garden Orache

Introduced (neophyte). A garden weed at Aylesford TQ75J, but not recorded elsewhere during the present survey. **1** (10).

Atriplex sagittata Borkh. Purple Orache

Introduced (neophyte). Recorded at Highsted quarry in 1958 and at a dump near Ashford 1956-7, but has not been noted since. **0** (0).

Atriplex micrantha Ledeb.

Introduced. Recorded as a casual wool-alien at Wateringbury 1971-80 but not seen since. **0** (1).

Atriplex prostrata Boucher ex DC. Spear-leaved Orache

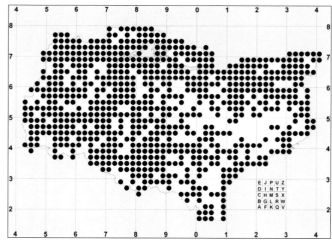

A native plant of cultivated and disturbed soils, particularly near the coast. It is a common plant on beaches, saltmarshes and other saline habitats, and in recent years has become particularly frequent along motorways and other main road verges. **756** (663).

Atriplex prostrata x glabriuscula

Recorded at Shellness, Sheppey in 1977, but has not been found during the present survey. **0** (1).

Atriplex prostrata x longipes Kattegat Orache
= **A. x gustafssoniana** Tascher.

Was recorded at Shellness, Sheppey in 1977, but has not been found during the present survey. **0** (1).

Atriplex glabriuscula Edmondston Babington's Orache

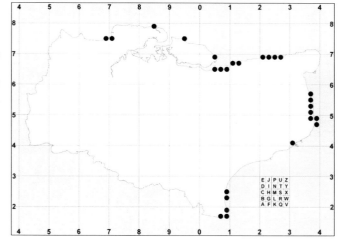

A native plant found along the strand-line on moderately exposed sand and shingle beaches. **27** (28).

Atriplex littoralis L.　　　Grass-leaved Orache　　*Atriplex patula* L.　　　Common Orache

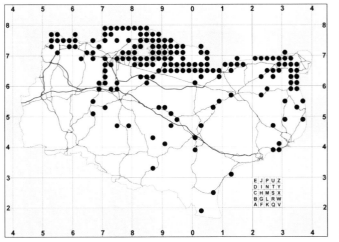

A native plant of sandy or silty areas on the coast, being particularly frequent at the edge of saltmarshes and along the drift-line on open beaches. In recent years it has increasingly been found along the verges of motorways and other inland main roads. **178** (116).

Native　On cultivated and waste ground throughout the county, although usually avoiding any brackish or saline habitats. **637** (769).

Wind turbines on Romney Marsh - landscape of the future? © E. Philp

Atriplex laciniata L.   Frosted Orache

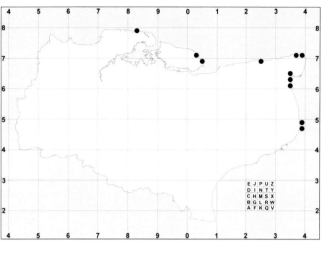

Native. Found on sandy shores at about high-tide level. Rather local and usually in small numbers or as single plants. **11** (8).

Atriplex halimus L.   Shrubby Orache

Introduced (neophyte). Regularly planted near the sea for ornament or as a windbreak. Recorded as naturalised at Folkestone TR23H. **1** (0).

Atriplex portulacoides L.   Sea-purslane

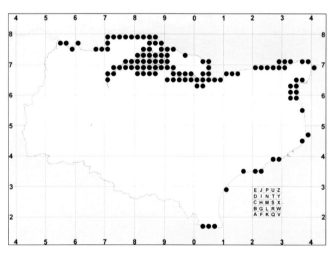

Native. On muddy or sandy saltmarshes that are regularly flooded by high tides, and occasionally on cliffs and other areas that are regularly splashed by the sea. It occurs in most suitable habitats around the coast. **114** (111).

Atriplex pedunculata L.   Pedunculate Sea-purslane

A native plant of the drier parts of saltmarshes, last recorded in 1924 and now considered extinct in the county. **0** (0).

Beta vulgaris L. ssp. *maritima* (L.) Arcang.   Sea Beet

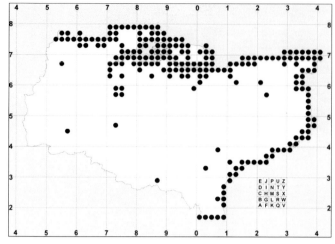

A native plant on shores and waste ground near the sea. Increasingly, plants have been found well inland, particularly on disturbed ground at roadsides. **213** (183).

Beta vulgaris L. ssp. *vulgaris*   Root Beet

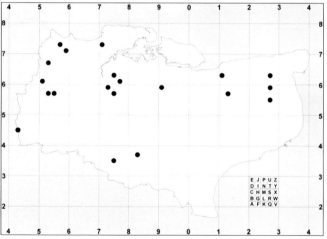

Introduced (neophyte). Plants found on roadsides and waste places, usually on disturbed soils. These records include a range of variants from cultivation and include some young plants which were difficult to identify and might have been ssp. *cicla* or inland seedlings of ssp. *maritima*. **20** (24).

Beta trigyna Waldst. & Kit.   Caucasian Beet

Introduced (neophyte). Claimed from a sand pit at Stone in 1973, but not recorded in the county since. **0** (1).

Sarcocornia perennis Perennial Glasswort
(Mill.) A.J. Scott

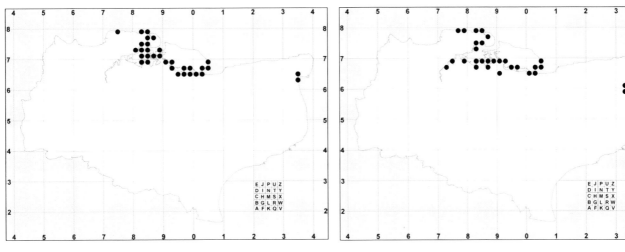

Native. On the middle and upper parts of salt-marshes. Scarce, but found in most suitable habitats. **32** (39).

Salicornia europaea L. Common Glasswort

Native. On muddy shores and salt-marshes. In spite of its English name, this is not the commonest glasswort in the county and is only found in sites that are regularly covered by high tide. No plants were recorded on the land side of the sea-wall. **29** (54).

Salicornia pusilla Woods One-flowered Glasswort

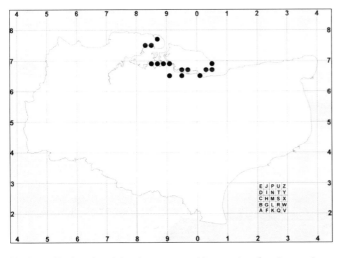

Native. Rather local in the upper, drier parts of salt-marshes. **15** (23).

Salicornia obscura Glaucous Glasswort
P.W. Ball & Tutin

Native. Plants fitting the description of this species were recorded from the middle part of salt-marshes along the Swale at Elmley TQ96N and Oare Marshes TR06C. **2** (0).

Salicornia ramosissima Woods Purple Glasswort

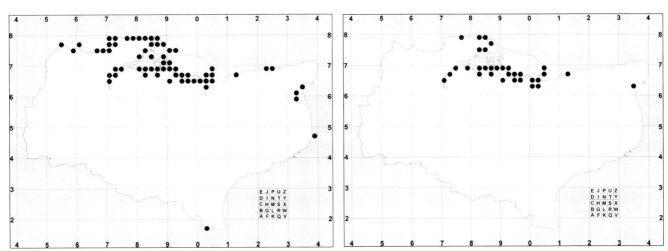

Native. The most frequent of the glassworts and found on the middle and upper parts of salt-marshes, on firm muddy shores and on brackish areas behind the sea-wall. **63** (74).

Salicornia fragilis P.W. Ball & Tutin Yellow Glasswort

Native. On bare mud in the lower-levels of salt-marshes and at the sides of channels. Frequent in suitable habitats. **32** (29).

Salicornia dolichostachya Moss Long-spiked Glasswort

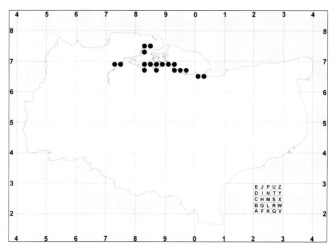

Native. On bare mud at the lowest level of salt-marshes and hence submerged for a greater period of time than any other species of glasswort. **18** (26).

Salsola kali L. ssp. kali Prickly Saltwort

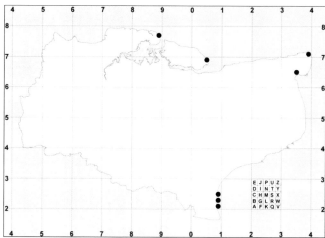

Native. A scarce plant of sandy beaches where is usually found along the drift-line. An annual, it can be erratic in its occurrence and is now listed in the Red List as Vulnerable. **7** (6).

Einadia trigonos (Schult.) Paul G. Wilson.

Introduced. A casual wool-alien, last recorded in the county in 1960. **0** (0).

Suaeda vera Shrubby Sea-blite
Forssk. ex J.F. Gmel.

Native. Well established and spreading along the sea-wall off the Lydd Ranges at TR01D, I & N where it might have originally been planted, and one mature bush at Shellness, Sheppey TR06N. Nationally a scarce plant. **4** (1).

AMARANTHACEAE

Amaranthus retroflexus L. Common Amaranth

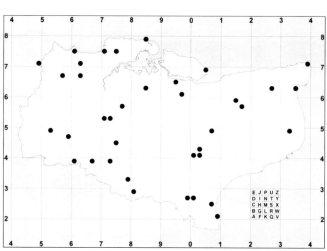

Introduced (neophyte). Escapes from gardens have been reinforced with plants from wool shoddy, bird seed and oil-seed waste, and it is now a regular casual in arable fields and disturbed ground by roadsides. **37** (15).

Suaeda maritima (L.) Dumort. Annual Sea-blite

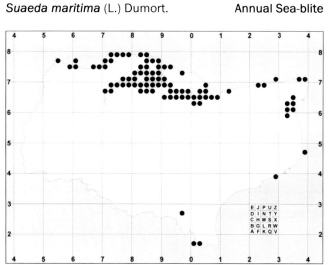

Native. A plant of the middle and lower parts of salt-marshes, but can also occur along the seashore and on sea walls that get covered by the highest spring tides. A small relic colony still persists on a grazing marsh at Fairfield TQ92T, now well inland, and long since it was a salt-marsh at the edge of the River Rother. **88** (98).

Amaranthus hybridus x *retroflexus*
= *A.* x *ozanonii* (Thell.) C. Schust. & M. Goldschm.

This species was recorded with both parents on a rubbish-tip at Dartford in the mid-1970s, but has not been seen since. **0** (1).

Amaranthus hybridus L.   Green Amaranth

Introduced (neophyte) with wool shoddy, oil-seed waste, agricultural seed and bird seed, and occasionally found growing on rubbish-tips, arable fields and waste places around built-up areas. Formerly more frequent, but during the present survey only found on rubbish-tips at Dartford TQ57M, Stone TQ57S and on disturbed ground at Gravesend TQ67M. **3** (7).

Amaranthus palmeri   Dioecious Amaranth
S. Watson

Introduced with oil-seed waste on rubbish-tips in the Dartford area in 1973, but not recorded since. **0** (2).

Amaranthus bouchonii Thell.   Indehiscent Amaranth

Introduced. On a disturbed roadside verge at Maidstone TQ75T in 2005. Had previously been recorded as a wool alien in a hop garden at Wateringbury in 1979. **1** (1).

Amaranthus cf. *powellii*   Powell's Amaranth
S. Watson

Introduced. A few casual plants found growing with *A.hybridus* on disturbed waste ground in Gravesend TQ67M. **1** (1).

Amaranthus albus L.   White Pigweed

Introduced. Casual records on rubbish-tips and waste places in north-west Kent in the past, but not recorded during the present survey. **0** (2).

Amaranthus quitensis Kunth   Mucronate Amaranth

Introduced. A wool alien and oil-seed waste casual on rubbish-tips and arable fields in the past, but not recorded during the present survey. **0** (5).

Amaranthus blitum L.   Guernsey Amaranth

Introduced. There have been a few casual records in the past, but not recorded in the county for over a hundred years. **0** (0).

Amaranthus thunbergii Moq.   Thunberg's Pigweed

Casual plants introduced with wool shoddy in 1960, but not recorded during the present survey. **0** (0).

Amaranthus blitoides S. Watson   Prostrate Pigweed

Introduced with wool shoddy, bird seed and oil-seed waste on rubbish-tips in the 1970s, but not recorded since. **0** (2).

Amaranthus aff. *arenicola* I.M. Johnston.

A plant resembling this species was recorded with oil-seed waste on a rubbish-tip at Stone in 1973. There are no subsequent records. **0** (2).

Amaranthus capensis Thell.   Cape Pigweed

Introduced. A wool alien recorded in a hop garden at Wateringbury in 1979, but not seen since. **0** (1).

Amaranthus spinosus L.   Spiny Amaranth

Introduced. A few casual plants were recorded with oil-seed waste on rubbish-tips in the Dartford area in 1975 and 1976, but there are no subsequent records. **0** (2).

Amaranthus caudatus L.   Love-lies-bleeding

Introduced. A casual garden escape recorded from waste ground at Northfleet TQ67H and Canterbury TR15J. **2** (1).

Amaranthus viridis L.

Introduced. Occasional plants were recorded with oil-seed waste in north-west Kent in the mid-1970s, but not since. **0** (2).

PORTULACACEAE

CARYOPHYLLACEAE

Portulaca oleracea L.   Common Purslane

Introduced (neophyte). A persistent weed in a garden at Aylesford TQ75J is the only record, but it would be expected to be found elsewhere. **1** (1).

Claytonia perfoliata Donn ex Willd.   Springbeauty

Introduced (neophyte). On sandy cultivated or disturbed ground. Rather local and only recorded from Sevenoaks TQ55H, Seal TQ55S, Wrotham Heath TQ65J and Greatstone TR02W. **4** (18).

Claytonia sibirica L.   Pink Purslane

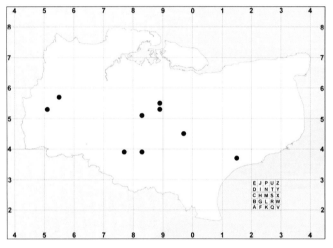

Introduced (neophyte). Not recorded in Kent until 1948 and now known only from a few damp shady woods and stream-sides. **9** (9).

Montia fontana L.   Blinks

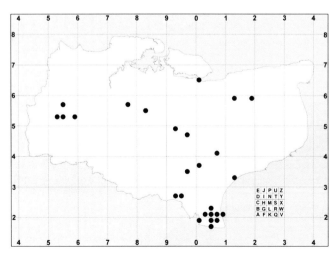

Native. Amongst short vegetation on sandy fields and roadsides, and also in damp meadows that dry out in the summer months. All specimens found have been checked and have proved to be ssp. *chondrosperma* (Fenzl) Walters. **26** (32).

Arenaria serpyllifolia L.   Thyme-leaved Sandwort
ssp. *serpyllifolia*

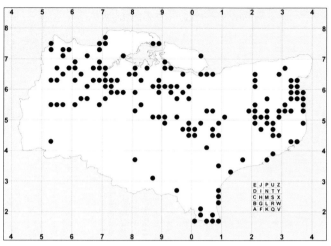

Native. On chalk downs, sand dunes and other open, dry fields and waste places. **153** (280).

Arenaria serpyllifolia L. ssp.   Slender Sandwort
leptoclados (Rchb.) Nyman

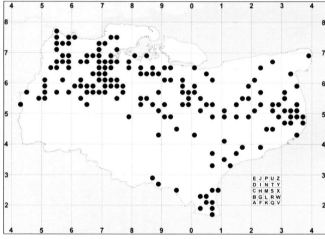

Native. In similar habitats to ssp. *serpyllifolia* and sometimes found growing together, but this subspecies is more regularly found near human habitation such as on old walls and cultivated ground. **169** (244).

Arenaria balearica L.   Mossy Sandwort

Introduced (neophyte). Has been recorded growing wild at Hever Castle, Tunbridge Wells and Scotney Castle in the past and may well still be present at these localities, but was not found during the present survey. **0** (3).

Arenaria montana L.   Mountain Sandwort

Introduced (neophyte). A garden escape which persisted for a few years at Stone but has now gone. **0** (0).

Moehringia trinervia (L.) Clairv.   Three-nerved Sandwort

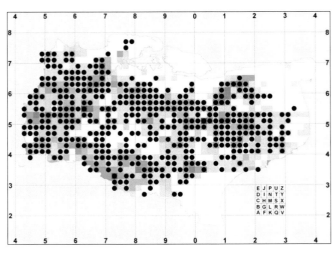

Native. On moist open ground, usually in woodlands or shady hedge banks. Common in suitable habitats. **444** (562).

Honkenya peploides (L.) Ehrh.   Sea Sandwort

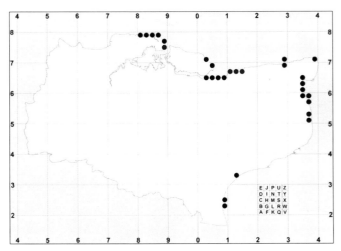

Native. On sand and shingle beaches, and found in most suitable habitats around the coast. **29** (34).

Minuartia hybrida   Fine-leaved Sandwort
(Vill.) Schischk.

A native plant, although probably introduced in Kent. Only now recorded from a few plants on the walls of the old castle at Eynsford TQ56M. It is listed in the Red List as 'Endangered'. **1** (1).

Stellaria media (L.) Vill.   Common Chickweed

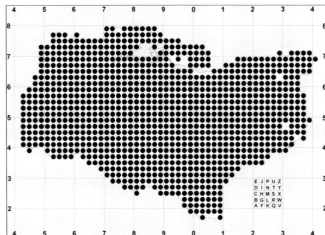

Native. A common plant of cultivated and waste ground, old walls and along the strand line on the coast, and found throughout the county. **1013** (1032).

Stellaria pallida (Dumort) Crép.   Lesser Chickweed

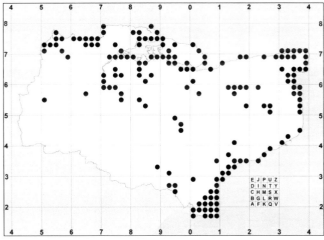

Native. On open, dry, well-drained soils, frequent on sand-dunes, shingle and other sandy places on the coast, and with scattered records on lawns and other sandy areas inland. **164** (55).

Stellaria neglecta Weihe   Greater Chickweed

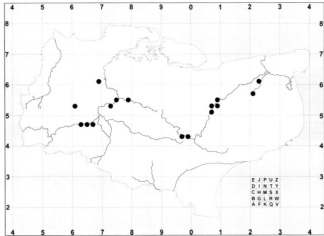

Native. Damp shady places by streams and rivers. Rather local, but easily overlooked. **16** (11).

Stellaria holostea L.   **Greater Stitchwort**

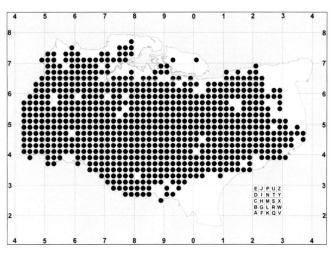

Native.   A common plant of hedgerows, copses and wood margins. **742** (804).

Stellaria graminea L.   **Lesser Stitchwort**

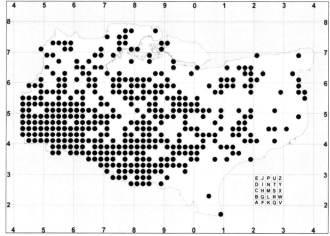

Native.   Open woods, heaths, pastures and other grassland. Widespread, but never abundant at any one site.   **432** (601).

Stellaria alsine Grimm   **Bog Stitchwort**

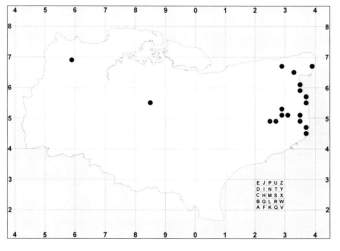

Native.   Stream-sides, wet woodlands and other boggy areas. Rather local and with some decline due to loss of habitat. **79** (128).

Cerastium arvense L.   **Field Mouse-ear**

Native.   On roadside banks and rough grassland on both chalk and sandy soils.   There appears to be some decline due to loss of suitable habitat.   **18** (48).

Greater Stitchwort *Stellaria holostea* © L. Rooney

Stellaria palustris Erh. ex Hoffm.   **Marsh Stitchwort**

Native. Not found during the present survey, but there is a chance that it might still exist on the Romney Marsh or along the Stour Valley. It is listed in the Red Data List as 'Vulnerable'. **0** (0).

Cerastium arvense x tomentosum.

Plants referable to this hybrid were found well established along a roadside verge at Acol TR26Y. **1** (2).

Cerastium tomentosum L.   Snow-in-summer

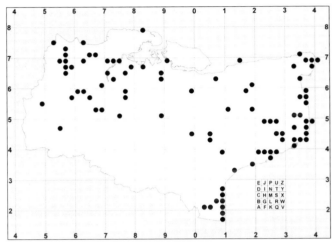

Introduced (neophyte). A garden plant that has escaped and is now well naturalised on roadsides, waste ground and coastal shingle and sand-dunes. It is particularly frequent along the east coast of the county. **92** (33).

Cerastium glomeratum Thuill.   Sticky Mouse-ear

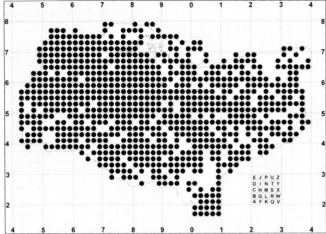

Native. A common plant that occurs on arable land and waste places. It is particularly found on sandy roadside banks, open sand-dunes, woodland rides and on old walls. **813** (649).

Cerastium brachypetalum Pers.   Grey Mouse-ear

Introduced (neophyte). First discovered in Kent in 1978 by J.R. Palmer where it was growing at the edge of a railway line near Longfield. The original site was destroyed with new railway works but the plant still survives in small numbers amongst nearby chalk vegetation in TQ56Z. However, its long-term survival must be in doubt as it has difficulty competing with the taller vegetation. **1** (1).

Cerastium fontanum Baumg.   Common Mouse-ear

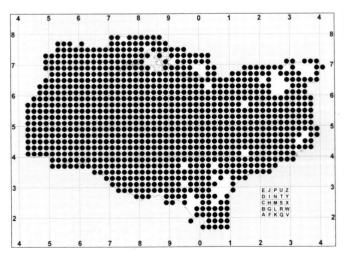

Native. A common plant of cultivated land, rough pastures, waysides and waste places. **978** (1003).

Cerastium diffusum Pers.   Sea Mouse-ear

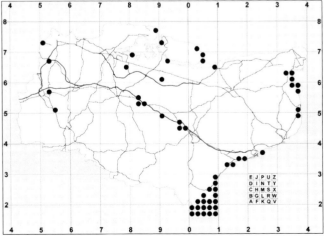

Native. On open grassland, fixed dunes, and sandy and shingle banks near the sea. During the survey it has also turned up inland on a number of sandy roadside verges in keeping with several other coastal species. **54** (39).

Cerastium pumilum Curtis   Dwarf Mouse-ear

Native. Always a rare plant in the county, and nationally in decline, this chickweed was not found during the present survey. It is listed in the Red List as 'Near Threatened'. **0** (2).

Moenchia erecta   Upright Chickweed
(L.) P. Gaertn., B. Mey. & Scherb.

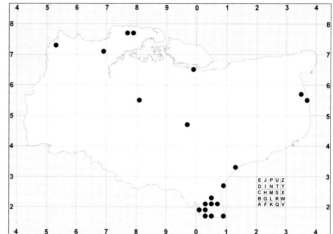

Native. On open dry sandy grassland, heathland, coastal dunes and sandy shingle. An inconspicuous species and easily overlooked. **20** (25).

Cerastium semidecandrum L.   Little Mouse-ear

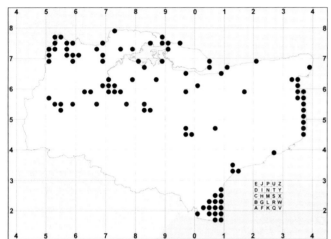

Native. In dry open habitats on calcareous or sandy soils such as roadside verges, sand-dunes and neglected lawns. **98** (93).

Sagina nodosa (L.) Fenzl.   Knotted Pearlwort

Native. In open dune slacks. In Kent only known from the Lydd/New Romney and Sandwich areas in the past, and during the present survey recorded from the RSPB Reserve at Dungeness TR01U and from Sandwich Bay TR35P. **2** (2).

Sagina subulata (Sw.) C. Presl   Heath Pearlwort

Native. Always a great rarity in the county, last recorded in 1957, and now probably extinct. **0** (0).

Myosoton aquaticum (L.) Moench   Water Chickweed

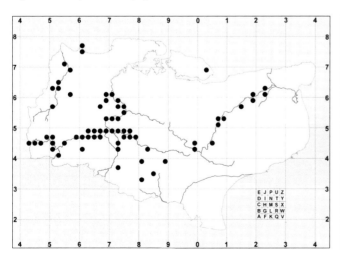

Native. On stream and river banks, and in marshes and wet woodlands. There have been some losses because of the destruction of habitat through housing and other building developments. **66** (102).

Sagina procumbens L.   Procumbent Pearlwort

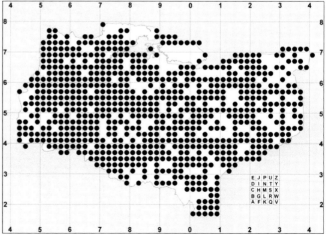

Native. On paths, lawns, roadside verges, woodland rides and between pavement slabs and on old walls throughout most of the county. **761** (767).

Sagina apetela Ard.   Annual Pearlwort

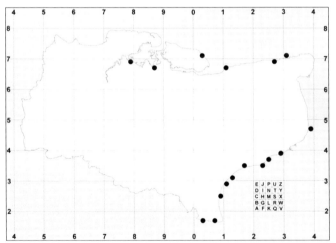

Native. On bare sandy ground and on old walls, pavements and other artificial habitats. Ssp. *apetala* with 153 records and ssp. *erecta* with 99 records were mapped separately but show no difference in pattern of distribution and are mapped together as the one species. Note that not all plants found were identifiable down to subspecies level, and in some tetrads both subspecies were found. **228** (304)

Sagina maritima Don   Sea Pearlwort

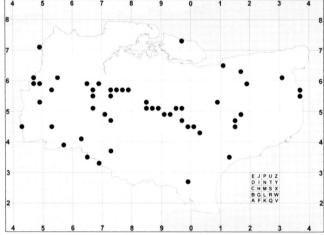

Native. On waste ground, sand-dunes, and in cracks in pavements and sea-defences on the coast. **16** (13).

Scleranthus annuus L.   Annual Knawel

Native. On dry sandy or gravelly ground, particularly on heathland and sandy roadside verges. In keeping with other counties in south-east England (and its national listing as 'Endangered'), this species appears to be on the decline, and during the present survey was only recorded from Farningham Wood TQ56J, Dartford Heath TQ57G, Addington TQ65P, Lydd TR02K and St. Mary's Bay TR02Y. All the specimens checked have proved to be ssp. *annuus* although ssp. *polycarpos* has been recorded from West Kent in the past. **5** (25).

Corrigiola litoralis L.   Strapwort

Introduced. Doubtfully recorded as a casual introduction at Sandwich Bay in the past, but there are no recent records. **0** (0).

Herniaria glabra L.   Smooth Rupturewort

Introduced (neophyte). On disturbed waste ground at Swanscombe TQ57X, coincidently the same area as for first record for the county in 1793. Also on waste ground at Staplehurst TQ74W, and in a car park at Detling TQ85E.   **3** (2).

Herniaria hirsuta L.   Hairy Rupturewort

Introduced. Recorded as a wool-alien in 1960, but there are no records since. **0** (0).

Illecebrum verticillatum L.   Coral-necklace

Introduced (neophyte). Known for over fifty years in woodland rides within the Bedgebury Forest, and still present in TQ73F, although usually in small quantity. **1** (1).

Spergula arvensis L.   Corn Spurrey

Native. In fields and other areas of disturbed, usually sandy, soil. Another plant that appears to be in decline, probably due to changes in farming practice and pointing to its listed status as 'Vulnerable'. **51** (183).

Spergula morisonii Boreau   Pearlwort Spurrey

Introduced (neophyte). Casual plants in a nursery in West Kent in the past, but there are no recent records. **0** (0).

Spergularia media (L.) C. Presl   Greater Sea-spurrey

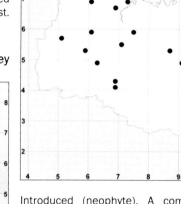

Native. On salt-marshes, muddy beaches and tidally inundated dune-slacks.   Found in suitable habitats around the coast. **76** (107).

Spergularia marina (L.) Griseb.   Lesser Sea-spurrey

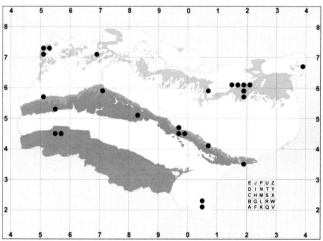

Native. On salt-marshes, muddy shingle and brackish grazing marshes.   In recent years it has become a regular inhabitant at the edge of salt-treated roads inland. **218** (126).

Spergularia rubra (L.) J. Presl & C. Presl   Sand Spurrey

Native. On open sandy and gravelly habitats such as heaths and roadside verges.   Rather local and never abundant at any one site. **25** (59).

Spergularia bocconei (Scheele) Graebn.   Greek Sea-spurrey

Introduced (neophyte). Discovered on a roadside verge on Bluebell Hill TQ76K in 1991 and still present. **1** (0).

Lychnis coronaria (L.) Murray   Rose Campion

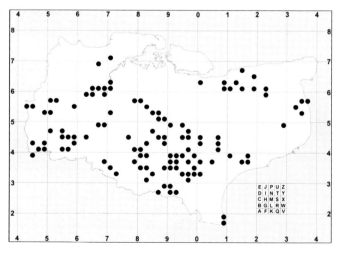

Introduced (neophyte). A common garden plant that sets abundant seed and regularly escapes into the wild. It is now found on roadside verges, sand-dunes and waste ground, and in some of these sites it is well established and persistent. **26** (12).

Lychnis flos-cuculi L.   Ragged-Robin

Native. In wet grassland, fen-meadow and in damp woodland. There appears to be some decline due to drying out, or the development, of its habitats. **115** (190).

Lychnis chalcedonica L.   Maltese-Cross

Introduced (neophyte). The only record is of a number of plants along a ride in Foal Hurst Wood TQ64S, where it might have been deliberately sown. **1** (2).

Lychnis x *haageana* Lem.

Introduced. Was reported from a beach at Shorne Marshes in the 1970s, but was not found during the present survey. **0** (0).

Agrostemma githago L.   Corncockle

Introduced (archaeophyte). Formerly a common weed in cornfields, first recorded from Kent in 1629 and listed by Hanbury & Marshall (1899) as "found in every district, but not very plentiful". However, by the end of the 20th century it had become virtually extinct due to improved seed cleaning. During this survey it was recorded from Sevenoaks TQ55H, East Malling TQ65X, Cuxton TQ66Y & Z and Grove Ferry TR26G. This plant is now a frequent component of wild-flower seed mixtures and it becomes difficult to be sure of the source of any plants growing wild, but the plants at East Malling appeared on disturbed soil that had not been cultivated for over a hundred years, and the plants in the Cuxton area were due to deliberately deeper ploughing. **5** (0).

Corncockle *Agrostemma githago* © L. Holland

Agrostemma gracile Boiss.

Introduced. Is recorded from near Swanley (Clement & Foster, 1994), but was not seen during the present survey. **0** (0).

Silene italica (L.) Pers.   Italian Catchfly

Introduced (neophyte). On roadside banks in the Greenhithe area TQ57X ,where it has been known since 1863. Its hold there is now very tenuous and it remains to be seen just how much longer this plant can survive at this site, the only regular one in Britain. **1** (2).

Silene nutans L.   Nottingham Catchfly

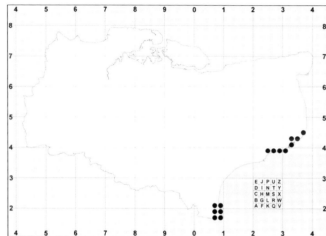

Native. On grassy or bare places on the shingle in the Dungeness-Greatstone area, and on chalk cliffs and the grassy area along the top of the cliffs between Folkestone–St. Margaret's Bay. Well established in these areas, but nationally a rare plant and in the Red List designated as 'Near Threatened'. **14** (18).

Silene vulgaris (Moench) Garcke ssp. *vulgaris*   Bladder Campion

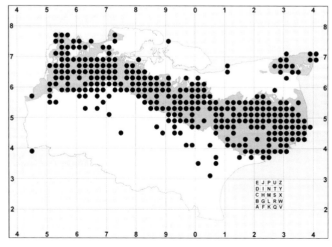

Native. On roadside banks, hedgerows, quarries and disturbed ground on the chalk and only rarely found in similar habitats elsewhere. **309** (467).

Silene uniflora Roth   Sea Campion

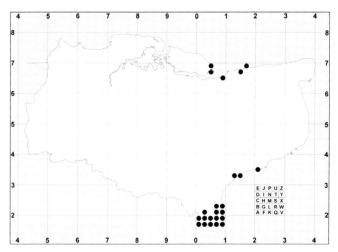

Native. On shingle, gravel and firm sand on the coast. It is a frequent plant over the shingle at Dungeness, but rather scarce at a few other sites on the coast. **23** (24).

Silene latifolia x *dioica*
= *S.* x *hampeana* Meusel & K. Werner

This hybrid is quite frequent on disturbed ground where the two parents grow close together, usually through disturbance with road building or other construction work. **77** (90).

Silene armeria L.   Sweet-William Catchfly

Introduced. A casual garden escape, last recorded wild in the county in 1960. **0** (0).

Silene noctiflora L.   Night-flowering Catchfly

Introduced (archaeophyte). A long established weed of arable fields on the chalk and sand, but one that has suffered through improved farming methods. During the present survey only recorded from some arable fields at Cuxton TQ66Y. Noted in the Red List Category, 'Vulnerable'. **1** (14).

Silene dioica (L.) Clairv.   Red Campion

Native. In copses and hedgerows, and in clearings and along rides in woodlands, usually in shady places. **496** (577).

Silene latifolia Poir.   White Campion

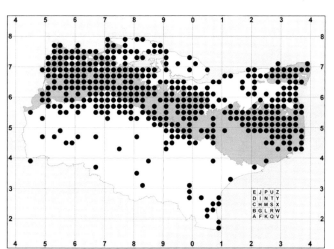

Native. A plant of roadsides, banks, cultivated and waste ground on light soils, particularly on the chalk. **442** (561).

Silene coeli-rosa (L.) Godr.   Rose-of-heaven

Introduced. A garden escape reported growing on a rubbish-tip in the past, but not found during the present survey. **0** (1).

Silene gallica L.   Small-flowered Catchfly

Introduced (archaeophyte). Formerly found in sandy arable fields or other disturbed soils. This plant has declined quite seriously in response to modern farming practices and is now reduced to a rare casual. During the present survey a single plant was found on a roadside verge at Gillingham TQ76Y plus a small colony of plants on some disturbed sandy soil (now built over) at Littlestone TR02X. Cited in the Red List as 'Endangered'. **2** (0).

Silene conica L.   Sand Catchfly

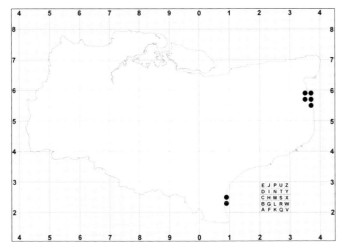

Native. On stabilised dunes and sandy shingle on the coast. Always rare in Kent, this plant still persists in the two ever only known localities in the county. Nationally its status in the Red List is given as 'Vulnerable'. **7** (3)

Silene dichotoma Ehrh.   Forked Catchfly

Introduced. A few casual plants occurred on disturbed soil on a roadside at Detling in 1966, but it has not been found since. **0** (0).

Saponaria officinalis L.   Soapwort

Introduced (archaeophyte). A plant of cultivation long well established on roadsides, hedge banks, quarries, railway banks and waste ground. **60** (131).

Saponaria ocymoides L.   Rock Soapwort

Introduced (neophyte). A rock-garden plant that occasionally establishes itself on old walls, but was not recorded during the present survey. **0** (0).

Vaccaria hispanica (Mill.) Rauschert   Cowherb

Introduced. There are casual records from rubbish-tips and waste ground in the past, but it was not noticed during the present survey. **0** (3).

Petrorhagia nanteuilii   Childing Pink
(Burnat) P.W. Ball & Heywood

Introduced (neophyte). Always a rare plant in Kent, it was last recorded in 1960 and is now considered extinct in the county. Noted as 'Vulnerable' in the Red List. **0** (0).

Petrorhagia saxifraga (L.) Link   Tunicflower

Introduced. A casual plant last recorded in the county in 1976. **0** (1).

Gypsophila paniculata L.   Baby's-breath

Introduced (neophyte). It still persists on sand-dunes at Sandwich Bay TR35P, where it has been known for many years. **1** (0).

Dianthus caryophyllus L.   Clove Pink

Introduced (neophyte). Still persists on the walls of Rochester Castle TQ76P, in spite of the 'conservation' work that takes place there, where it has been known since 1666. Surely this plant is as historically deserving as the castle itself! It was also recorded, probably as a garden escape, on a chalky bank on Bluebell Hill TQ76K. **2** (2).

Dianthus plumarius L.   Pink

Introduced. A garden plant that has occasionally been found established on old walls and disturbed ground. Last recorded wild in the county in 1971. **0** (1).

Dianthus deltoides L.   Maiden Pink

Native. At the edge of a track on the Snodland Marshes TQ76B is the only record. Always a rare plant in Kent and listed nationally as 'Near Threatened'. **1** (0).

Dianthus barbatus L.   Sweet-William

Introduced (neophyte). A common garden plant, but during this survey it was only noted growing 'wild' on a roadside bank near Newnham TQ95U. **1** (9).

Dianthus armeria L.   Deptford Pink

Native. On dry sunny banks and field edges by Farningham Wood TQ56I & 56N where it has long been known. It appears to have gone from its locality near Littlebourne, perhaps through use of herbicide sprays, and, although it might still be present, could not be found at a former site at Sandwich Bay. Noted in the Red List Category, 'Endangered'. **2** (3).

Persicaria amplexicaulis   Red Bistort
(D. Don) Ronse Decr.

Introduced. A casual garden escape (or as a garden throw-out) on waste ground near Cowden, TQ44V, Penshurst TQ54G, Dartford TQ57R and Sutton TR34E. **5** (5).

POLYGONACEAE

Persicaria campanulata   Lesser Knotweed
(Hook. f.) Ronse Decr.

Introduced. Noted as a casual garden escape in the past, but not recorded during the present survey. **0** (1).

Persicaria amphibia (L.) Delarbre   Amphibious Bistort

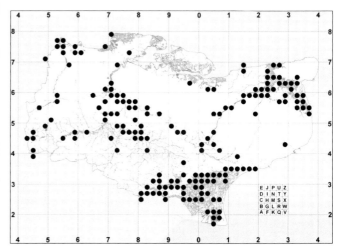

Native. In ponds, slow-flowing rivers, streams and ditches, and at times as a terrestrial form in damp meadows, marshes and dune-slacks. **174** (172).

Persicaria wallichii   Himalayan Knotweed
Greuter & Burdet

Introduced (neophyte). Naturalised on roadside verges near Ightham TQ55S & 55T, and on a laneside near Hawkhurst TQ73L. **3** (8).

Persicaria mollis (D. Don) H. Gross   Soft Knotweed

Introduced (neophyte). Was known on some waste ground at Tunbridge Wells, but not found during the present survey. **0** (1).

Persicaria bistorta (L.) Samp.   Common Bistort

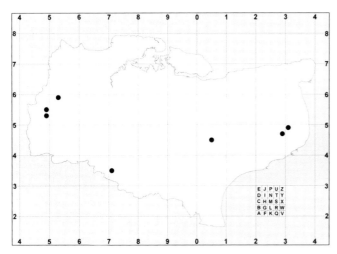

Native. In damp meadows and grassy roadside verges. Never a common plant in the county, this species appears to have declined further since the last survey. **7** (18).

Persicaria maculosa Gray   Redshank

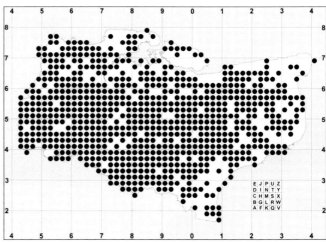

Native. A common plant of cultivated and disturbed soils, particularly those that are rich in nutrients. It also occurs on banks by rivers and ditches and on waste plots in built-up areas. **756** (895).

Persicaria lapathifolia (L.) Delarbre — Pale Persicaria

Native. In cultivated and waste ground, and by ponds and ditches. Widespread but not as frequent as the previous species. **228** (497).

Persicaria pensylvanica (L.) M. Gómez — Pinkweed

Introduced. A casual plant on rubbish-tips and other places where soya waste had been deposited during the 1970s, but there are no recent records. **0** (4).

Persicaria hydropiper (L.) Delarbre — Water-pepper

Native. On damp mud at the margins of lakes, ponds, rivers and streams, and along damp woodland rides. Frequent in suitable habitats. **294** (362).

Persicaria mitis (Schrank) Assenov — Tasteless Water-pepper

Native. A rare plant of damp habitats, first found in the county in 1855, last recorded in 1955, and now considered extinct in Kent. Its status in the Red List is given as 'Vulnerable'. **0** (0).

Persicaria minor (Huds.) Opiz — Small Water-pepper

Native. A rare plant of damp places by ponds, ditches and winter-flooded meadows. The only record during the present survey was of a few plants alongside a ditch near Sandhurst TQ82D. In the Red List its status is given as 'Vulnerable'. **1** (5).

Persicaria capitata (Buch.-Ham. ex D. Don) H. Gross — Pink-headed Knotweed

Introduced. A frequently grown pot-plant, and sometimes planted in gardens where it is quite hardy. Found completely naturalised between pavement slabs at Aylesford TQ75J in 1998 and still present, but surprisingly not recorded elsewhere. **1** (0).

Fagopyrum esculentum Moench — Buckwheat

Introduced (neophyte). A casual plant of rubbish-tips, and in areas where game bird food is put down. Noted at Knockholt TQ45U, Sutton-at-Hone TQ57K, Darenth TQ57Q, near Badlesmere TR05H and Barham TR25A. **5** (14).

Fagopyrum tataricum (L.) Gaertn. — Green Buckwheat

Introduced. A few casual plants were noted where game bird food had been put down in the 1970s, but this species has not been recorded since. **0** (1).

Polygonum oxyspermum C.A. Mey. & Bunge — Ray's Knotgrass

Native. A rare plant found on sand or shell-sand beaches, usually just above the limit of the highest tides. This plant has been specifically searched for at all the suitable localities but has only been found near Leysdown-on-Sea TR06P, Warden Bay TR07F, and at Whitstable TR16D. **3** (7).

Polygonum arenastrum Boreau — Equal-leaved Knotgrass

Considered to have been introduced (archaeophyte) but appears as a native. On tracks, paths, roadside verges and other open, well-drained, and usually trampled, areas. Widespread and common. **754** (799).

Polygonum aviculare L.   Knotgrass

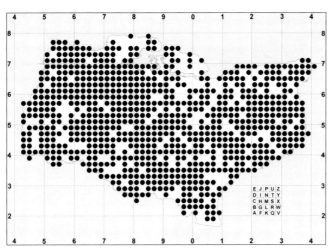

Native. On arable fields, gardens, seashores and other areas of disturbed or open land. Very common, and probably to be found throughout the county. **804** (1000).

Polygonum rurivagum   Cornfield Knotgrass
Jord. ex Boreau

Introduced (archaeophyte). Some authorities do not regard this plant as a good species, but just a form of *P. aviculare* that occurs in cornfields on the chalk. Plants fitting the description were found at Knockholt TQ45U, Istead Rise TQ66P, near Chilham TR05W, Waltham TR14E, and at Stodmarsh TR26A. **5** (90).

Polygonum arenarium   Lesser Red-knotgrass
Waldst. & Kit.

Introduced. There are previous casual records from rubbish tips in West Kent, but it was not found during the present survey. **0** (0).

Fallopia japonica   Japanese Knotweed
(Houtt.) Ronse Decr.

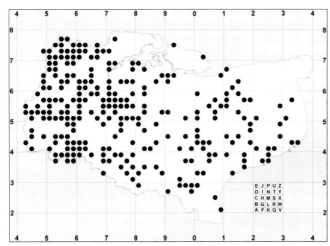

Introduced (neophyte). Formerly planted in parks and large gardens; the first report of it growing wild in the county was in 1931. It is now a widespread weed of roadsides, railway banks and waste places. **263** (306).

Fallopia japonica x *sachalinensis*
= *F.* x *bohemica* (Chrtek & Chrková) J.P. Bailey

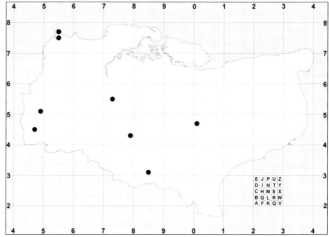

Introduced (neophyte). On roadsides, railway banks, riversides and waste places. Not previously recorded in the county, but probably over-looked and more frequent than the few records suggest. **8** (0).

Fallopia sachalinensis   Giant Knotweed
(F. Schmidt) Ronse Decr.

Introduced (neophyte). Planted by lakes and ponds in parks and large gardens and rarely found as a true escape. During the present survey only noted growing wild in Vinters Park, Maidstone TQ75T. **1** (6).

Fallopia baldschuanica   Russian-vine
(Regel) Holub

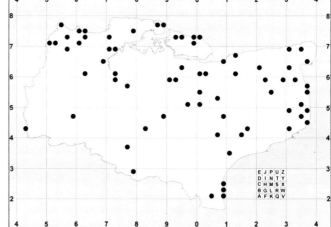

Introduced to British gardens in about 1894, and first reported growing in the wild in 1936 (neophyte). Now frequently found along hedgerows and derelict ground near houses, and at times in woodland and field edges away from habitation where garden rubbish has been dumped. **69** (35).

Fallopia convolvulus (L.) Á. Löve   Black-bindweed

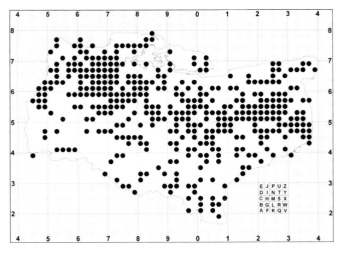

Native.   In gardens, on arable land and disturbed soil in waste places.   There appears to be some decline, probably due to more efficient farming on agricultural land. **408** (693).

Fallopia dumetorum (L.) Holub   Copse-bindweed

Native. A rare plant of hedgerows, thickets and woodland edges. In spite of specifically searching in all the previous recorded sites, this plant was not found during the present survey.   In the Red List this plant is listed as 'Vulnerable'. **0** (1).

Rheum palmatum L.   Ornamental Rhubarb

Introduced. Reported as a garden escape at Sandling in the past (Clement & Foster, 1994), but was not found during the present survey. **0** (0).

Rheum x hybridum Murray   Rhubarb

Introduced (neophyte).   A garden relic noted growing wild, well away from present gardens, at Northfleet TQ67H, East Malling Heath TQ65X, Maidstone TQ75S, near Leeds TQ86H, Hothfield TQ94T, and Sandgate TR13X. **6** (3).

Rumex acetosella L.   Sheep's Sorrel

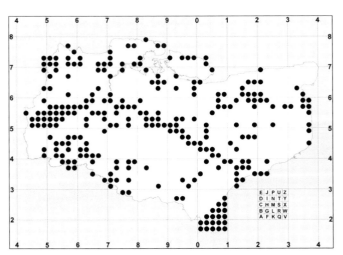

Native. On open grassland on sandy soils, dry heaths, and non-calcareous sand-dunes and shingle beaches. The taxon with narrow linear leaves, best regarded as var. *tenuifolius* Wallr., is frequent over the shingle at Dungeness and Hythe ranges, and on fixed sand-dunes at Sandwich Bay. **268** (442).

Rumex scutatus L.   French Sorrel

Introduced. Was recorded as a garden casual at Maidstone in 1879, but not since. **0** (0).

Rumex acetosa L.   Common Sorrel

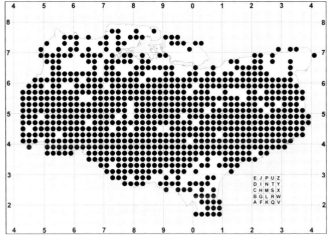

Native. Meadows, roadsides, churchyards and other open grassy areas. Common throughout most of the county, although reduced in some areas where large areas have been developed for building. **790** (910).

Rumex salicifolius T. Lestib.   Willow-leaved Dock

Introduced. Casual plants found on a rubbish-tip at Dartford in 1968 and in a disused quarry at Stone in 1971 and 1972 are the only records for the county. **0** (1).

Rumex confertus Willd.   Russian Dock

Introduced (neophyte).   Well naturalised and persistent on a roadside south of Headcorn TQ84L, this is perhaps now the only English locality. **1** (1).

Rumex confertus x crispus
= *R. x skofitzii* Blocki

One plant recorded in TQ84L in 2002 but site destroyed by roadworks. **1** (0).

Rumex hydrolapathum Huds.   Water Dock

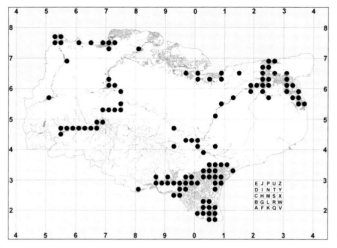

Native. At the margins of slow-flowing rivers and streams, by ponds and in ditches. **118** (180).

Rumex hydrolapathum x conglomeratus = R. x digeneus Beck

Recorded in the past from East Kent, but not found during the present survey. **0** (0).

Rumex cristatus DC.   Greek Dock

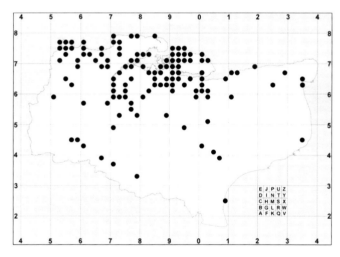

Introduced (neophyte). On roadsides, river banks, sea-walls and waste places. Well naturalised in the north of the county, and spreading. **124** (29).

Rumex cristatus x crispus = R. x dimidiatus Hausskn.

Recorded from West Kent in the past, but not during the present survey. **0** (0).

Rumex cristatus x obtusifolius = R. x lousleyi D.H. Kent

On waste ground at Denton TQ67R. **1** (0).

Rumex patientia L.   Patience Dock

Introduced (neophyte). Persistent on a roadside verge at Green Street Green TQ57Q and in good quantity on waste ground near Denton TQ67R. Perhaps over-recorded in mistake for *R. cristatus* in the past. **2** (20).

Rumex patientia x crispus = R. x confusus Simonk.

Several plants at the edges of disused fields on Westcourt Marshes TQ67R. **1** (0).

Rumex patientia x conglomeratus = R. x philpii Kitchener

A specimen was collected from at the edge of a marsh at Snodland in 1978, but the plant has not been seen since. **0** (1).

Rumex patientia x obtusifolius = R. x erubescens Simonk.

Numerous plants at the edges of disused fields on Westcourt Marshes near Denton TQ67R. **1** (2).

Rumex crispus L.   Curled Dock

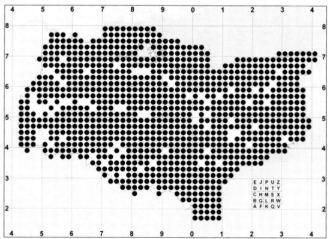

Native. A common plant of cultivated and waste land, dune-slacks and shingle beaches. The common plant is ssp. *crispus*, although ssp. *littoreus* has been noted on some sand and shingle beaches, and ssp. *uliginosus* on tidal mud in the River Medway, but these have not been mapped separately. **945** (1013).

Rumex crispus x conglomeratus = R. x schulzei Hausskn.

Plants of this hybrid were found at Bough Beech TQ44Z, Westcourt Marshes TQ67R, Shorne Marshes TQ67W, Higham Marshes TQ77H, Potman's Heath TQ82U, Stoke Marshes TQ87M & 87N, Oare Marshes TR06C and Ebbsfleet TR36G. **9** (0).

Rumex crispus x sanguineus = R. x sagorskii Hausskn.

Plants of this hybrid were found at Bough Beech TQ44Y & 44Z, Tonbridge TQ54N, Offham TQ65T and Eastry TR35C. **5** (0).

Rumex crispus x pulcher
= *R.* x *pseudopulcher* Hausskn.

Found near Lane End TQ57Q and Norton Court TQ96Q. **2** (0)

Rumex crispus x obtusifolius
= *R.* x *pratensis* Mert. & W.D.J. Koch

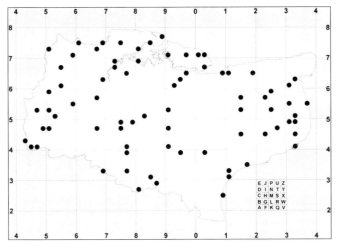

On fields, roadsides, river banks and other waste or disturbed ground, usually, but not always, with both parents. **76** (21).

Rumex crispus x palustris = R. x *heteranthos* Borbás

Found growing with both parents on the Shorne Marshes TQ67X. **1** (0).

Rumex crispus x maritimus = R. x *fallacinus* Hausskn.

Recorded, growing with both parents, on Stoke Marshes TQ87M. **1** (0).

Rumex conglomeratus Murray   Clustered Dock

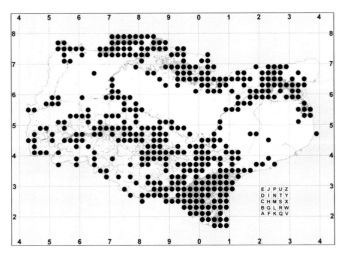

Native. In wet meadows, river and stream banks and ditches. Practically always in wet areas or places that flood at least for part of the year. **421** (540).

Rumex conglomeratus x pulcher
= *Rumex* x *muretii* Hausskn.

Has been recorded from East Kent in the past but was not found during the present survey. **0** (0).

Rumex conglomeratus x obtusifolius
= *Rumex* x *abortivus* Ruhmer

Recorded from Otford TQ55J, Denton TQ67R, Potman's Heath TQ82U, Teynham TQ96S and Canterbury TR15N. **5** (2).

Rumex conglomeratus x palustris = R. x *wirtgenii* Beck

Recorded together with both parents on the Shorne Marshes TQ67X. **1** (0).

Rumex conglomeratus x maritimus
= *Rumex* x *knafii* Celak.

Recorded growing with both parents on the Cooling Marshes TQ77T and the Stoke Marshes TQ87M & N. **3** (0).

Rumex sanguineus L.   Wood Dock

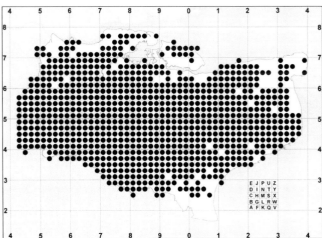

Native. In woods, particularly along the rides and edges, in hedgerows, roadsides and waste places. **844** (825).

Rumex sanguineus x pulcher
= *R.* x *mixtus* Lamb.

Recorded at Lane End TQ57V (Kitchener, 1996) is the only record. **1** (0).

Rumex sanguineus x obtusifolius
= *R.* x *dufftii* Hausskn.

Plants were found at Tonbridge TQ54N, Green Street Green TQ57V, Rolvenden TQ83L and Denge Wood TR15A. **4** (0).

Rumex brownii Campd.   Hooked Dock

Introduced. Casual records with wool shoddy in arable fields, mainly hop-gardens, in the 1960s and 1970s, but this dock has not been found since. **0** (2).

Rumex pulcher L.   Fiddle Dock

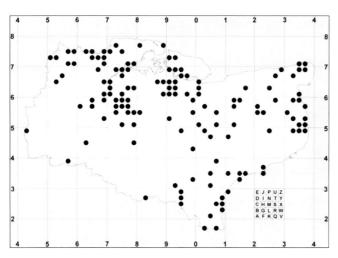

Native. On roadsides, churchyards, village greens and dry pastures, particularly near the coast. **141** (125).

Rumex pulcher x obtusifolius
= R. x ogulinensis Borbás

Has been recorded in the past but not as part of this survey. **0** (0).

Rumex obtusifolius L.   Broad-leaved Dock

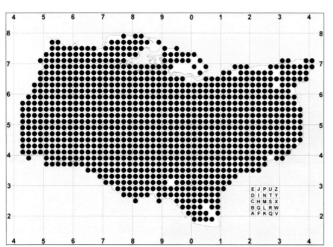

Native. Roadsides, field margins, river banks, ditches, neglected cultivated gardens and fields, and disturbed waste ground. The commonest dock in the county. **967** (983).

Rumex palustris Sm.   Marsh Dock

Native. Only known regularly from the Shorne Marshes TQ67X, and about pools and ditches in the Dungeness area TR01P & 01U, but there are healthy populations in both these areas. **3** (3).

Rumex maritimus L.   Golden Dock

Native. Recorded from the Cooling-High Halstow Marshes TQ77T & 77Y, Stoke Marshes TQ87M & 87N, and from the Chislet Marshes TR02I. **5** (6).

Rumex bequaertii De Wild.

Introduced. Casual records from East and West Kent in the past from fields treated with wool shoddy, but not seen during the present survey. **0** (0).

PLUMBAGINACEAE

Limonium vulgare Mill.   Common Sea-lavender

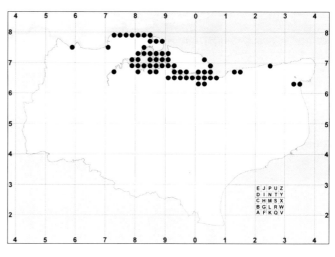

Native. In muddy saltmarshes and in grazing marshes that are covered at times by the highest tides. **61** (71).

[**Limonium humile** Mill.   Lax-flowered Sea-lavender

Recorded in the past, but no voucher material to support these claims has been found. During the present survey a special search was made to find this plant, but without success. However, it does occur on the north side of the Thames Estuary and is a plant that one would expect to be found in the county. **0** (0).]

Limonium platyphyllum Lincz.   Florist's Sea-lavender

Introduced. An casual escape from cultivation recorded from the north-west of the county in the past, but not found during the present survey. **0** (0).

Limonium binervosum　　　　Rock Sea-lavender
(G.E. Sm.) C.E. Salmon

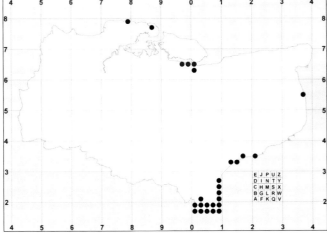

Native.　On chalk cliffs and other exposed chalky ground on the coast and occasionally on the drier parts of salt-marshes.　Ssp. *binervosum* (a slender plant) and ssp. *cantianum* (a more robust plant) occur in Kent and their recorded distributions overlap. However, in the field it is not always possible to place every plant as there appears to be a gradation between the two extremes, and so no attempt has been made to map the two subspecies separately.　**19** (17).

Armeria maritima (Mill.) Willd.　　　　Thrift

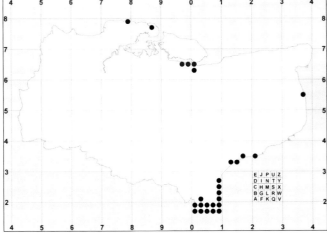

Native.　On the drier parts of salt-marshes, shingle beaches and other bare, sand-shingle areas on the coast.　It appears to have been lost from some areas in recent years, but not all of these losses can be attributed to new building and construction work. **26** (59).

PAEONIACEAE

Paeonia lactiflora Pall.　　　　Chinese Peony

Introduced.　Casual plants were found growing on rubbish-tips in the Dartford area during the 1970s, but this species has not been recorded since.　**0** (4).

ELATINACEAE

Elatine hexandra　　　　Six-stamened Waterwort
(Lapierre) DC.

A native species found growing at the edge of a pond at Bedgebury in 1948, but not seen there, or anywhere else in the county, since.　**0** (0).

CLUSIACEAE

Hypericum calycinum L.　　　　Rose-of-Sharon

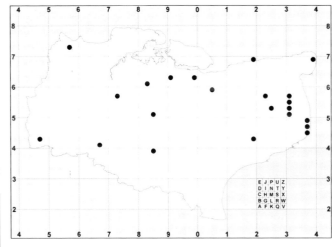

Introduced (neophyte).　Well naturalised in shrubberies, hedgerows, roadside and railway banks.　**22** (26).

Hypericum androsaemum L.　　　　Tutsan

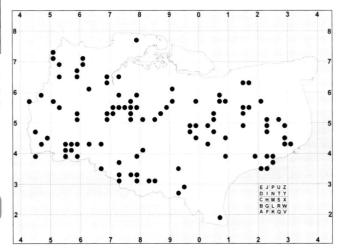

Native.　In woods and shady hedgerows, and looking completely native there. It is also found on rubbish-tips, railway banks, gardens and other disturbed soils near human habitation, and in these sites it is difficult to be sure if these are relics from native populations or escapes from gardens.　**102** (66).

Hypericum androsaemum x *hircinum*   Tall Tutsan
= *H.* x *inodorum* Mill.

Recorded in the past but not noted during the present survey.
0 (0).

Hypericum maculatum   Imperforate St John's-wort
Crantz

Native. Always a rare species in Kent, this plant was not recorded
during the present survey and could now well be extinct in the
county. **0** (8).

Hypericum hircinum L.   Stinking Tutsan

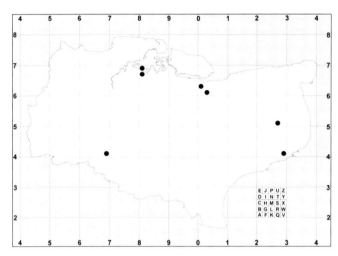

Introduced (neophyte). Well naturalised on roadsides and waste
ground in several localities in the county. **7** (1).

Hypericum tetrapterum Fr.   Square-stalked
St John's-wort

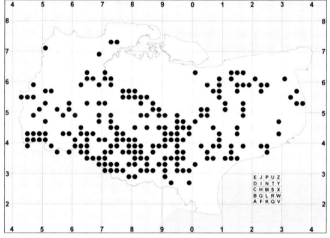

Native. Usually found in damp meadows, marshes, stream-sides
and wet ditches, but occasionally in woodland on the chalk.
Scattered records and never abundant. **216** (252).

Hypericum perforatum L.   Perforate St John's-wort

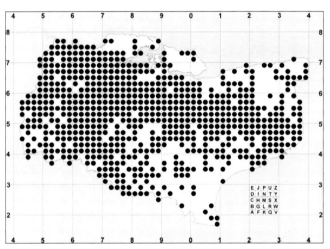

Native. In open woods, roadsides, railway and hedgerow banks,
and in meadows and other grassland. **701** (780).

Hypericum humifusum L.   Trailing St John's-wort

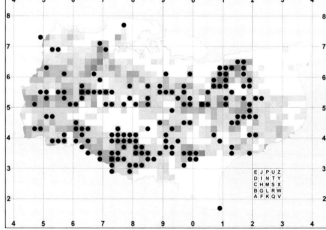

Hypericum maculatum x *perforatum*   Des Etang's
= *H.* x *desetangsii* Lamotte   St John's-wort

Found in the absence of one or both parents at the edge of a ditch
on the Kent/Sussex border at Pokehill TQ53N; on the banks of the
River Medway at Wateringbury TQ65W; and at the edge of a small
stream in Bedgebury Forest TQ73F. **3** (1).

Native. On heaths, woodland rides and dry sandy area on light
acid soils. There appears to be some decline in the distribution
of this plant. **158** (231).

Hypericum pulchrum L.   Slender St John's-wort

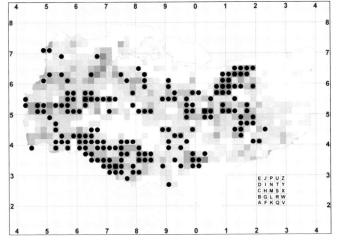

Native. On dry sandy heaths and open woodland on non-calcareous soils. **180** (237).

Hypericum hirsutum L.   Hairy St John's-wort

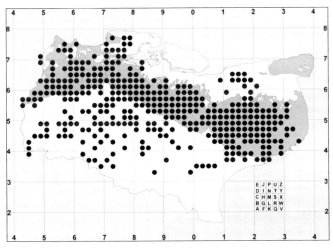

Native. Open woodland, rough and ungrazed grassland and roadside verges, particularly on the chalk. It also occurs along river and stream banks. **379** (405).

Hypericum montanum L.   Pale St John's-wort

Native. A rare and declining species, now in the Red List Category, 'Near Threatened'. The only record is of a small colony in a woodland ride near Woolage Village TR25K. **1** (2).

Hypericum elodes L.   Marsh St John's-wort

Native. In a boggy area by Louisa Lake in Bedgebury Forest TQ73G, and in Hothfield Bog TQ94S are the only present sites. **2** (3).

Hypericum olympicum L.

Introduced. A garden plant found well established on disturbed waste ground near Stodmarsh TR26A. **1** (0).

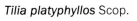

Tilia platyphyllos Scop.   Large-leaved Lime

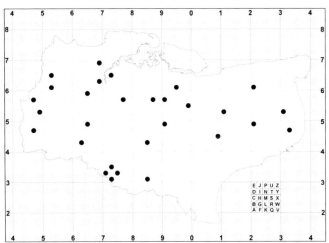

Perhaps always introduced (neophyte) in Kent. Widely planted in parks and large gardens, but only trees that are not obviously planted, or are self-seeded trees, have been mapped. **29** (7).

Tilia cordata x *platyphyllos*   Lime
= *T.* x *europaea* L.

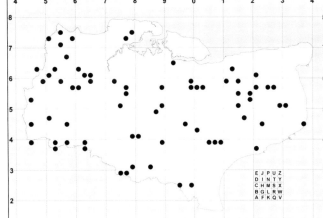

Introduced (neophyte). A widely planted tree in parks, large garden and roadside verges. Only not obviously planted trees have been mapped. **71** (166).

Tilia cordata Mill.   Small-leaved Lime

Native. Recorded from Tunbridge Wells Common TQ53U, Farningham Wood TQ56J, and Clowes Wood TR16G. **3** (2).

MALVACEAE

Sida spinosa L.   Prickly Mallow

Introduced. Casual records from rubbish-tips and other sites in the Dartford area where oil-seed waste had been deposited in the 1970s, but not recorded since. **0** (4).

Sida rhombifolia L.   Queensland-hemp

Introduced. Casual plants found growing on oil-seed waste on a rubbish-tip at Dartford in 1975, but not recorded since. **0** (1).

Sida cordifolia L.   Flannel Weed

Introduced. A casual wool-alien found in a hop-garden at Wateringbury in the 1970s, but not recorded since. **0** (1).

Malvastrum coromandelianum   Broomweed
(L.) Garcke

Introduced. As a casual wool-alien in hop-gardens near Wateringbury during the 1970s, but not recorded since. **0** (2).

Urocarpidium shepardae (I.M. Johnst.) Krapov.

Introduced. A wool-alien found growing in a hop-garden near Wateringbury in the 1970s, but not recorded since. **0** (1)

Anisodontea scabrosa   Scabrous Mallow
(L.) D. M. Bates

Introduced. On a rubbish-tip at Stone in 1978, possibly a greenhouse throw-out. Not recorded since. **0** (1).

Malva moschata L.   Musk mallow

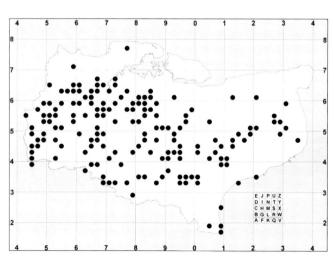

Native. On grassy banks, roadsides and woodland edges. On occasion it is sown with wild-flower seed mixes and some records could be as a result of this. **166** (195).

Malva sylvestris L.   Common Mallow

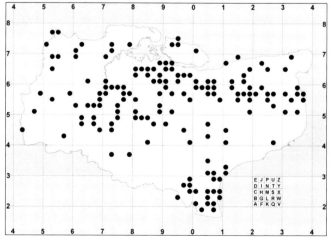

Introduced (archaeophyte). Long established and looking native on roadsides, railway-banks, field-borders and neglected land. Common throughout most of the county but scarce or absent from some parts of the Weald. **900** (861).

Malva nicaeensis All.   French Mallow

Introduced. A casual wool-alien last recorded in the county in 1970. **0** (0).

Malva parviflora L.   Least Mallow

Introduced. A casual wool, bird seed and esparto-grass alien, last recorded in the 1970s. **0** (5).

Malva pusilla Sm.   Small Mallow

Introduced. A casual wool, grain and bird seed alien, but with no records since 1978. **0** (3).

Malva neglecta Wallr.   Dwarf Mallow

Introduced (archaeophyte). Long established in arable fields, gardens, edges of footpaths and disturbed waste ground. Scattered records, but often persistent where it does occur. **158** (194).

Malva verticillata L.   Chinese Mallow

Introduced. Several plants in a farmyard at Waltham TR14E in 1999, constitute the only record. **1** (0).

Lavatera arborea L.   Tree-mallow

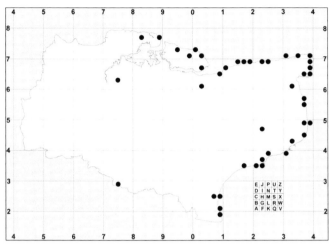

Probably introduced (neophyte), and certainly so inland. However, it is now well established and spreading by self-sown seed, particularly on or near the coast. **42** (20).

Lavatera thuringiaca sens. lat.   Garden Tree-mallow

Introduced (neophyte). A complex of plants, much planted in gardens, parks and at times on roadside verges. Recorded as naturalised and un-cared for at Lynsted TQ96K, New Romney TR02S, Swingfield Minnis TR24B and Dover TR33E. **4** (0).

Marsh-mallow *Althaea officinalis* © J. Shorter

Lavatera trimestris L.   Royal Mallow

Introduced (neophyte). Last recorded on a beach at Whitstable in 1989, probably as a garden escape. **0** (3).

Althaea officinalis L.   Marsh-mallow

Native. On the banks of tidal rivers and brackish dykes and ditches. The population over the Romney Marsh appears to be in decline through modern ditch management and through grazing marshes being turned to arable. A strong colony on the verges of a country lane near Bethersden appear to be a relic population from when the sea was nearer that area, but a small population on the banks of the river Darent at Eynsford is probably deliberately planted or an escape from cultivation. **49** (70).

Althaea hirsuta L.   Rough Marsh-mallow

Introduced (neophyte). Known from arable fields and woodland rides in the Cobham area TQ66Y & 66Z since 1792, and still present there. The number of plants appears to fluctuate from year to year depending on how much disturbance of the soil takes place. Also a few plants have persisted on some banks at Haysden TQ54S which were almost certainly introduced with imported soil. **3** (3).

Alcea rosea L.   Hollyhock

Introduced (neophyte). A common garden plant that often escapes and becomes established, at least temporarily, on roadside verges, cracks between buildings and pavements, and on waste ground. **40** (30).

Abutilon theophrasti Medik.   Velvetleaf

Introduced (neophyte) with wool shoddy, bird seed and oil-seed and now found as a casual adventive. Recorded from rubbish-tips at Stone TQ57S, Northfleet TQ67G, and from cultivated ground at Aylesford TQ75J and near Headcorn TQ84L. **4** (7).

Abutilon pictum   Chinese-lantern
(Gillies ex Hook. & Arn.) Walp.

Introduced. Casual plants, recorded as a greenhouse escapes, on a rubbish-tip near Maidstone in the past, but not seen during the present survey. **0** (0).

Pavonia urens Cav.

Introduced. A casual wool-alien recorded from a hop-garden near Maidstone in the 1970s, but not seen since. **0** (1).

Hibiscus trionum L.   Bladder Ketmia

Introduced (neophyte). A wool, bird seed and oil-seed casual recorded from scattered localities 1971-76, but there are no recent records. **0** (6).

SARRACENIACEAE

Sarracenia purpurea L.   Pitcherplant

Introduced. Deliberately planted in the bog in the L.N.R. at Hothfield TQ94S in the 1990s where it thrived and reproduced itself. Thankfully it has now been removed. **1** (0).

DROSERACEAE

Drosera rotundifolia L.   Round-leaved Sundew

Native. In the bog on the L.N.R. at Hothfield TQ94S is now the only locality left in Kent. **1** (2).

Round-leaved Sundew *Drosera rotundifolia* © A. Witts

CISTACEAE

[*Cistus* x *corbariensis* Pourret   Corbières Rock-rose

Reported from Crockenhill in Clement & Foster (1994), but the plants had actually been planted at the entrance to a nursery and have no claim to be wild. **0** (0).]

Helianthemum nummularium   Common Rock-rose
(L.) Mill.

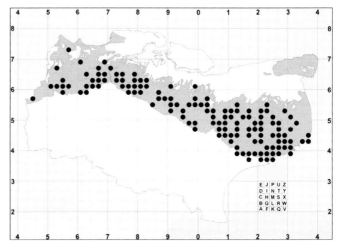

Native. On roadside banks, downland and open grassy or light scrub areas on the chalk. **134** (176).

VIOLACEAE

Viola odorata L.   Sweet Violet

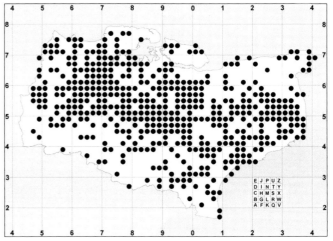

Native. Open woodland, hedge banks and scrub, particularly on the chalk. A range of flower colours have been noted from the usual violet to deep purple or white, and occasionally pinkish or apricot. It is a regular inhabitant in churchyards, although here in most cases it would have been originally planted. **503** (361).

Viola odorata x hirta
= *V.* x *scabra* F. Braun

Although this hybrid has been recorded in the past it was not noted during the present survey, but could have been over-looked. **0** (1).

Viola riviniana x reichenbachiana
= *V.* x *bavarica* Schrank

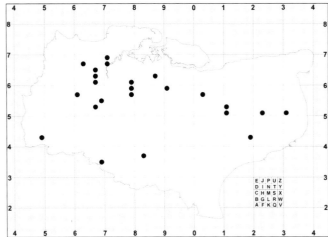

Scattered records of this hybrid, usually, but not always, growing with both parents. **23** (2).

Viola hirta L.   Hairy Violet

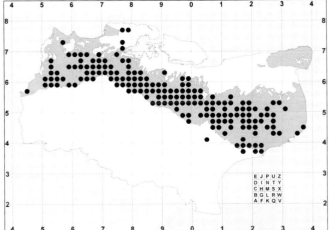

Native. In short grassland, scrub and roadside banks, nearly always on the chalk. **173** (220).

Viola riviniana x *canina* = *V.* x *intersita* Beck

Recorded from Dartford Heath TQ57B & 57G, and also from Borough Green TQ65D. **3** (1).

Viola riviniana x *lactea*

Plants referable to this hybrid (specimen in **MNE** collected by F. Rose) were found near Leigh in 1955 but have not been seen since. **0** (0).

Viola riviniana Rchb.   Common Dog-violet

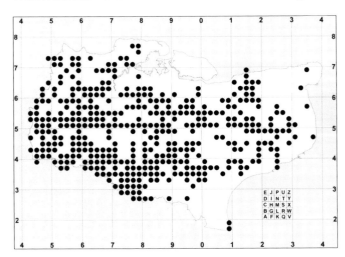

Native. Open deciduous woodland, hedge banks and roadside verges. **422** (627).

Viola reichenbachiana Jord. ex Boreau   Early Dog-violet

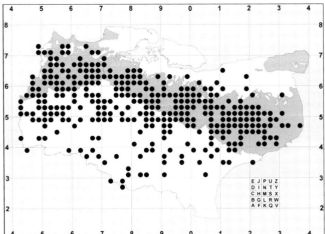

Native. In deciduous woodland and hedgerows, particularly on the chalk. **331** (333).

Viola canina L.   Heath Dog-violet

Native. Heaths, coastal dunes and grassland on acid soils. This plant was specifically searched for, but was only found on Dartford Heath TQ57B and 57G, in acid grassland in the Pembury area TQ54W and 64B, a few plants in open woodland near Elmstead TR14C, and on fixed sand-dunes at Sandwich Bay TR35N. Nationally, it is listed as 'Near Threatened'. **6** (8).

Viola canina x lactea

Was once recorded in the 19th century from near Tunbridge Wells, but has not been seen since. **0** (0).

Viola lactea Sm.   Pale Dog-violet

Native. Old records suggest that it used to occur in the Tunbridge Wells area where it was last recorded in 1897. **0** (0).

Viola palustris L.   Marsh Violet

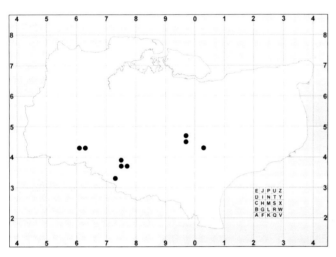

Native. In bogs, wet heaths and wet woodland. Rather scarce and apparently decreasing. **9** (12).

Viola x wittrockiana Gams ex Kappert   Garden Pansy

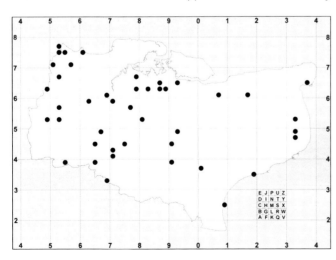

Introduced (neophyte). Much grown in gardens and escaping to rubbish-tips, rough ground and cultivated fields. Many plants revert back and are almost indistinguishable from Viola tricolor. **43** (25).

Viola tricolor L.   Wild Pansy

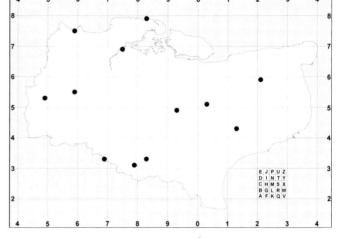

Native. On cultivated fields and marginal ground. In common with many other arable weed species, the wild pansy has decreased over the years and is now a scarce plant, giving relevance to its national listing as 'Near Threatened'. **12** (35).

Viola tricolor x arvensis = V. x contempta Jord.

Plants referable to this hybrid were found in arable fields near Charing TQ95Q and at Cheeseman's Green TR03J. **2** (1).

Viola arvensis Murray   Field Pansy

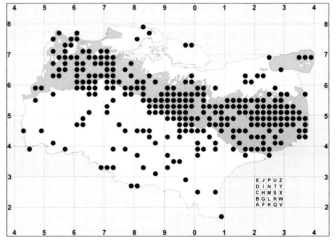

Native. In cornfields and other cultivated land, roadsides and disturbed waste ground, particularly on the chalk. **290** (327).

TAMARICACEAE

Tamarix gallica L. — Tamarisk

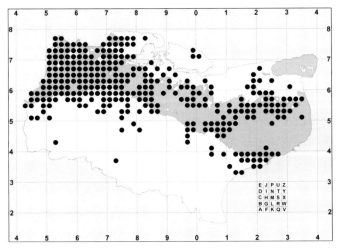

Introduced (neophyte). Often planted in coastal areas and all records are of well established naturalised plants. **28** (8).

FRANKENIACEAE

Frankenia laevis L. — Sea-heath

Native. A few plants at the edges of saline pools on the Lydd ranges at TR01D and 01I; in good quantity on shingle at Pen Bars, near Dungeness TR01T; abundant on the chalk cliffs at Lydden Spout TR23U where it has been known since at least 1829; and a few plants on the chalk cliffs at Shakespeare Cliff TR33E. In the Red List Category as 'Near Threatened'. **5** (3).

CUCURBITACEAE

Bryonia dioica Jacq. — White Bryony

Native. In hedgerows, woodland borders and scrub, particularly on the chalk. In the past, superstition considered it unlucky to dig up this plant as the swollen roots are often grotesque and in the form of a human body. **310** (396).

Ecballium elaterium (L.) A. Rich. — Squirting Cucumber

Introduced. Reported as 'naturalised' at Westgate in 1961, but has not been seen wild in the county since. **0** (0).

Sicyos angulatus L. — Bur Cucumber

Introduced. Casual plants have been reported on a few occasions in the past from rubbish-tips and waste ground, but the species has not been seen since last recorded at Stone in 1981. **0** (1).

Cucumis melo L — Melon

Introduced. Casual records as growing on rubbish-tips from a few localities in the north-west of the county in the 1970s, but there are no recent records. **0** (7).

Citrullus lanatus (Thunb.) Matsum. & Nakai — Water Melon

Introduced. Occasional plants were reported as growing on rubbish-tips in the 1970s, but there are no recent records. **0** (5).

Cucurbita pepo L. — Marrow

Introduced. Casual plants recorded on a rubbish-tip at Dartford TQ57M, on waste ground at Swanscombe TQ67C, and on a disturbed roadside near Lenham TQ95G. **3** (12).

Cucurbita maxima Duchesne ex Lam. — Pumpkin

Introduced. A casual plant was reported as growing on a rubbish-tip in West Kent in 1979, but there are no other records. **0** (1).

SALICACEAE

Populus alba L. — White Poplar

Introduced (neophyte). Much planted, particularly in coastal areas. It spreads by sucker growth and is now well established in many places throughout the county. **150** (151).

Populus alba x *tremula*   Grey Poplar
= *P.* x *canescens* (Aiton) Sm.

Populus nigra 'Italica'   Lombardy Poplar

Introduced (neophyte). Much planted in parks, farmland hedgerows and for screening and was noted as 'wild and not being cared for' at TQ65V, TQ75D, TQ85D, TQ94E, TR26A and TR36G, but nowhere can it be really claimed as naturalised. 6 (5).

Populus x *canadensis* Moench   Hybrid Black-poplar

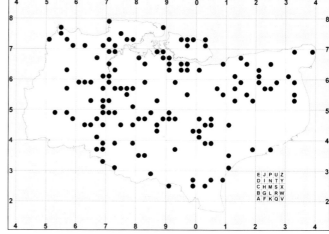

Introduced (neophyte). Much planted in windbreaks or as an amenity tree, and found naturalised as scattered trees in hedgerows or wood borders. 25 (52).

Introduced (neophyte). Planted in plantations, hedgerows and as an amenity tree in parkland and along roadsides. Recorded naturalised and spreading by suckers, but no attempt has been made to identify various cultivars. 138 (143).

Populus tremula L.   Aspen

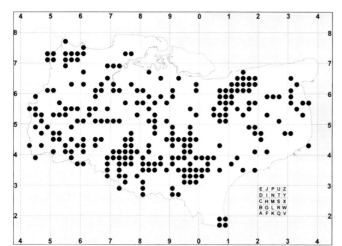

Populus x *jackii* Sarg.   Balm-of-Gilead

Introduced (neophyte). Is occasionally planted in parks and by roadsides, and although recorded in the past, no wild established trees were noted during the present survey. 0 (5).

Native. In woodland, heathland, and in waste places such as in old sand quarries. Frequent throughout most of the county. 260 (367).

Populus trichocarpa   Western Balsam-poplar
Torr. & A. Gray ex Hook.

Introduced (neophyte). Frequently planted for ornament and for timber. Noted as looking 'wild' at East Sutton TQ84J and Tilmanstone TR35A. 2 (0).

Populus nigra ssp. *betulifolia*   Black Poplar
(Pursh) Dippel

Salix pentandra L.   Bay Willow

Native. Recorded from Bough Beech TQ44Y; Shornmead Fort TQ67X; edge of Bedgebury Forest TQ73H; a fine stand of stunted trees on St. Mary's Marsh TQ87E; and from Dymchurch TR12E. 5 (2).

Introduced (neophyte). Occasionally planted and reported naturalised in the past, but was not noted during the present survey. 0 (1).

Salix fragilis L. — Crack-willow

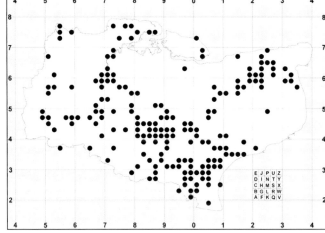

Introduced (archaeophyte)   Long established, but much planted in the past.   Twigs pushed into damp ground soon root and it is still regularly planted in this way, particularly by fishermen, around ponds and flooded gravel pits.   By rivers, streams, wet woods and other damp areas.   **459** (538).

Salix fragilis x triandra
= S. x *alopecuroides* Tausch ex Opiz

Recorded from Rusthall Common in 1803, and this is the only record from the county.   **0** (0).

Salix alba x fragilis — Hybrid Crack-willow
= S. x *rubens* Schrank

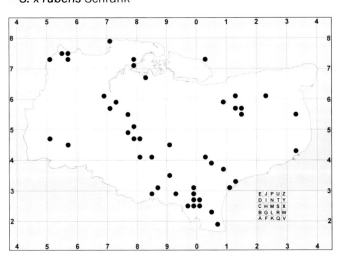

By ponds, ditches, rivers and streams, and in marshy areas. Whether any of these records refer to naturally occurring hybrids is open to doubt as this tree is easily propagated and much planted.   **48** (65).

Salix fragilis x babylonica — Weeping Crack-willow
= S. x *pendulina* Wender.

Found growing in the wild away from cultivation at Haysden TQ54M, Wateringbury TQ65W, Teston TQ75B, Maidstone TQ75S & 75T, Leybourne TQ76A, Oare TR06C and at Canterbury TR15N although in each case it must have originally been planted. **8** (3).

Salix alba L. — White Willow

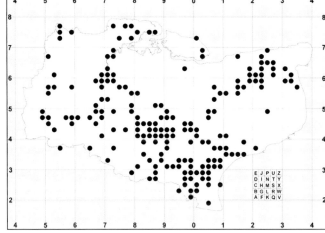

Introduced (archaeophyte).   Long established although many records must refer to trees that were originally planted.   By lakes, ponds rivers and ditches.   **189** (237).

Salix alba x babylonica — Weeping Willow
= S. x *sepulcralis* Simonk.

Introduced (neophyte).   A completely naturalised tree by a river at Maidstone must have originally been planted.   **1** (2).

Salix triandra L. — Almond Willow

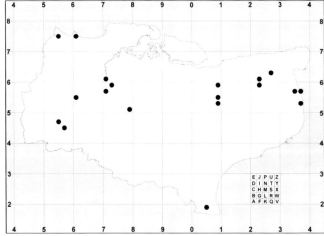

Introduced (archaeophyte).   Long established and completely naturalised in wet places by lakes, rivers, ponds and in marshes. **19** (18).

Salix purpurea L.   Purple Willow

Native. By ponds, ditches and in marshes. Recorded from Nettlestead Green TQ65Q, Harrietsham TQ85Q, Fairfield TQ92T and from near Brookland TR02C. **4** (12).

Salix purpurea x *viminalis*   Green-leaved Willow
= *S.* x *rubra* Huds.

There no recent records for this hybrid willow, last recorded in the county more than a hundred years ago. **0** (0).

[*Salix daphnoides* Vill.   European Violet-willow

Introduced (neophyte). Only seen as obviously planted and cared for trees, as must have been the previous record for the county. **0** (1).]

[*Salix acutifolia* Willd.   Siberian Violet-willow

Introduced (neophyte). Only seen as obviously planted and cared for trees. **0** (1).]

Salix viminalis L.   Osier

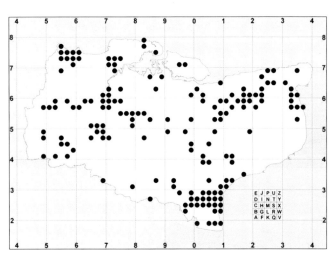

Introduced (archaeophyte). Long established, but much planted and many records must refer to such trees or to their offspring. In damp places by rivers, streams and in marshes.   **164** (207).

Salix viminalis x *caprea*   Broad-leaved Osier
= *S.* x *sericans* Willd.

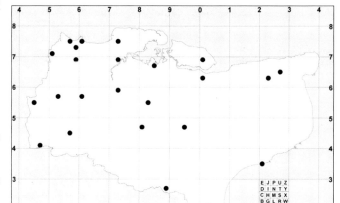

Native, although on occasion it is planted and some records might refer to these. At the edge of woodland, on river banks and in hedgerows. **24** (16).

Salix viminalis x *caprea* x *cinerea*   Holme Willow
= *S.* x *calodendron* Wimm.

Recorded from damp scrub at Pegwell Bay TR36G, the only record in this survey. However, it could not be re-found at its only previous locality at Aylesford where it occurred in the 1970s. **1** (1).

Salix viminalis x *cinerea*   Silky-leaved Osier
= *S.* x *smithiana* Willd.

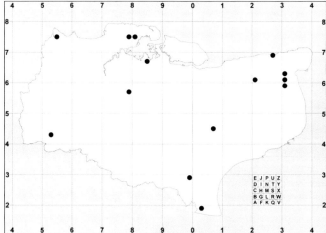

Native. In gravel pits and other disturbed damp area, usually, but not always with both parents. **14** (13).

Salix caprea L.   Goat Willow   *Salix cinerea* L.   Grey Willow

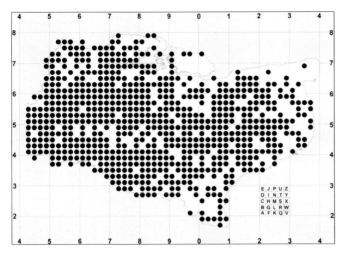 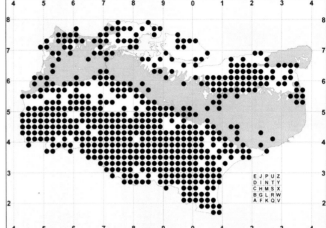

Native. In open woodland, wood margins, scrub, hedgerows, at the edge of lakes and ponds, and in old quarries. It is the only sallow to be met with regularly on the chalk. **725** (757).

Native. In damp areas in woods and hedgerows, in marshes, and by lakes ponds and streams. The common plant is ssp. *oleifolia*. Ssp. *cinerea* does occur rarely in very wet marshy or fen areas, but has not been mapped separately. **571** (666).

Salix cinerea x aurita = S. x *multinervis* Döll

Has been recorded in the past, but there are no recent records. **0** (0).

**Salix caprea x cinerea
= S. x *reichardtii* A. Kern.**

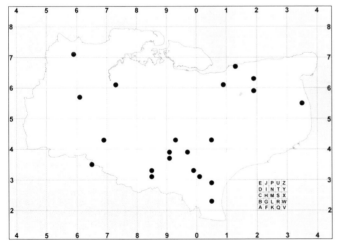

Salix cinerea x *myrsinifolia*

This species has been recorded from West Kent in the past (Stace, 1975) but there are no recent records. **0** (0).

Salix aurita L.   Eared Willow

Native. Scattered records where both parents occur; almost certainly under-recorded. **21** (13).

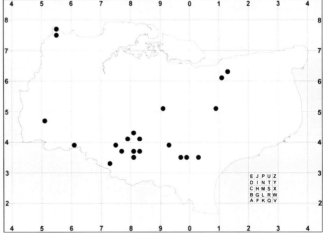

**Salix caprea x aurita
= S. x *capreola* Jos. Kern. ex Andersson**

Native. Has been recorded in the past, but there are no recent records. **0** (0).

Native. On heathland and damp woods on acidic soils. Rather local. **21** (30).

Salix aurita x repens = S. x ambigua Ehrh.

Has been recorded in the past but there are no recent records. **0** (0).

Salix repens L.   Creeping Willow

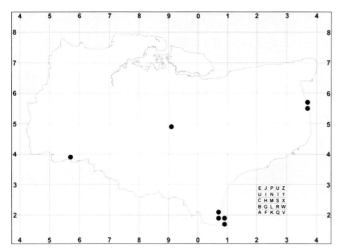

Native. The var. *repens* occurs on damp heathland inland, and the var. *argentea* on coastal shingle and sand-dunes. **8** ((9).

Salix babylonica L. var.   Corkscrew Willow
pekinensis Henry 'Tortuosa'

Introduced (neophyte). Several trees, growing wild, in scrub and marshland at Snodland TQ76A, on waste ground at Kemsley TQ96C, and at the edge of a dyke at Oare TR06C must have all originally been planted. **3** (0).

CAPPARACEAE

Cleome sesquiorygalis   Spider-flower
Naudin ex C. Huber

Introduced. A casual garden escape found on a rubbish-tip at Dartford in 1976, but not recorded since. **0** (1).

BRASSICACEAE

Sisymbrium irio L.   London-rocket

Introduced (neophyte), although known as a wild plant in Britain since about 1650. At present only recorded from arable fields on the Wade Marshes TR26P and at Acol TR36D. **2** (1).

Sisymbrium loeselii L.   False London-rocket

Introduced (neophyte). The False London-rocket was introduced to cultivation in Britain in 1787 and first recorded wild in 1883, and with the first Kent record in 1898. It has always been a scarce plant in the county and the only present records are from disturbed waste ground at Dartford TQ57N, Swanscombe TQ67C and Naccolt TR04M. **3** (2).

Sisymbrium altissimum L.   Tall Rocket

Introduced (neophyte). There appears to have been a great reduction in the range and numbers of this plant since the 1970s. During this survey it was only recorded from disturbed waste ground on Dartford Marshes TQ57N, disturbed waste ground at Murston TQ96M, and from fixed sand-dunes at Sandwich Bay TR35P & 35U. **4** (30).

Sisymbrium orientale L.   Eastern Rocket

Introduced (neophyte). First recorded wild in Kent in 1892, and now with scattered records throughout the county. It occurs on disturbed waste land, roadsides, and frequently around buildings in built-up areas. **84** (99).

Sisymbrium erysimoides Desf.   French Rocket

Introduced (neophyte). Has been recorded as a wool shoddy alien in the past, but the only present record is from a roadside in Borough Green TQ65D. **1** (0).

Sisymbrium officinale (L.) Scop.   Hedge Mustard

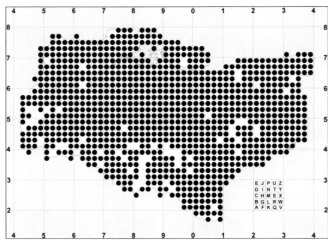

Introduced (archaeophyte). Long established and a common plant of roadsides, hedgerows, cultivated and waste ground. **943** (977).

Arabidopsis thaliana (L.) Heynh.   Thale Cress

Native. On old walls, dry sandy banks, in pavement cracks and on other open or recently disturbed areas with little or no other competition. **318** (353).

Descurainia sophia (L.) Webb ex Prantl   Flixweed

Introduced (archaeophyte). Long established, the Flixweed is another one of the yellow cresses that appears to be in decline and was only recorded from arable fields or disturbed roadside verges at Teston TQ75B, Linton TQ75K, Gillingham TQ76Z, Cliffe TQ77I and Faversham TR06A. **5** (32).

Isatis tinctoria L.   Woad

Introduced (archaeophyte). A casual alien, not recorded since before 1899. **0** (0).

Alliaria petiolata   Garlic Mustard
(M. Bieb.) Cavara & Grande

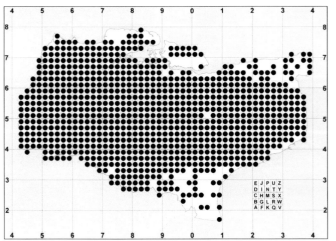

Native. Roadsides, hedgerows, woodland edges, gardens and other disturbed ground. Common except in a few coastal areas. **885** (912).

Bunias orientalis L.   Warty-cabbage

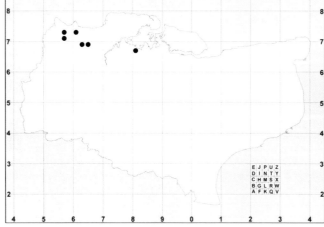

Introduced (neophyte). Roadsides, railway banks and waste places. **6** (14).

Erysimum cheiranthoides L.　Treacle-mustard

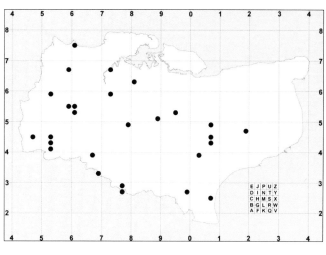

Introduced (archaeophyte). On cultivated and waste ground particularly in arable fields. It appears to have declined in recent years, probably through changes in farming practices. **27** (100).

Hesperis matronalis L.　Dame's-violet

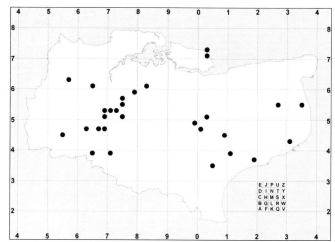

Introduced (neophyte). A garden escape that has become naturalised along roadsides, on river banks and in waste places. At some localities it has been long established and there are records, and voucher specimens, for some sites along the Medway Valley dating back more than a hundred years. **29** (73).

Erysimum x marshallii (Henfr.) Bois　Siberian Wallflower

Introduced A casual garden outcast, recorded in the past, but not during the present survey. **0** (3).

Malcolmia maritima (L.) W.T. Aiton　Virginia Stock

Introduced. A casual garden escape that has been recorded on a few occasions in the past, but not during the present survey. **0** (8).

Erysimum cheiri (L.) Crantz　Wallflower

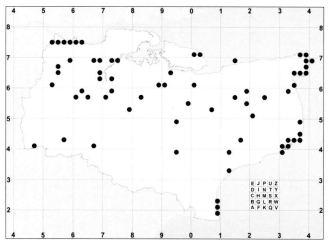

Introduced (archaeophyte). A common garden plant but has long been well naturalised on sea-cliffs, old walls and railway cuttings on the chalk. In fact in 1899 Hanbury and Marshall wrote "Now far too well established to be classed as an alien; indeed, a fair case might be made out for claiming it as a native on the cliffs of Thanet, and again from St. Margaret's to Folkestone." This argument still holds good today. **67** (95).

Matthiola incana (L.) W.T. Aiton　Hoary Stock

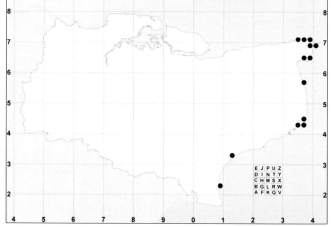

Introduced (neophyte). On coastal chalk cliffs and sand-dunes and looking completely native there. **13** (13).

Matthiola longipetala (Vent.) DC.　Night-scented Stock

Introduced. A casual garden escape last recorded wild in the county in 1950. **0** (0).

Barbarea vulgaris   Winter-cress
W.T. Aiton

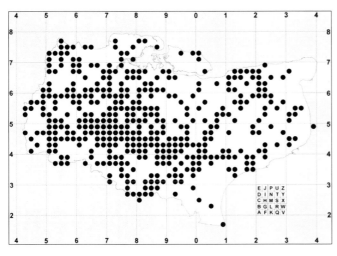

Native. At the edge of rivers, streams and ponds, and also in damp areas on roadsides, cultivated and waste land. **426** (517).

Rorippa nasturtium-aquaticum/microphylla   Water-cress species

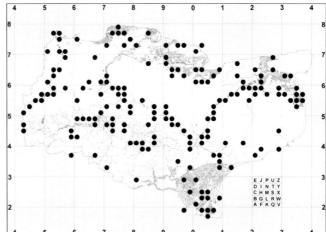

The two water-cress species are only reliably identified when in fruit and it has not been possible to confirm the identification of all plants. Observations were often made at the wrong time of year, or the heads had been grazed off and so the aggregate was recorded. The above map shows the combined distribution of both species plus all those plants that were not able to be determined to species level. **176**.

Barbarea intermedia   Medium-flowered Winter-cress
Boreau

Introduced. A casual plant of disturbed waste areas. Recorded from near Longfield TQ56Z, Hawkhurst TQ73K and Dungeness TR01Y. **3** (12).

Barbarea verna (Mill.) Asch.   American Winter-cress

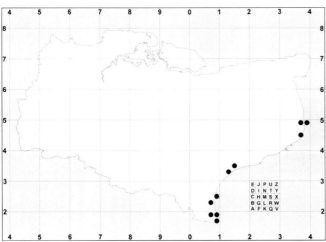

Introduced (neophyte). Well established on shingle and sandy areas in a few areas between Dungeness to Deal. Has been recorded as a casual plant elsewhere in the past but not during the present survey. **10** (16).

Rorippa nasturtium-aquaticum   Water-cress
(L.) Hayek

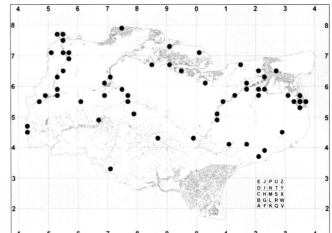

Native. In and beside clear shallow rivers, streams, ponds and ditches, particularly those influenced by calcareous substrata. **58** (207).

Rorippa nasturtium-aquaticum x   Hybrid Water-cress
microphylla = R. x *sterilis* Airy Shaw

This hybrid is the most widely cultivated water-cress and was first grown in the country near Gravesend in 1808. Recorded from near Gravesend TQ67C and Littlebourne TR25D, at both these sites probably originating from former cultivation. **2** (3).

Rorippa microphylla (Boenn.)   Narrow-fruited Water-cress
Hyl. ex Á. Löve & D. Löve

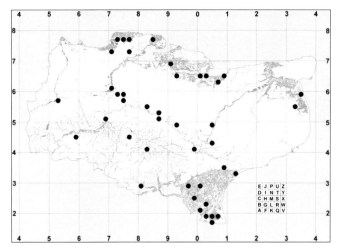

Native. In and beside clear shallow rivers, streams, ponds and ditches. The distribution of this species does not appear to be restricted by the ground geology. **42** (109).

Rorippa palustris (L.) Besser   Marsh Yellow-cress

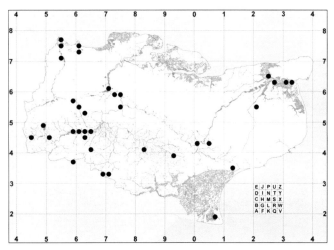

Native. On river banks, pond edges and marsh ground that either partly dries out in the summer, or floods in the winter. Appears to be in decline. **35** (93).

Rorippa sylvestris (L.) Besser   Creeping Yellow-cress

Native. In damp ground by rivers and ponds where it floods in winter, and on cultivated and waste ground. **26** (104).

Rorippa sylvestris x *amphibia*
= *R. x anceps* (Wahlenb.) Rchb.

Several plants found along the banks of the River Rother at Newenden TQ82N. **1** (0).

Rorippa amphibia (L.) Besser   Great Yellow-cress

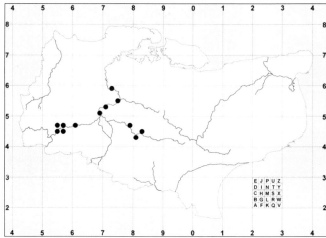

Native. By rivers and streams and in marshy areas by lakes and ponds. **12** (44).

Rorippa austriaca   Austrian Yellow-cress
(Crantz) Besser

Introduced. Has been recorded as a casual from East Kent in the past, but there are no recent records. **0** (0).

Armoracia rusticana   Horse-radish
P. Gaertn., B. Mey. & Scherb.

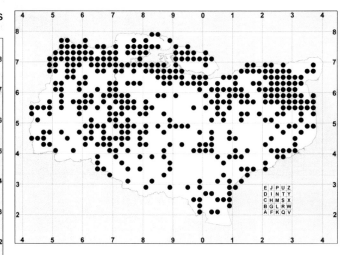

Introduced (archaeophyte). Long cultivated for use in hot relishes, and now widely naturalised on roadsides and waste ground. Seed-set is not known in this country and spread is by dispersal of root fragments. **429** (650).

Cardamine bulbifera (L.) Crantz)　　　　　　Coralroot

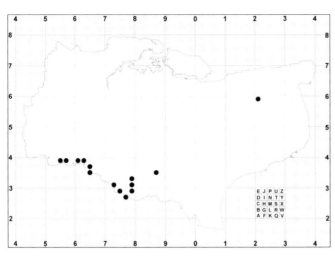

Native. A scarce plant of damp woodland over clay in the Weald. Plants near Trenleypark Wood, originally discovered by D. Worsfold, are in a totally new locality for Kent, but look completely native and with no suggestion of being introduced. **14** (9).

Cardamine pentaphyllos　　　　Five-leaved Coralroot
(L.) Crantz

Introduced.　A casual plant on a roadside at Ashurst recorded by M. Page in 1980 has not been re-found and had probably escaped from a nearby garden. **0** (1).

Cardamine amara L.　　　　　　Large Bitter-cress

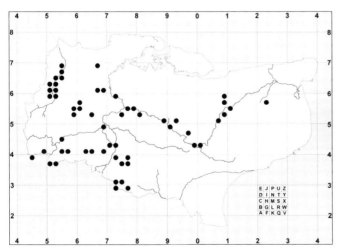

Native. By stream-sides, and in marshes, spring flushes, wet meadows and wet woodlands. **56** (45).

Cardamine pratensis L.　　　　　　Cuckooflower

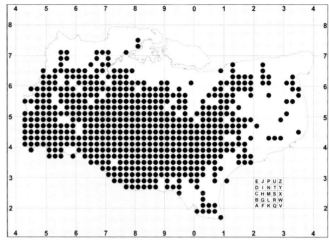

Native. In damp areas by rivers, streams, woods, churchyards, meadows and roadside ditches. A common wild flower away from most coastal areas. **589** (641).

Cuckooflower *Cardamine pratensis* © L. Manning

Cardamine pratensis x *flexuosa*
= *C.* x *fringsii* F. Wirtg.

On a damp roadside verge on Sevenoaks Common TQ55G in 2001, but the site has now been destroyed through housing development. The first Kent record. **1** (0).

Cardamine impatiens L.   Narrow-leaved Bitter-cress

Native. On banks and in damp meadows along the Medway Valley. Appears to be in decline and only recorded from Chiddingstone TQ54C, Haysden Park TQ54T and Aylesford TQ75J. Listed nationally as 'Near Threatened'. **3** (15).

Cardamine flexuosa With.   Wavy Bitter-cress

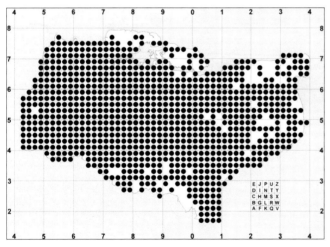

Native. In damp areas at the edge of ponds, rivers and streams, and it is particularly frequent along damp woodland rides. It is also found at times in gardens and on other cultivated soils. **407** (420).

Cardamine hirsuta L.   Hairy Bitter-cress

Native. On fixed sand-dunes, shingle beaches, dry roadside banks and on old walls. It is also a common weed of gardens, nurseries and other cultivated ground. **907** (743).

Cardamine corymbosa   New Zealand Bitter-cress
Hook. f.

Introduced (neophyte). This plant, looking like a diminutive *Cardamine hirsuta*, was first recorded in the county by C. Foord in her garden at Rochester TQ76N in 1992. It has subsequently been found elsewhere in a garden at Rochester TQ76P and in a nursery at Charing Heath TQ94J. It is easily over-looked and should be searched for in gardens and particularly garden nurseries. **3** (0).

Arabis glabra (L.) Bernh.   Tower Mustard

Native, but now probably extinct in the county. It was last recorded in the wild in 1958, although four plants turned up in a garden at Rochester in 1985. **0** (0).

Arabis caucasica Willd. ex Schltdl.   Garden Arabis

Introduced. A plant of garden origin that has been reported as a casual escape in the past, but was not recorded during the present survey. **0** (5).

Arabis hirsuta (L.) Scop.   Hairy Rock-cress

Native. On dry chalky banks and at the edges of arable fields on chalk. Never very common in the county, this plant appears to have declined even further in recent years and is now known only from Stockbury TQ86F and Kingsdown TR34T. **2** (7).

Aubrieta deltoidea (L.) DC.   Aubretia

Introduced (neophyte). A garden escape noted naturalised on old walls and waste places at Offham TQ65N, Hunton TQ74J, Sandling TQ75P, near Aldington TR03S, Kennington TR04H and Stanford TR13J, and is probably elsewhere. **6** (19).

Lunaria annua L.   Honesty

Introduced (neophyte). A common garden plant that is now well naturalised on roadside banks, secondary woodland, hedgerows and waste ground. **236** (195).

Alyssum alyssoides (L.) L.   Small Alison

Introduced (neophyte). A garden escape, not recorded in the county since before 1899. **0** (0).

Alyssum saxatile L.   Golden Alison

Introduced (neophyte). A garden plant occasionally naturalised on old walls and only noted at South Darenth TQ56U during the present survey. **1** (5).

Berteroa incana (L.) DC.   Hoary Alison

Introduced. A casual plant that has occasionally become naturalised, but was not noticed during the present survey. Last recorded in the county in 1978. **0** (1).

Lobularia maritima (L.) Desv.   Sweet Alison

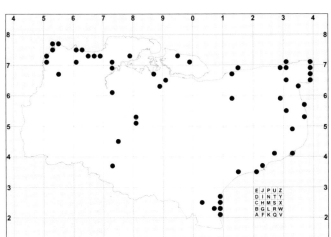

Introduced (neophyte). A common garden plant, well naturalised on sand-dunes, coastal cliffs, open waste ground and roadsides, particularly in pavement cracks. Scattered records but particularly frequent in some coastal areas. **53** (86).

Draba muralis L.   Wall Whitlowgrass

Introduced (neophyte). Recorded from near Wye in the late 19th century, and from Riverhead in 1985 and 1986. **0** (0).

Erophila verna (L.) DC.   Common Whitlowgrass

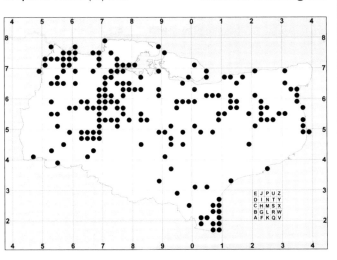

Native. Found on old walls, sand-dunes, roadside banks, old quarries, cracks in pavements and other well-drained areas. This cress is one of the first plants to come into flower at the beginning of the year and is soon over and hence, easily missed. The genus has recently been split into three species and great care has been taken over the identification of these plants. However many plants varied from with just the odd hair through to having scattered hairs on the stem, and with petals bifid from a quarter through to three quarters of their length all on the same plant, characters that are supposed to distinguish this species from *E. glabrescens*. All doubtful plants have been recorded as *E. verna*. The third species, *Erophila majuscula*, was looked for but not found. **188** (189).

Erophila glabrescens Jord.   Glabrous Whitlowgrass

Native. Plants that fitted the description of this species were recorded from Teston TQ75B, Eccles TQ76A, and Greatstone TR02W. **3** (0).

Cochlearia anglica L.   English Scurvygrass

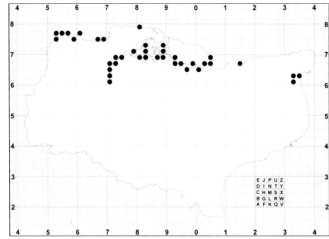

Native. In saltmarshes and at the edge of sheltered sea-walls. **38** (60).

Cochlearia danica L.   Danish Scurvygrass

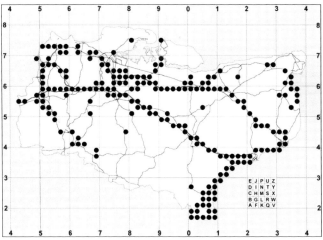

Native. On sandy and shingle areas on the coast from the Sussex border through to Pegwell Bay. However, since 1980 this plant has taken a liking to the edges of salt-treated roads and is now found along all the major roads in the county and is beginning to spread into some of the minor roads as well. Now recorded from 209 tetrads, a great increase since the 1971-80 Atlas. **209** (17).

Camelina sativa (L.) Crantz.   Gold-of-pleasure

Introduced. Recorded in the past as a casual plant of rubbish tips and waste ground, but not found during the present survey. **0** (3).

Neslia paniculata (L.) Desv.   Ball Mustard

Introduced.   A casual plant of rubbish tips, last recorded in the county in 1948. **0** (0).

Capsella bursa-pastoris (L.) Medik.   Shepherds's-purse

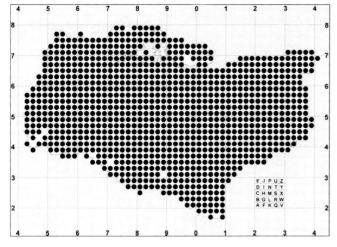

Introduced (archaeophyte).   On cultivated and disturbed ground in fields, gardens, roadsides and waste places throughout the county, and looking very native. **1009** (1021).

Jonopsidium acaule (Desf.) Rchb.   Violet Cress

Introduced.   A garden casual recorded from Darenth Wood in the 1970s, but has not been seen since. **0** (1).

Teesdalia nudicaulis (L.) W.T. Aiton   Shepherd's Cress

Native. Frequent on sandy ridges among the shingle beaches on the Dungeness peninsular, but not known elsewhere in the county.   Nationally, it is listed as 'Near Threatened'.   **13** (15).

Thlaspi arvense L.   Field Penny-cress

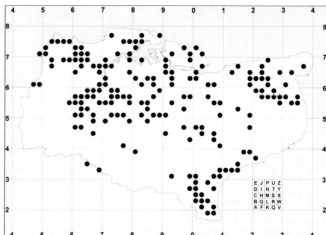

Introduced (archaeophyte). Long established in arable fields and disturbed waste places. In line with many other arable weeds there appears to have been a serious decline in the occurrence of this plant in recent years.   **191** (469).

Thlaspi alliaceum L.   Garlic Penny-cress

Introduced (neophyte). Well naturalised at the edge of arable fields in the Ripper's Cross area TQ94L, 94R & 94W, where it has been known since 1923. **3** (2).

Iberis sempervirens L.   Perennial Candytuft

Introduced.   A casual garden escape recorded from the Gravesend area in the past, but with no recent records. **0** (1).

Iberis amara L.   Wild Candytuft

Native. Recorded in small quantity from chalk banks in an old quarry at Snodland TQ66W & 76B, and from a chalky bank at Folkestone TR23I. A scarce plant listed as 'Vulnerable'. **3** (1).

Iberis umbellata L.   Garden Candytuft

Introduced. A garden plant found growing as a casual escape on a roadside verge at Edenbridge TQ44N and at the top of a beach at Swalecliffe TR16P. **2** (13)

Lepidium sativum L.   Garden Cress

Introduced. Casual plants recorded from Dartford TQ57H, Maidstone TQ75X and Hoath TR26C. **3** (13).

Lepidium campestre (L.) W.T. Aiton   Field Pepperwort

Lepidium hyssopifolium Desv.   African Pepperwort

Introduced. A casual wool alien last recorded in Kent, as *L.. africanum,* in 1962. **0** (0).

Lepidium latifolium L   Dittander

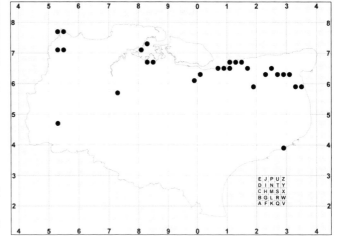

Introduced (archaeophyte). Another long-established plant that looks completely native in open grassland, roadside verges and arable fields. **60** (120).

Lepidium heterophyllum Benth.   Smith's Pepperwort

Native. On sandy areas on the shingle beach at Dungeness TR01Y and on fixed sand-dunes at Pegwell Bay TR36G. **2** (3).

Lepidium virginicum L.   Least Pepperwort

Introduced (neophyte). Several plants on a roadside verge at Dover TR24W in July 1996. **1** (0).

Native. A scarce plant of river banks, sea-walls and brackish ditches, and occasionally on roadside verges. A stable population occurs along the River Great Stour but there appears to be a slight increase in sites along the north coast of the county. **28** (12).

Lepidium ruderale L.   Narrow-leaved Pepperwort

Lepidium draba L.   Hoary Cress

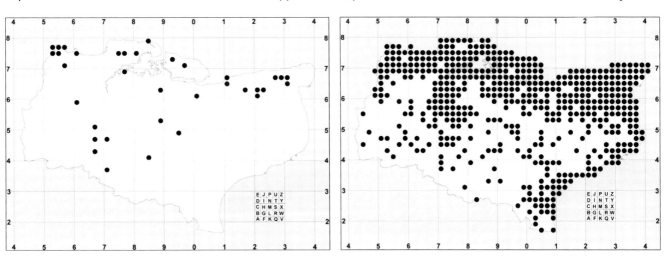

Introduced (archaeophyte). Long established on disturbed waste ground along the coast in the north of the county, elsewhere as a casual introduction on roadside verges. **35** (70).

Introduced (neophyte). This was introduced into Kent with the bedding-straw of invalid troops disembarked at Ramsgate from the Walcheren Expedition. It subsequently became distributed with manure to many parts of the Isle of Thanet and the plant was first recorded in 1835. It is now a common plant of roadsides, arable land and waste ground throughout a large part of the county. **532** (548).

Coronopus squamatus (Forssk.)   Swine-cress

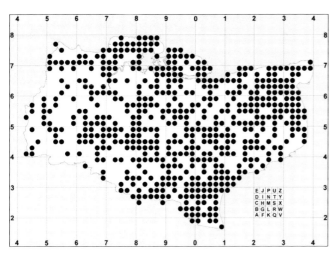

Introduced (archaeophyte). Long established on pathways, particularly by gateways, in farmyards and on nutrient-rich arable fields. **564** (652).

Coronopus didymus (L.) Sm.   Lesser Swine-cress

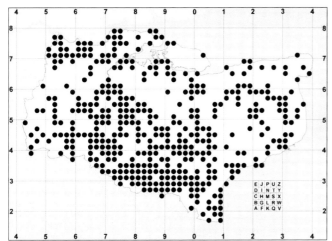

Introduced (neophyte). First recorded in Kent in 1892 and now frequent over most of the county, particularly in the Weald and in the more urban areas. It occurs on cultivated and waste ground, especially in gardens and poorly maintained lawns. **437** (301).

Conringia orientalis (L.) Dumort.   Hare's-ear Mustard

Introduced. A casual plant of arable fields and rubbish-tips, but not recorded in the county for over eighty years now. **0** (0).

Diplotaxis tenuifolia (L.) DC.   Perennial Wall-rocket

Introduced (archaeophyte). On coastal cliffs, chalk quarries, railway banks, roadside verges and on old walls. It looks completely native in some coastal sites. **284** (331).

Wild Cabbage *Brassica oleracea* © D. Mills

Diplotaxis muralis (L.) DC.   Annual Wall-rocket

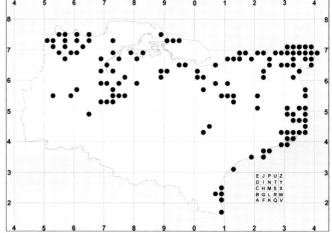

Introduced (neophyte). First recorded in Britain on Thanet in 1778 where it was found amongst oats raised from seed rescued from a ship which had been wrecked on the coast. On waste ground by roads and railways, old walls and on cultivated ground, particularly gardens, and still common on Thanet. **131** (250).

Brassica oleracea L.   Wild Cabbage

The native plant is var. *oleracea* and is found on chalk cliffs and banks on the coast from Folkestone through to Deal and again on some of the chalk cliffs in Thanet. It was first recorded in Kent from Dover in 1551 and the population remains much the same now save for some losses through development. Various other varieties and cultivars of cabbage are regularly grown on farms and gardens and odd escapes are noted as open circles on the map. **19 + 5** (20 + 42).

Brassica napus L. ssp. oleifera (DC.) Metzg.   Oil-seed Rape

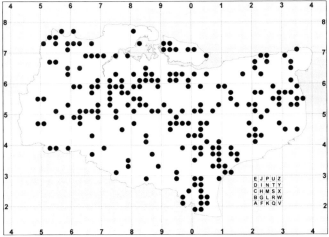

Introduced (neophyte). Oil-seed rape is a major crop in the farming industry and is now widely grown. The plants mapped are those found growing on road verges and other waste places away from the arable fields in which the crop is grown. The Swede var. *rapifera*, although recorded in the past, was not noted during the present survey. **215** (36).

Brassica rapa L.   Turnip

Introduced. A casual plant of roadsides and waste places; all recent records probably originating from bird seed. Noted from Dunton Green TQ55D, Swanscombe TQ67C, Appledore TQ92U, Conyer TQ96S and Greatstone TR02W. **5** (60).

Brassica tournefortii Gouan   Pale Cabbage

Introduced. A casual wool-alien, last recorded in the county in 1964. **0** (0).

Brassica juncea (L.) Czern.   Chinese Mustard

Introduced (neophyte). Recorded in the past as a casual plant on rubbish-tips from bird seed, and as a wool-alien in arable fields. It is now frequently grown in gardens as a salad crop. In my own garden a few plants appear each year, in spite of being an annual, now some ten years after I sowed a short row. It is then surprising that the only plants noted growing wild during this survey were in a church car park at Tudeley TQ64H. **1** (6).

Brassica nigra L.   Black Mustard

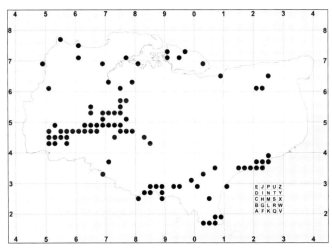

Native. Along river banks and by other waterways and on sand and shingle banks near the coast. In the 1982 Atlas it was obviously over-recorded by inexperienced observers in mistake for *Hirschfeldia incana*. **92** (235).

Sinapis arvensis L.   Charlock

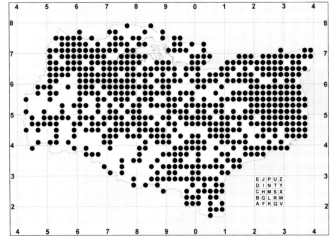

Introduced (archaeophyte). A weed of cultivation, and also found on roadsides, railway banks and waste places. **646** (875).

Sinapis alba L.   White Mustard

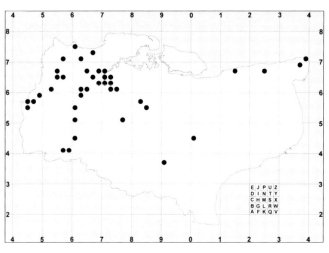

Introduced (archaeophyte). A casual plant of arable fields, roadsides and waste ground, particularly on the chalk. It is now much less grown than in the past and this is reflected in its present scarcity as a wild plant. **40** (159).

Eruca vesicaria (L.) Cav.   Garden Rocket

Introduced. A casual plant on roadsides and waste places, as an escape from gardens or from bird seed. Only recorded from Hextable TQ57F and Gravesend TQ67M, but because of its recent popularity as a salad vegetable one would expect it to turn up more frequently in the future. **2** (1).

Erucastrum gallicum
(Willd.) O.E. Schulz   Hairy Rocket

Introduced. A casual plant of arable and waste land, last recorded in the county in 1978. **0** (2).

Hirschfeldia incana (L.) Lagr.-Foss.   Hoary Mustard

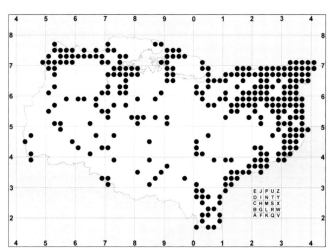

Introduced (neophyte). On roadsides, railway sidings, sand-dunes and waste places. In the 1950s this plant was only known from East Kent in the Thanet-Sandwich area, but since then has extended its range widely over the county, and this extension of range continues. **309** (101).

Cakile maritima Scop.   Sea Rocket

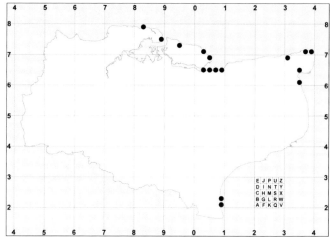

Native. On sandy shores just above the high-tide line. Still found in suitable habitats but there have been some losses due to development, cleansing of beaches, and work on new sea-walls. **16** (27).

Sea Rocket *Cakile maritima* © D. Mills

Rapistrum rugosum (L.) Bergeret   Bastard Cabbage

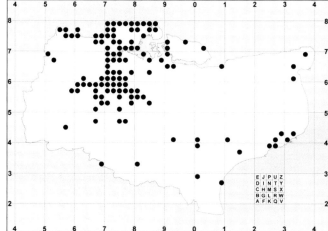

Introduced (neophyte). On roadsides and waste ground, particularly where there has been recent disturbance such as with road widening. **120** (96).

Rapistrum perenne (L.) All.   Steppe Cabbage

Introduced (neophyte). Recorded from Sandwich Bay in 1975 but there are no subsequent records. **0** (1).

Crambe maritima L.   Sea-kale

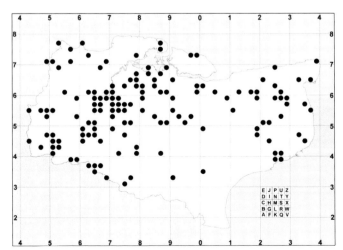

Native. On shingle, shingle-sand and cliffs on the coast. In contrast to the Sea Rocket which has more specific habitat requirements, this species has been extending its range on the Kent coast. **50** (31).

Crambe cordifolia Steven   Greater Sea-kale

Introduced. A casual garden throw-out noted from a roadside in 1966, but there are no subsequent records. **0** (0).

Raphanus raphanistrum L.   Wild Radish
ssp. *raphanistrum*

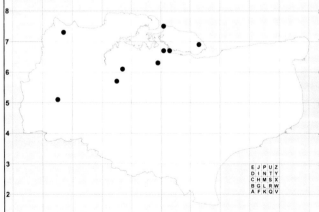

Introduced (archaeophyte). A casual or persistent weed of arable fields, roadsides and waste places. Appears to be much less frequent than formerly. **144** (322).

Raphanus raphanistrum L.   Sea Radish
ssp. *maritimus* (Sm.) Thell.

Native. Always a rare plant in Kent and last recorded from Broadstairs in 1869. Within Britain this plant has been extending its range in recent years and during the present survey convincing plants were found a little above high-tide mark at Minster TQ97R and Kingsdown TR34Y. **2** (0).

Raphanus sativus L.   Garden Radish

Introduced. Has been recorded as a casual plant in the past, mainly on rubbish-tips or as a relic of cultivation, but was not noted during the present survey. **0** (19).

RESEDACEAE

Reseda luteola L.   Weld

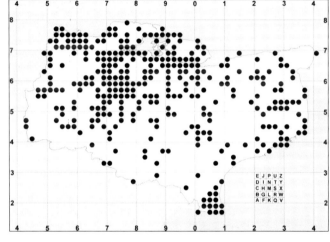

Introduced (archaeophyte). On roadsides, railway sidings, quarries, waste ground and brown-field sites. **335** (348).

Reseda alba L.   White Mignonette

Introduced (neophyte). A casual plant around docklands, by roadsides and on waste places. **9** (7).

Reseda lutea L.   Wild Mignonette

Gaultheria shallon Pursh   Shallon

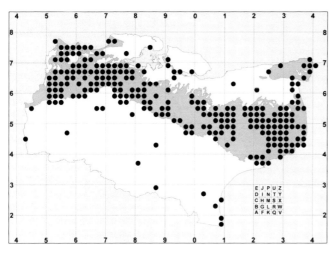

Native. On arable fields and other disturbed soils on the chalk, and at times on sand-dunes and other well-drained areas on sand. **250** (352).

Introduced (neophyte). Originally planted for cover and food for game birds and now well naturalised in a few areas on acid sandy and peaty soils. **13** (13).

Gaultheria mucronata   Prickly Heath
(L. f.) Hook. & Arn.

Introduced (neophyte). A plant of garden origin now well established in woodland near Westerham TQ45G and Brasted Chart TQ45R. **2** (5).

Reseda phyteuma L.   Corn Mignonette

Introduced (neophyte). Although specifically looked for in its former known sites, this plant was not found during the present survey and this cornfield weed is now probably extinct in the county. **0** (2).

Arbutus unedo L.   Strawberry-tree

Introduced (neophyte). Trees looking completely naturalised and certainly not being tended were noted at Higham TQ77A and Goodnestone TR25N. **2** (1).

ERICACEAE

Rhododendron ponticum L.   Rhododendron

Calluna vulgaris (L.) Hull   Heather

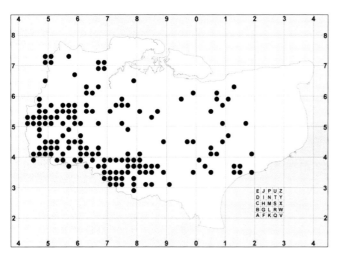
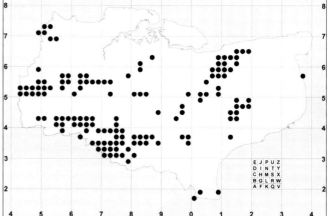

Introduced (neophyte). Often planted in parks and woodland and now well naturalised and spreading by runners and by seed, particularly on peaty or sandy soils. **161** (173).

Native. On heaths, commons and open woodlands on peaty or sandy soils. The plants on shingle and sand beaches at Dungeness and Sandwich are in unusual habitats but look completely native there. **140** (157).

Erica tetralix L.   Cross-leaved Heath

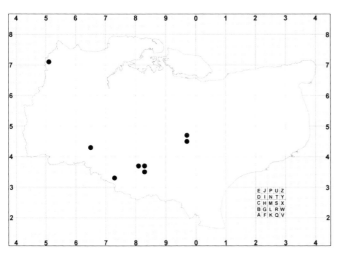

Native. In bogs and wet heathland areas. Becoming a very scarce plant in the county. **8** (13).

Vaccinium myrtillus L.   Bilberry

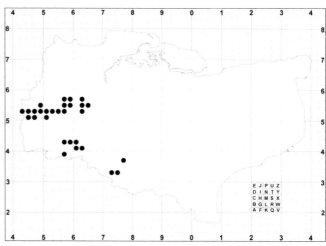

Native. On heaths and in acid woodland. The bilberry rarely regenerates from seed and there appears some slight decline in range through loss of habitat. **29** (36).

Erica cinerea L.   Bell Heather

Native. On dry heaths and along dry woodland rides. Appears to have gone from some sites through loss of habitat. **34** (52).

Erica x darleyensis Bean   Darley Dale Heath

Introduced (neophyte). An escaped garden plant now well established at one site at South Foreland TR34L. **1** (0).

Erica vagans L.   Cornish Heath

Introduced (neophyte). A very large patch that has long been established in Longrope Wood TQ93X. **1** (1).

PYROLACEAE

Pyrola minor L.   Common Wintergreen

Native. A rare plant of damp woodland. In spite of searching in former known sites, this plant has not been found during the present survey and could now be extinct in the county. **0** (2).

Round-leaved Wintergreen *Pyrola rotundifolia* © S. Poyser

Pyrola rotundifolia L.   Round-leaved Wintergreen

Native. In an old quarry in Beacon Wood Country Park TQ57V, a disused chalk quarry at Swanscombe TQ57X, along a disused chalk quarry railway track at Swanscombe TQ67C and in an old chalk quarry within the Berengrave Nature Reserve TQ86I. The two subspecies do not seem to hold good, at least in Kent. Some plants measured up and checked ran to ssp. *rotundifolia* whilst other specimens ran to ssp. *maritima*, whilst most plants showed characters of both reputed subspecies. Subspecies *rotundifolia* nationally is listed as 'Near Threatened'. **4** (4).

MONOTROPACEAE

PRIMULACEAE

Monotropa hypopitys L.   Yellow Bird's-nest

Primula vulgaris Huds.   Primrose

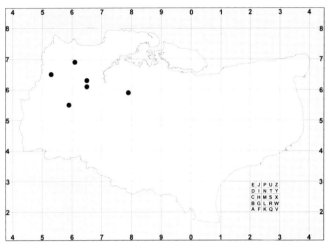

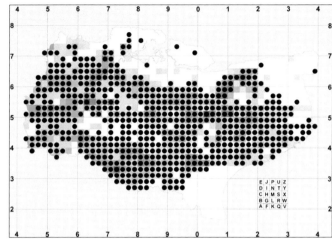

Native. A rare plant usually found in woodland with deep leaf litter. In keeping with the rest of southern England this plant appears to be in decline and is now only recorded from half the number of sites recorded in the 1971-80 survey. Nationally it is listed as 'Endangered'. **6** (12).

Native. In woods, hedgerows and north-facing banks. Less frequent in or absent from most coastal areas. **610** (693).

Primrose *Primula vulgaris* © S. Poyser

Primula vulgaris x veris
= P. x polyantha Mill.

False Oxlip

Cyclamen hederifolium Aiton

Sowbread

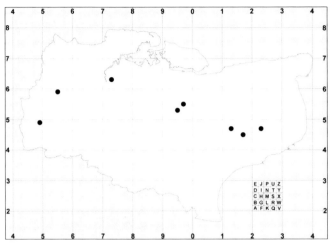

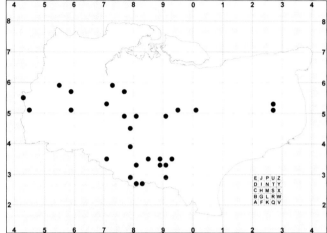

Occasional plants where the two parent plants occur such as in woodland edges or on open downland near wooded areas. **8** (15).

Introduced (neophyte). On roadsides, hedgerows and disturbed waste ground. With seed now easily available and much grown in gardens, this plant is increasingly being found as an escape from cultivation. **28** (1).

Primula veris L.

Cowslip

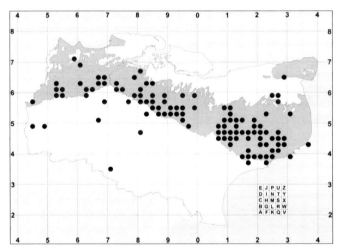

Cyclamen coum Mill.

Eastern Sowbread

Introduced (neophyte). Another plant now much grown in gardens and recorded growing 'wild' on a roadside verge near Ightham Mote TQ55W and in open woodland near Bluebell Hill TQ76K. **2** (0).

Native. In meadows and other open grassy areas on light soils, particularly on the chalk. **111** (172).

Hottonia palustris L.

Water-violet

Lysimachia nemorum L.

Yellow Pimpernel

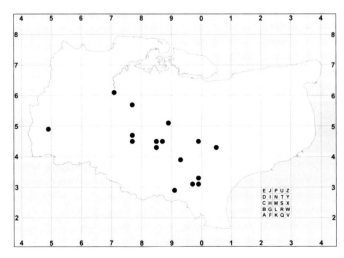

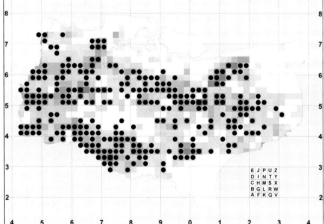

Native. In ponds and marsh dykes. The slow decline mentioned in the previous Atlas continues through loss or destruction of suitable habitats. **16** (32).

Native. In open woodlands, particularly along the rides and along shady hedgerows. Widespread in suitable habitats but never abundant. **275** (353).

Lysimachia nummularia L.   Creeping-jenny

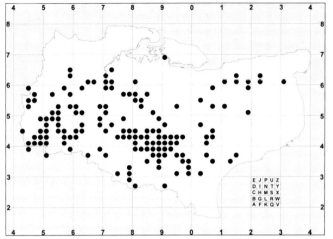

Native. In damp grassy roadside banks, streamsides, marshes and in damp woodlands. **151** (215).

Lysimachia vulgaris L.   Yellow Loosestrife

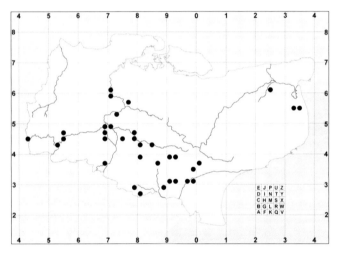

Native. At the edge of ponds and marsh dykes, and in wet copses. Rather local and perhaps decreasing. **34** (68).

Lysimachia punctata L.   Dotted Loosestrife

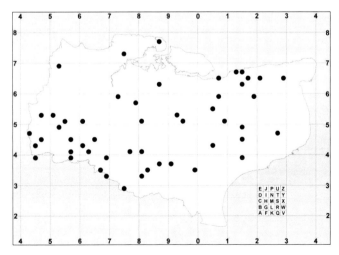

Introduced (neophyte). Much grown in gardens and now increasingly found on roadsides, woodland edges and waste ground. **51** (40).

Trientalis borealis Raf.   Starflower

Introduced (neophyte). Long established in the grounds of a nursery near Ightham TQ55S. **1** (1).

Anagallis tenella (L.) L.   Bog Pimpernel

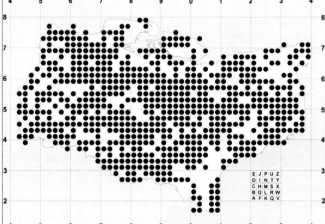

Native. In bogs and damp peaty areas. Rare and decreasing through loss of habitat. **4** (5).

Anagallis arvensis L.   Scarlet Pimpernel

Native. On cultivated and disturbed ground, open downland and coastal dunes. The blue-flowered form was found on a few occasions and the true Blue Pimpernel ssp. *caerulea* was recorded from open fields near Rolvenden TQ83G and from Pluckley TQ94G. **708** (825).

Anagallis minima (L.) E.H.L. Krause — Chaffweed

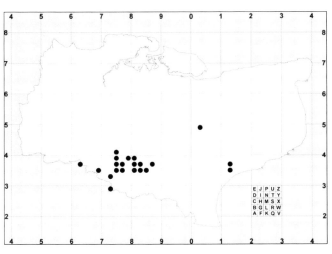

Native. In woodland rides on damp sandy soils. This plant has been specifically searched for and the increased number of records in comparison with the previous Atlas now reflects a truer picture of its distribution within the county. It is listed in the Red List as 'Near Threatened'. **21** (8).

Glaux maritima L. — Sea-milkwort

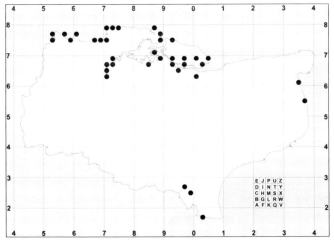

Native. In the upper parts of salt-marshes, on banks of tidal rivers, and in other grassy places on a firm muddy substratum in coastal areas. There appear to be some reductions due to loss of habitat. **37** (62).

Sea Milkwort *Glaux maritima* © D. Mills

Samolus valerandi L. — Brookweed

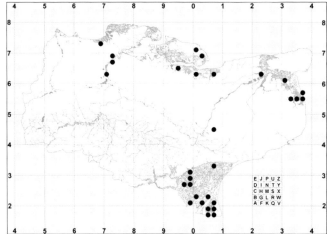

Native. At the edge of dykes and in marshy areas, usually near the coast. Another plant that appears to have been lost from several sites, either through development or from drying out. **30** (52).

HYDRANGEACEAE

Philadelphus coronarius L. — Mock-orange

Introduced (neophyte). A garden plant recorded in the past, but not found growing wild during the present survey. **0** (6).

Philadelphus x virginalis Rehder — Hairy Mock-orange

Introduced (neophyte). A garden relic recorded from Shoreham TQ56G, near Harrietsham TQ85L, Brookland TQ92X and Hothfield TQ94T. **4** (0).

Hydrangea petiolaris Siebold & Zucc. — Climbing Hydrangea

Introduced (neophyte). Appears have been lost from the site at South Darenth. There are no other records. **0** (1).

GROSSULARIACEAE

Ribes rubrum L.   Red Currant

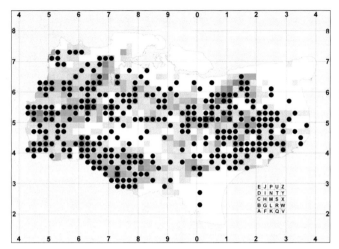

Introduced (neophyte). Widespread in old or well established woodland where it looks completely native. It is also occasionally found in marshes and hedgerows. **332** (260).

Ribes sanguineum Pursh   Flowering Currant

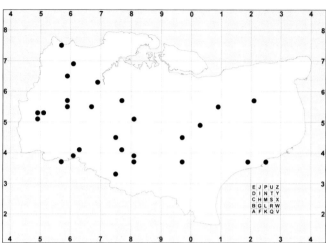

Introduced (neophyte). A common garden shrub now widely established, either originally bird sown or from garden rubbish, in hedgerows, commons, woodland edges and waste ground. **27** (26).

Ribes odoratum H.L. Wendl.   Buffalo Currant

Introduced (neophyte). Has been recorded rarely in the past but was not seen during the present survey. **0** (1).

Ribes nigrum L.   Black Currant

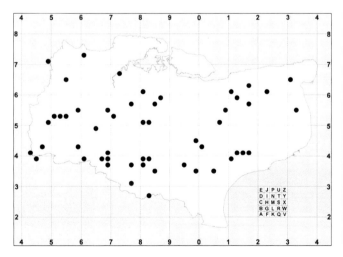

Introduced (neophyte). An escape from cultivation, but thoroughly naturalised in damp or wet woodlands, roadside banks and waste ground. **52** (110).

Ribes uva-crispa L.   Gooseberry

Introduced (neophyte). In deciduous woodland where it looks completely native, and occasionally in hedgerows and on derelict land. **140** (173).

CRASSULACEAE

Crassula tillaea Lest.-Garl.   Mossy Stonecrop

Native. Recorded at Sandwich Bay c. 1900 but there are no subsequent records for the county. **0** (0).

Crassula helmsii (Kirk) Cockayne   New Zealand Pygmyweed

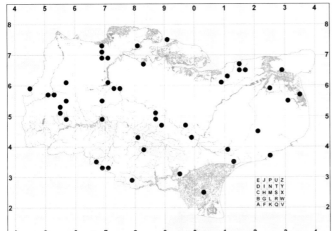

Introduced (neophyte). First recorded wild in Britain in 1956 and in Kent in 1960. Since then it has steadily spread through the county in ponds, rivers, reservoirs and occasionally on damp ground. In some waterways it has formed dense stands but overall it has not as yet become the pest that some predicted. **46** (0).

Umbilicus rupestris (Salisb.) Dandy   Navelwort

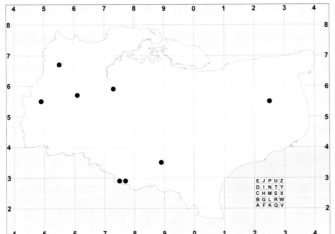

Native, although perhaps originally introduced at some of the localities in the county. However at Aylesford TQ75J in appeared on an old ragstone wall near the church in 2002 and has persisted, and increased, ever since. This is many miles away from any known wild or cultivated population, so it is difficult to be sure of the status of any plants, but all those mapped appear to be genuinely wild. **8** (6).

Sempervivum tectorum L.   House-leek

Introduced (neophyte). On old walls and roofs, perhaps sometimes planted as a supposed protection from lightning. **6** (1).

Sedum rosea (L.) Scop.   Roseroot

Introduced. Was reported as a casual from a rubbish-tip near Dartford in 1978 but did not persist and has not been found elsewhere. **0** (1).

Sedum spectabile Boreau   Butterfly Stonecrop

Introduced (neophyte). A garden throw-out found established near Pembury TQ64B, on a shingle beach at Lade TR02V, at the edge of a footpath at Faversham TR06F, and along the sea-wall on the Wade Marshes TR26P. **4** (4).

Sedum telephium L.   Orpine

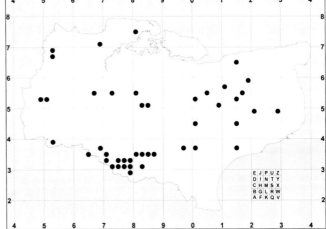

Native. In woods, hedgerows and on shaded roadside banks. **44** (85).

Sedum spurium M. Bieb.   Caucasian Stonecrop

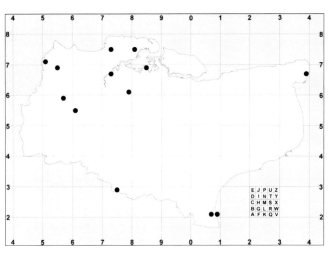

Introduced (neophyte). A garden escape that is occasionally naturalised on old walls and roadside banks. **13** (11).

Sedum acre L.   Biting Stonecrop

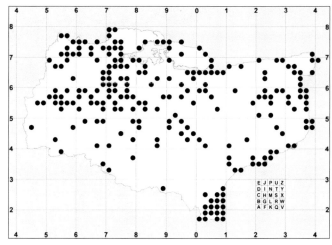

Native. On dry sandy grassland, sand-dunes and shingle beaches on the coast, and also on walls, gravel tracks, pavements and dry road verges inland. **232** (290).

Sedum sexangulare L.   Tasteless Stonecrop

Introduced. There have been a few casual records in the past but it has not been found during the present survey. **0** (1).

Sedum rupestre L.   Reflexed Stonecrop

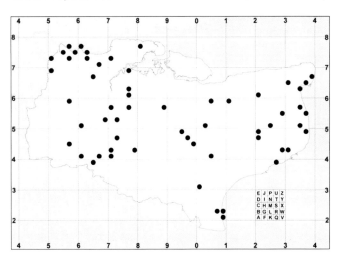

Introduced (neophyte). In cultivation since the 17th century, this plant is now well naturalised on old walls, roadside banks and waste places. **58** (59).

Sedum album L.   White Stonecrop

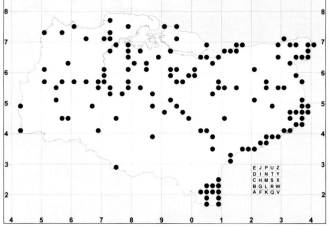

Introduced (archaeophyte), although looking very native on the coast from Dungeness through to Thanet. On old walls, roadsides, sand-dunes and shingle beaches. **143** (115).

Sedum fosterianum Sm.   Rock Stonecrop

Introduced (neophyte). Long and widely established on shingle at Walmer TR34U & 34Z, and on waste ground at Dartford TQ57S. **3** (6).

Sedum lydium Boiss.   Least Stonecrop

Introduced. A few casual records in the past but not found during the present survey. **0** (4).

Sedum anglicum Huds.   English Stonecrop

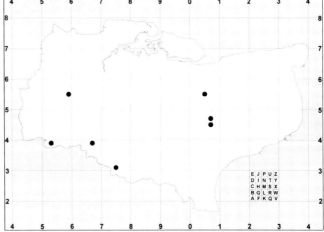

Native. On shingle and sandy beaches and on waste ground near the sea. **15** (22).

Sedum dasyphyllum L.   Thick-leaved Stonecrop

Introduced. A casual garden escape, last recorded in the county in 1860. **0** (0).

SAXIFRAGACEAE

Bergenia crassifolia (L.) Fritsch   Elephant-ears

Introduced (neophyte). Widely planted around towns and new developments and found naturalised, probably from garden rubbish, at Badger's Mount TQ46W, Rochester TQ76I and Kingsdown TR34U. **3** (2).

Saxifraga x *urbium* D.A. Webb   Londonpride

Introduced (neophyte). A garden escape found naturalised on roadsides and waste places near Westerham TQ45G, Harvel TQ66L, near Tenterden TQ93C and Barham TR24E. **4** (12).

Saxifraga granulata L.   Meadow Saxifrage

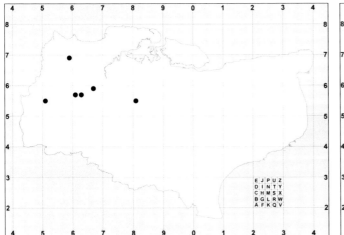

Native. Damp meadows, railway banks and grassy places, especially on sandy and gravelly soils. Appears to have been lost from several former sites through land improvement or development. **6** (22).

Saxifraga hypnoides L.   Mossy Saxifrage

Introduced. A casual throw-out from cultivation noticed in a ditch at Darenth Wood in the 1970s, but did not persist. **0** (1).

Saxifraga tridactylites L.   Rue-leaved Saxifrage

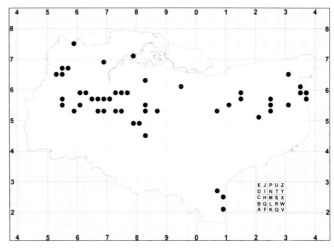

Native. On fixed sand-dunes and sandy heathland, and also on old walls and buildings. **49** (62).

Heuchera sanguinea Engelm.   Coralbells

Introduced (neophyte). A casual garden escape recorded in the 1970s but not since. **0** (1).

Tolmiea menziesii
(Pursh) Torr. & A. Gray   Pick-a-back-plant

Introduced (neophyte). A large flowering clump in woodland near Edenbridge TQ44I in 1994 is the only record. **1** (0).

Tellima grandiflora (Pursh) Douglas ex   Fringecups

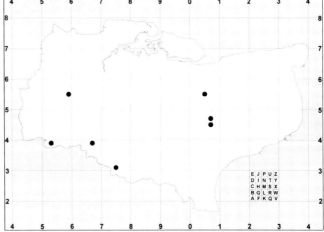

Introduced (neophyte). A garden escape on roadsides, woodland edges and waste places. This plant sets seed very readily and would be expected to extend its range in future years. **7** (4).

Chrysosplenium oppositifolium L.   Opposite-leaved Golden-saxifrage

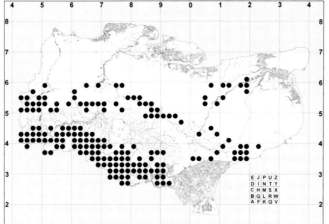

Native. On boggy ground and seepages in woods and stream-sides, usually in shade. The population appears stable at present with actually more records and with no serious losses since the 1971-80 survey. **177** (140).

Chrysosplenium alternifolium L.   Alternate-leaved Golden-saxifrage

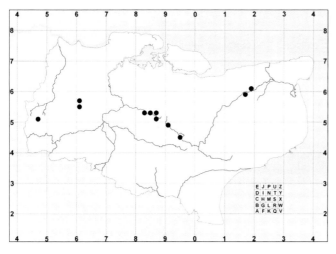

Native. On boggy ground in woods and by streams, particularly where alders are growing. **11** (13).

ROSACEAE

Sorbaria sorbifolia (L.) A. Braun   Sorbaria

Introduced (neophyte). Recorded near Bean in 1963 (Burton, 1983) but there are no subsequent records. **0** (0).

Sorbaria tomentosa (Lindl.) Rehder   Himalayan Sorbaria

Introduced (neophyte). On old walls and in scrub. The only record during the present survey was from an old wall at Rochester TQ76J. **1** (5).

Sorbaria kirilowii (Regel) Maxim.   Chinese Sorbaria

Introduced. A casual garden relic at the edge of Darenth Wood in 1988, but not noted during the present survey. **0** (0).

Spiraea x *pseudosalicifolia* Silverside   Confused Bridewort

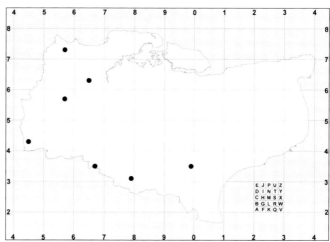

Introduced (neophyte). A hybrid of garden origin found naturalised in hedgerows and roadside banks. Some of the older records of various species of *Spiraea* probably refer to this plant. **7** (0).

Spiraea douglasii Hook.   Steeple-bush

Introduced (neophyte). In a hedgerow near Tonbridge TQ65A is the only record. **1** (10).

Spiraea canescens D.Don   Himalayan Spiraea

Introduced (neophyte). A garden plant reported in 1980 from near Longfield but there are no subsequent records. **0** (1).

Spiraea x *arguta* Zabel   Bridal-spray

Introduced (neophyte). A garden relic at the edge of Darenth Wood reported in 1975 but with no subsequent records. **0** (1).

Aruncus dioicus (Walter) Fernald   Buck's-beard

Introduced. A casual garden outcast recorded from a disused chalk-pit in 1952 but with no subsequent records. **0** (0).

Holodiscus discolor (Pursh) Maxim.   Oceanspray

Introduced (neophyte). The plant long naturalised on an old wall at Sevenoaks now appears to have been lost. There are no other records. **0** (1).

Filipendula vulgaris Moench — **Dropwort**

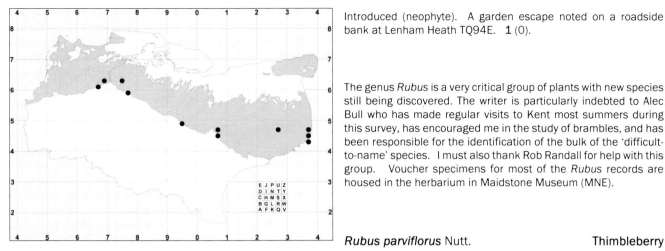

Native. On open chalk downland and on roadside banks on the chalk. Rather local and in decline. **11** (19).

Dropwort *Filipendula vulgaris* © S. Poyser

Filipendula ulmaria (L.) Maxim. — **Meadowsweet**

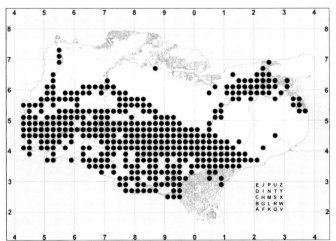

Native. By rivers and streams, in marshes and damp woods and by roadside ditches. A common plant in wet habitats, but strangely absent from most of the Romney Marsh. **407** (465).

Kerria japonica (L.) DC. — **Kerria**

Introduced (neophyte). A garden escape noted on a roadside bank at Lenham Heath TQ94E. **1** (0).

The genus *Rubus* is a very critical group of plants with new species still being discovered. The writer is particularly indebted to Alec Bull who has made regular visits to Kent most summers during this survey, has encouraged me in the study of brambles, and has been responsible for the identification of the bulk of the 'difficult-to-name' species. I must also thank Rob Randall for help with this group. Voucher specimens for most of the *Rubus* records are housed in the herbarium in Maidstone Museum (MNE).

Rubus parviflorus Nutt. — **Thimbleberry**

Introduced (neophyte). Recorded from East Kent in 1956 but not noted since. **0** (0).

Rubus idaeus L. — **Raspberry**

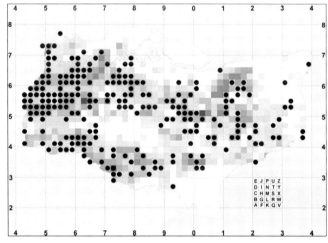

Native. In woods, scrub, heaths and hedgerows. **233** (253).

Rubus caesius x *idaeus*
= *R.* x *pseudoidaeus* (Weihe) Lej.

Has been recorded from East Kent in the past but was not found during the present survey. **0** (0).

Rubus phoenicolasius Maxim. — **Japanese Wineberry**

Introduced (neophyte). Has been recorded from East Kent in the past but was not noted during the present survey. **0** (1).

Rubus spectabilis Pursh — **Salmonberry**

Introduced (neophyte). Well naturalised in the Sandling Park area TR13N. **1** (5).

Rubus loganobaccus L.H. Bailey   Loganberry

Introduced (neophyte). Has been recorded as a relic of cultivation in the past but was not noted during the present survey. **0** (1).

Rubus fruticosus L. **agg.**   Bramble

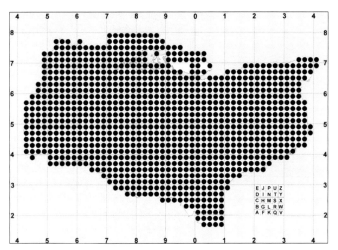

Included here are all the various species of *Rubus*, except those mentioned above, which can all be lumped together as 'brambles'. All those that have been named are listed below, and it will be seen that many species have a discrete and interesting distribution within the county. **1016** (1009).

Rubus arrheniiformis W.C.R. Watson

Native. Previously recorded from TQ53 & 54. **0** (0).

Rubus bertramii G. Braun

Native. Previously recorded from TQ73 & 83. **0** (0).

Rubus divaricatus P.J. Müll.

Native. Previously recorded from TQ57 & TR15. **0** (1).

Rubus fissus Lindl.

Native. Previously recorded from TQ53 & 54. **0** (0).

Rubus integribasis P.J. Müll. ex Boulay

Native. Previously recorded from TQ75. **0** (0).

Rubus nessensis Hall

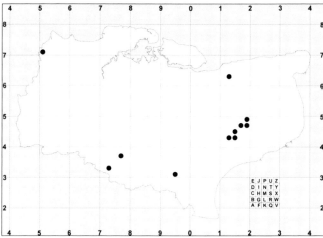

Native. On heaths and open heathy woodland. **11** (4).

Rubus nitidiformis Sudre

Native. Previously recorded from TQ53 & TR05. **0** (0).

Rubus nobilissimus (W.C.R. Watson) Pearsall

Native. Woodland ride in Causton Wood TQ83I. **1** (0).

Rubus plicatus Weihe & Nees

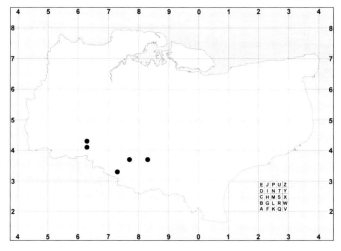

Native. On dry open woodland and heaths. **5** (0).

Rubus scissus W.C.R. Watson

Native. Previously recorded from TQ53, TQ54, TR14 & TR24. **0** (0).

Rubus sulcatus Vest

Native. Previously recorded from TR15. **0** (0).

Rubus adspersus Weihe ex H.E. Weber

Native. Previously recorded from TR13. **0** (0).

Rubus albionis W.C.R. Watson

Native. In hedgerows and open woodland at Kiln Wood TR23I and at Acrise Wood TR14V. **2** (1).

Rubus averyanus W.C.R. Watson

Native; a local endemic to West Sussex, West Kent and Surrey. Previously recorded from TQ53 & TQ64. **0** (0).

Rubus calvatus Lees ex A. Bloxam

Native. Long known and still present in open woodland at Willesborough Lees TR04G & TR04L. **2** (0).

Rubus canterburiensis Edees

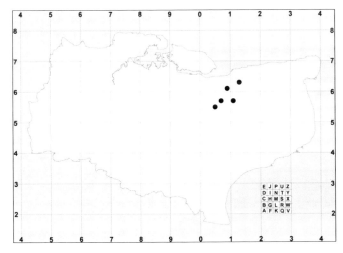

Native. In open woodland and along woodland rides. The type locality is Denstead Wood. **5** (2).

Rubus chloophyllus Sudre

Native. Recorded from the area of Kent/Sussex border in the past but has not been found during the present survey. **0** (0).

Rubus crespignyanus W.C.R. Watson

Native, endemic to East Sussex and West Kent. Recorded from along woodland rides and open sandy heath in the Pembury area TQ64B, 64C, 64L & 64S. **4** (0).

Rubus errabundus W.C.R. Watson

Native. Recorded from Dartford Heath TQ57B and East Blean Wood TR16X. **2** (0).

Rubus gratus Focke

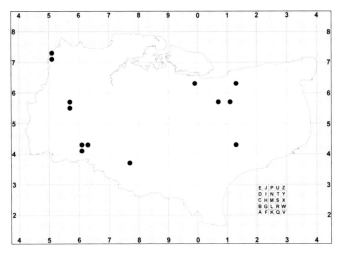

Native. On heathland and open deciduous woodland. **13** (4).

Rubus imbricatus Hort

Native. Recorded from Rusthall Common TQ53U, Tunbridge Wells Common TQ53Z, Pembury Walks TQ54G and Sandling Park TR13N. **4** (2).

Rubus laciniatus Willd.

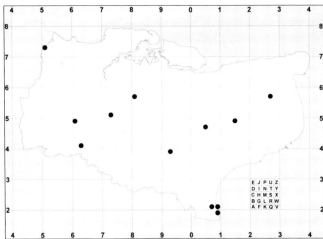

Introduced (neophyte). Grown in gardens and allotments and naturalised in woods, by roadsides and on open heathy ground. **12** (18).

Rubus leucandriformis Edees & A. Newton

Native. Woodland edge in Oaken Wood, Barming TQ75C is the only record. **1** (0).

113

Rubus lindleianus Lees

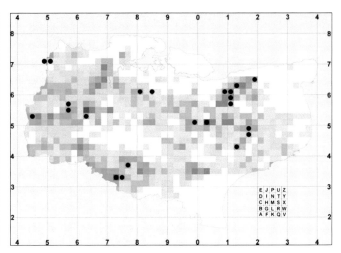

Native. In hedgerows and woodland edges. Widespread but rather local. **5** (2).

Rubus pyramidalis Kaltenb.

Native. On heaths, woodlands and hedge banks, usually on well-drained soils. **22** (8).

Rubus macrophyllus Weihe & Nees

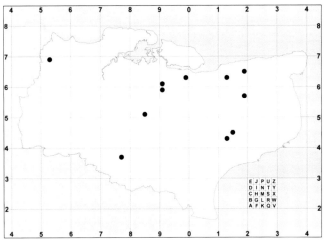

Native. At the edge of woods, heaths and in hedgerows. **11** (3).

Rubus sciocharis (Sudre) W.C.R. Watson

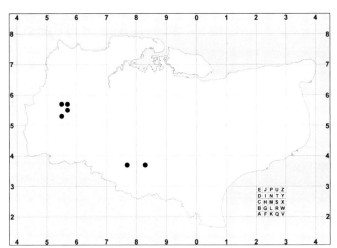

Native, Wood borders and hedgebanks. **6** (2).

Rubus platyacanthus P.J. Müll. & Lefèvre

Native. Previously recorded from TQ57, TQ85 & TR13. **0** (1).

Rubus amplificatus Lees

Native. In hedgerows and wood borders at Park Wood, Appledore TQ93K, Faggs Wood TQ93X, Ashford Warren TR04C and near Littlebourne TR15Y. **4** (2).

Rubus pliocenicus
(W.C.R. Watson) Edees & A. Newton

Native, endemic to Kent. Plentiful in a roadside hedgerow at Halstead TQ46V is the only record. **1** (2).

Rubus cardiophyllus Lefèvre & P.J. Müll.

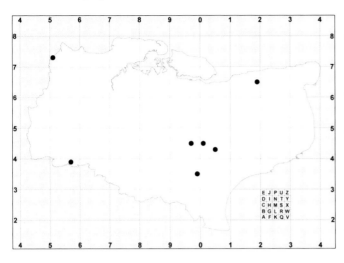

Native.   Woodland edges, heaths and hedgerows.   **7** (4).

Rubus cissburiensis W.C. Barton & Ridd.

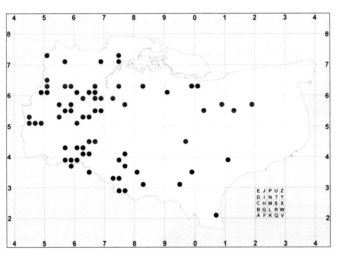

Native.   Hedgebanks, heaths and wood borders. Locally common.
69 (20).

Rubus dumnoniensis Bab.

Native.   Only recorded from a railway bank near Shorne TQ67W.
1 (1).

Rubus elegantispinosus (A. Schumach.) H.E. Weber

Introduced (neophyte). Several plants found at woodland edge at
Scroggers Hill TR05T in June 2004 were the first for Kent.
1 (0).

Rubus incurvatus Bab.

Native. Previous records from Kent have not been confirmed.
0 (0).

Rubus milfordensis Edees

Native.   Previously recorded from TQ65 & TR14, but not found
during the present survey. **0** (0).

Rubus nemoralis P.J. Müll.

Native.   Old records from TQ57 & TR13, but not recorded during
the present survey. **0** (0).

Rubus patuliformis Sudre

Native. Restricted to the Tunbridge Wells area of East Sussex and
West Kent, but not found during the present survey. **0** (1).

Rubus pervalidus Edees & A. Newton

Native. Endemic to Surrey and South Essex to which East Kent
can now be added, having been found along an open ride in the
Blean Woods TR06V in 1999. **1** (0).

Rubus polyanthemus Lindeb.

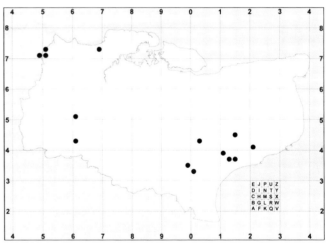

Native.   Hedgerows, wood borders and heaths.   **14** (3).

Rubus prolongatus Boulay & Letendre ex Corb.

Native. Open woodland and heathland in the Tunbridge Wells
area TQ53U & 53Z. **2** (0).

Rubus prolongatus x ulmifolius

Recorded from Tunbridge Wells Common over fifty years ago but
there are no recent records. **0** (0).

Rubus rhombifolius Weihe ex Boenn.

Native. Frequent amongst scrub on the shingle in the Dungeness
area TR01Z & TR02Q. **2** (0).

Rubus rubritinctus W.C.R. Watson

Native. Recorded from West Kent in the past, but not found during the present survey. **0** (0).

Rubus subinermoides Druce

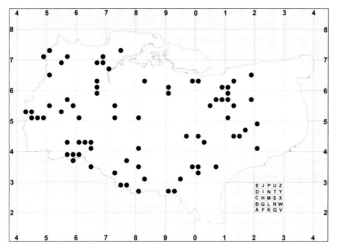

Native. A common and widespread bramble of woods, wood borders and shady hedgebanks. **76** (20).

Rubus subinermoides x ulmifolius

Has been recorded in the past but was not found during the present survey. **0** (1).

Rubus brevistaminosus Edees & A. Newton

Native. Only noted on Tunbridge Wells Common TQ53U during the present survey. Endemic to East Sussex and West Kent. **1** (1).

Rubus sprengelii Weihe

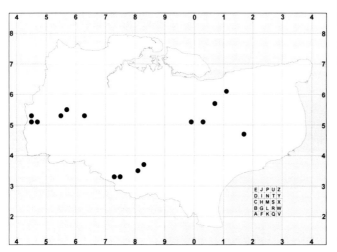

Native. Heaths and woodland on sandy and gravelly soils. **15** (7).

Rubus armeniacus Focke

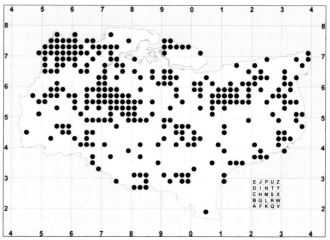

Introduced (neophyte). This plant, known as the Himalayan Giant, has been in cultivation for over a century, but its true origin is unclear. Grown widely in gardens and allotments, it is readily bird-sown in hedgerows and waste land and is now the most frequent bramble in built-up areas. **299** (25).

Rubus armipotens W.C. Barton ex A. Newton

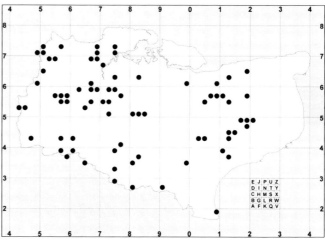

Native. Wood borders, hedgerows and heathland. One of the commoner species of bramble in the county. **77** (20).

Rubus armipotens x ulmifolius

Has been recorded in the past but was not found during the present survey. **0** (1).

Rubus ulmifolius Schott

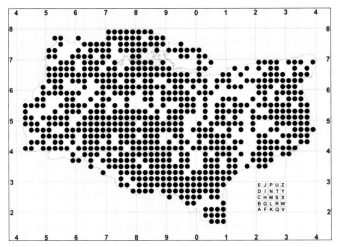

Native. A common species of hedgerows and waste ground. It occurs throughout the county and is not restricted by soil type, but does not occur in mature woodland and other very shaded areas. **718** (349).

Rubus ulmifolius x caesius

This hybrid has been noted in the county in the past but was not found during the present survey. **0** (2).

Rubus ulmifolius x vestitus

Recorded in the past but not found during the present survey. **0** (2).

Rubus adscitus Genev.

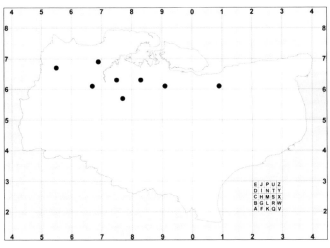

Native. Hedgebanks and wood borders. **8** (1).

Rubus andegavensis Bouvet

Native. Hosey Common TQ45L and Queendown Warren near Stockbury TQ86G are the only recorded British localities for this bramble, otherwise only known from France. **2** (1).

Rubus conspersus W.C.R. Watson

Native, endemic to south-east England. Recorded from Farningham Wood TQ56P and from Park Wood and West Wood area of the Lyminge Forest TR14G, 14L & 14M. **4** (0).

Rubus criniger (E.F. Linton) W.M. Rogers

Native. Has been recorded in the past but there were no confirmed records during the present survey. **0** (0).

Rubus infestisepalus Edees & A. Newton

Native. Recorded in the past but not found during the present survey. **0** (2).

Rubus leucostachys Schleich. ex Sm.

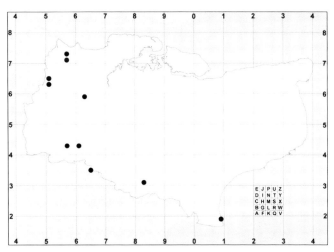

Native. In woods, open scrub and heathland. **10** (0).

Rubus surrejanus W.C. Barton & Ridd.

Native. Recorded from Tunbridge Wells Common TQ53U, Cromer's Wood TQ96A and West Wood TR14L. **3** (0).

Rubus vestitus Weihe

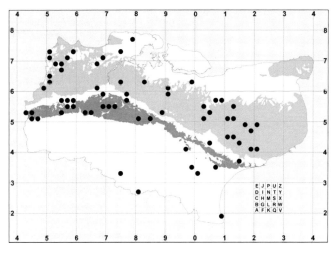

Native. In woods, wood margins and hedgerows, particularly on the more calcareous soils. **66** (22).

Rubus erythrops Edees & A. Newton

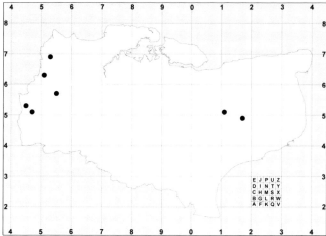

Native. Woods, woodland edges and heathland. **7** (3).

Rubus egregius Focke

Native. On Langley Heath TQ85A in 1991 was the first record for the county. **1** (0).

Rubus wirralensis A. Newton

Native. Several plants on Rusthall Common TQ53U in 2000 were a rather unexpected find, and the first for Kent. **1** (0).

Rubus decussatus W.C. Barton ex A. Newton

Native. Recorded from Rustall Common TQ53U and Chartham Hatch TR15D. **2** (1).

Rubus glareosus W.M. Rogers

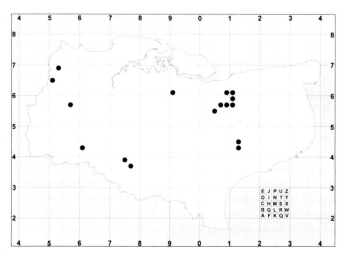

Native. In woods, woodland edges and heaths. **16** (0).

Rubus diversus W.C.R. Watson

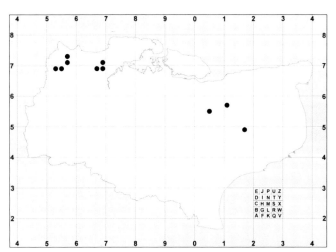

Native. In woods, particularly in remnants of ancient forest. **10** (4).

Rubus longifrons W.C.R. Watson

Native. Endemic to the Tunbridge Wells area of East Sussex and West Kent, but not recorded during the present survey. **0** (0).

Rubus micans Godr.

Native. Previously recorded from TQ66 and TR15 but not found during the present survey. **0** (0).

Rubus moylei W.C. Barton & Ridd.

Native. Woodland edge at Tank Wood TQ74Q and Oaken Wood TQ75H. **2** (0)

Rubus raduloides (W.M. Rogers) Sudre

Native. On Dartford Heath TQ57B and at Mereworth Wood TQ65G. **2** (0).

Rubus trichodes W.C.R. Watson

Native. By a footpath through Sandling Wood TR13N. **1** (2).

Rubus adamsii Sudre

Native. Open woodland at Hosey Common TQ45L. **1** (0).

Rubus anisacanthos G. Braun

Native. Recorded from Farningham Wood TQ56J and woodland edge at Bigbury TR15D. **2** (0).

Rubus campaniensis Winkel ex A. Beek

Native. Recorded from Hosey Common TQ45L. **1** (0).

Rubus cinerosus W.M. Rogers

Native. Previously recorded from TQ65, TQ75 & TR15, but not found during the present survey. **0** (0).

Rubus dentatifolius (Briggs) W.C.R. Watson

Native. Has been recorded from Kent in the past, but was not found during the present survey. **0** (0)

Rubus hartmanii Gand.

Native. Recorded from Rusthall Common TQ53U and Shorne Wood TQ67V. **2** (1).

Rubus leyanus W.M. Rogers

Native. Recorded from the Acrise area in East Kent in the past but not found during the present survey. **0** (1).

Rubus bloxamii (Bab.) Lees

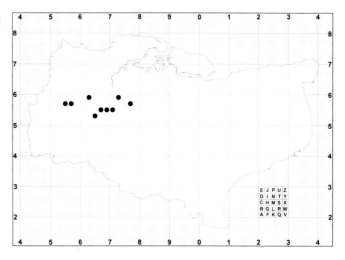

Native. Wood borders and hedgerows, particularly on the Lower Greensand. **9** (4).

Rubus cantianus (W.C.R. Watson) Edees & A. Newton

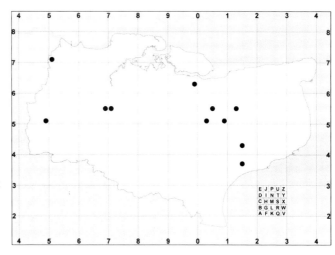

Native. Wood borders, hedgerows and heaths. **11** (2).

Rubus echinatoides (W.M. Rogers) Dallman

Native. Recorded from Dartford Heath in the past but not found during the present survey. **0** (0).

Rubus echinatus Lindl.

Native. Past records from TQ45, TQ66 and TR05, but not found during the present survey. **0** (1).

Rubus euryanthemus W.C.R. Watson

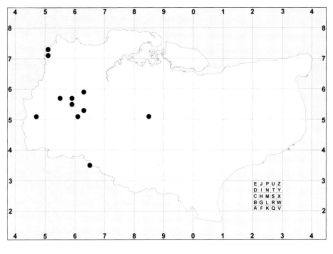

Native. Woodland rides, wood borders and hedgerows. **11** (6).

Rubus flexuosus P.J. Müll. & Lefèvre

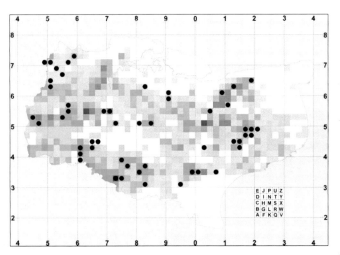

Native. Common in open woods and wood borders. **52** (9).

Rubus hyposericeus Sudre

Native. Plants matching this endemic species in Causton Wood TQ83I and Langley Heath TQ85A. **2** (0).

Rubus insectifolius Lefèvre & P.J. Müll.

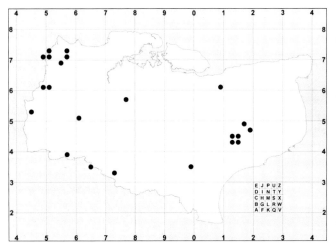

Native. Heaths, hedgebanks and wood borders. **22** (4).

Rubus largificus W.C.R. Watson

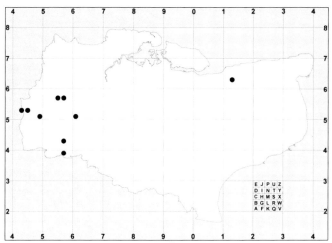

Native. Open woodland, wood borders and hedgebanks. **9** (6).

Rubus longithyrsiger Lees ex Focke

Native. A rare species in Kent and recorded from Joyden's Wood TQ57A and Faggs Wood TQ93X. **2** (0).

Rubus pallidus Weihe

Native. Another rare species in the county and recorded only from Longbeech Wood TQ95V and from the Challock Forest TR05F. **2** (0).

Rubus pannosus P.J. Müll. & Wirtg.

Native. Recorded from the Chartham Hatch-Bigbury area in the past and, although searched for, was not found during the present survey. **0** (0).

Rubus radula Weihe ex Boenn.

Native. Has been recorded rarely in the past, but was not found during the present survey. **0** (0).

Rubus rudis Weihe

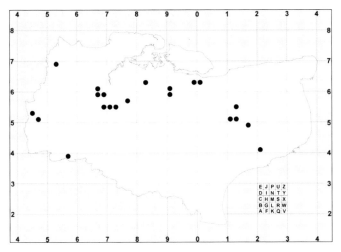

Native.   Woods, wood borders and hedgebanks.   **21** (7).

Rubus rufescens Lefèvre & P.J. Müll.

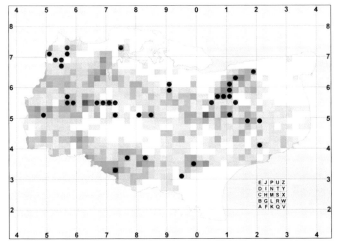

Native.   A woodland species, often very common in coppiced woods.   **38** (19).

Rubus sectiramus W.C.R. Watson

Native.   Recorded from Cinderhill Wood TQ64L, Oaken Wood, Barming TQ75C and Ham Street Woods TR03C.   **3** (0).

Rubus spadix W.C.R. Watson

Native. An endemic species previously thought to be restricted to parts of the London area of West Kent. However, during the present survey good plants were found in Earley Wood TR15A. **1** (0).

Rubus atrebatum A. Newton

Native.   Woodland edge at Seal Chart TQ55N.   **1** (0).

Rubus bercheriensis (Druce ex W.M. Rogers) W.M. Rogers

Native.   Recorded from Larkeyvalley Wood TR15H; Kiln Wood, Newingreen TR13I: Sandling Park TR13M and West Wood TR14G & 14L.   **5** (0).

Rubus dasyphyllus (W.M. Rogers) E.S. Marshall

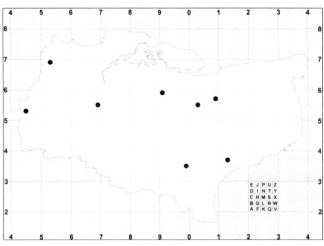

Native.   Woods, heaths and hedgerows, usually on sandy or acid soils.   **8** (0).

Rubus infestior Edees

Native.   Recorded from Joyden's Wood TQ57A and Farningham Wood TQ56N.   **2** (0).

Rubus marshallii Focke & W.M. Rogers

Native. Recorded from Hosey Common TQ45L and Toy's Hill TQ45Q.   **2** (2).

Rubus asperidens (Sudre ex Bouvet) Bouvet

Native.   Recorded from Toy's Hill TQ45Q; Kiln Wood, Westenhanger TR13I and edge of a footpath near Littlebourne TR15Y.   **3** (1).

Rubus murrayi Sudre

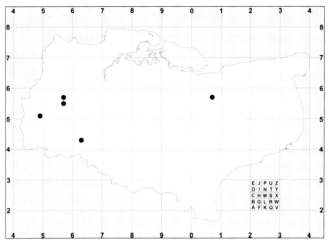

Native. Wood borders and heaths. Has been recorded more widely in the past. **5** (4).

Rubus newbridgensis W.C. Barton & Ridd.

Native. Has been recorded from the Westerham area in the past, but was not found during the present survey. **0** (0).

Rubus phaeocarpus W.C.R. Watson

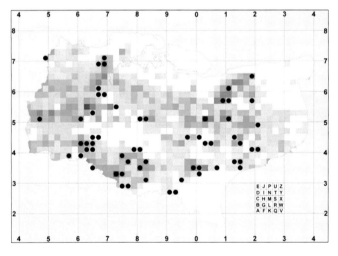

Native. Heaths, hedgerows and wood borders. Widely distributed. **60** (17).

Rubus tardus W.C.R. Watson

Native, endemic to Kent and Surrey. Recorded from Cinderhill Wood TQ64L and Fullingpits Wood TQ75H. **2** (0).

Rubus watsonii W.H. Mills

Native. Recorded from Crockenhill Common TQ45L and Beechen Wood TQ56C. These are the first British records for south of the Thames. **2** (0).

Rubus angloserpens Edees & A. Newton

Native. In Longbeech Wood TQ95V in 1998 was the first record for the county. **1** (0).

Rubus hylonomus Lefèvre & P.J. Müll.

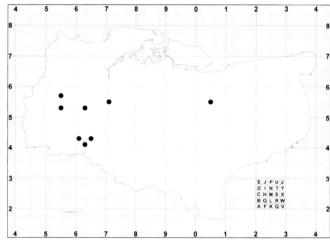

Native. Woods, wood borders and heathland. **8** (1).

Rubus leptadenes Sudre

Native. Several bushes in Larkeyvalley Wood TR15H in 2005 are the only record outside Buckinghamshire for this rare species. **1** (0).

Rubus praetextus Sudre

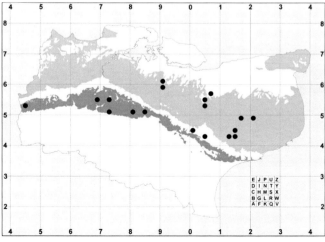

Native. On heaths and in hedgerows. **18** (4).

Rubus scaber Weihe

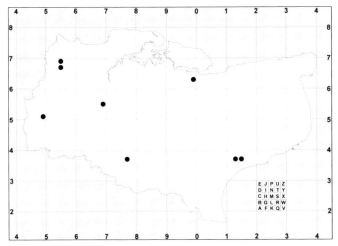

Native. In woods and hedge banks in wooded areas. **8** (1).

Rubus conjungens (Bab.) W.M. Rogers

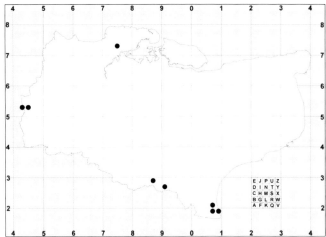

Native. In hedgerows, well vegetated banks and in scrub on shingle beaches. **8** (2).

Rubus halsteadensis W.C.R. Watson

Native. In hedgerows and roadside banks at Halstead TQ46V, Joyden's Wood TQ57A, Dartford Heath TQ57B and Darenth Wood TQ57Q & R. **5** (0).

Rubus britannicus W.M. Rogers

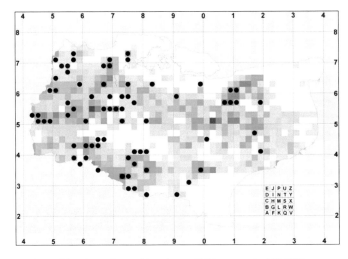

Native. Woods and wood borders. Widespread. **73** (10).

Rubus hindii A.L. Bull

Native. Recorded from Ightham Common TQ55X, Queendown Warren TQ86G, Bysing Wood TQ96W and Clowes Wood TR16G. **4** (0).

Rubus intensior Edees

Native. Found in reasonable quantity in West Wood TR14L & M in 2001. These are the first records for this species for south-east England. **2** (0).

Rubus nemorosus Hayne & Willd.

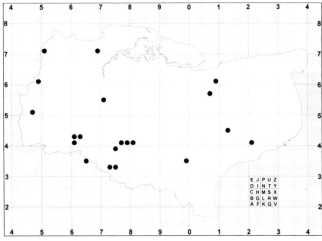

Native. In hedges damp woods on sand or clay. Widespread. **20** (6).

Rubus cantabrigiensis A.L. Bull & A.C. Leslie

Native. Described new to science in 2005 from material collected at Little Boxhurst TQ82 by R.J. Pankhurst in 1982. Searching at the original location failed to re-find the plant there, but later in 2005 this bramble was found on a roadside bank in Mintching Wood TQ95E. **1** (0).

Rubus pruinosus Arrh.

Native. The only record is from Hothfield Common TQ94S. **1** (0).

Rubus tuberculatus Bab.

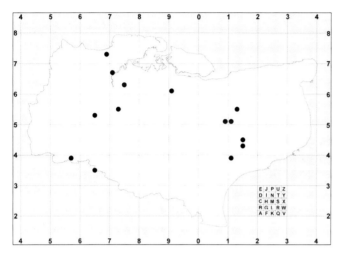

Native. Hedgerows, wood borders and disturbed waste ground. Scattered records. **14** (1).

Rubus caesius L.   Dewberry

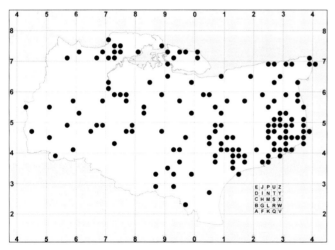

Native. Roadside banks, wood borders, river banks and sand-dunes, being more common near the coast. Great care has to be taken in the identification of this plant as it will frequently hybridize with other brambles. **145** (285).

Potentilla palustris (L.) Scop   Marsh Cinquefoil

Native. Only known from dykes and other damp areas in the Dungeness area TR01T & 01U. **2** (3)

Potentilla anserina L.   Silverweed

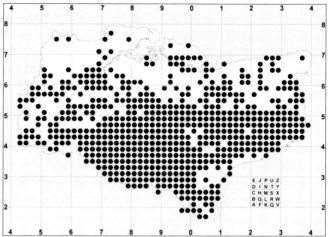

Native. On dry roadside verges, open grassland, and also on open, sparsely vegetated areas that are inundated during the winter months. **626** (807).

Potentilla argentea L.   Hoary Cinquefoil

Native. A rare and declining species, mainly though loss or destruction of habitat. Although looked for at all former known sites, it was only found on Dartford Heath TQ57G; on a laneside over Dartford Marshes TQ57N; an open area in Putt Wood TQ96Q; and on a footpath near Littlebourne TR15Y. It is listed in the Red List as 'Near Threatened'. **4** (9).

Potentilla inclinata Vill.   Grey Cinquefoil

Introduced. A casual plant last recorded in 1974 and not seen during the present survey. **0** (1).

Potentilla recta L.   Sulphur Cinquefoil

Introduced (neophyte). A garden plant noted growing wild at Shoreham TQ56A, Darenth TQ57Q, and Maidstone TQ75H. **3** (9).

Potentilla intermedia L.   Russian Cinquefoil

Introduced (neophyte). A garden plant recorded naturalised in the past but not seen during the present survey. **0** (1).

Potentilla norvegica L.   Ternate-leaved Cinquefoil

Introduced. A casual plant noted in the past, but not seen during the present survey. **0** (1).

Potentilla erecta (L.) Raeusch. Tormentil

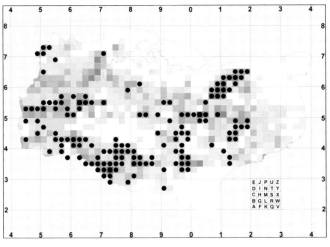

Native. Woodland rides, heaths and boggy areas, usually on the more acid soils. Locally common. **150** (242).

Potentilla erecta x **anglica**
= *P.* x *suberecta* Zimmeter

There are a few past records, but it was not found (but perhaps over-looked) during the present survey. **0** (3).

Potentilla erecta x **reptans** = *P.* x *italica* Lehm.

One doubtful record from over a hundred years ago, and not seen during the present survey. **0** (0).

Potentilla anglica Laichard. Trailing Tormentil

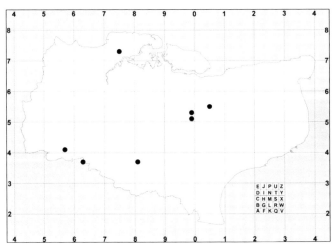

Native. In woodland rides, woodland edges, heaths and sandy banks, usually on the more acidic soils. A scarce, and probably declining, plant. **7** (14).

Potentilla anglica x **reptans**
= *P.* x *mixta* Nolte ex Rchb.

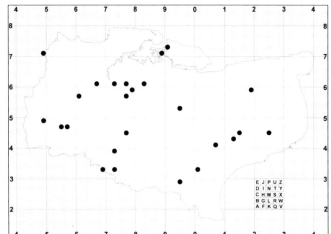

Scattered records over a large part of the county and never with the parent *P. anglica*. Great care has been taken over these plants and only recorded when identification is absolutely sure; the result is that it is probably under-recorded. **25** (49).

Potentilla reptans L. Creeping Cinquefoil

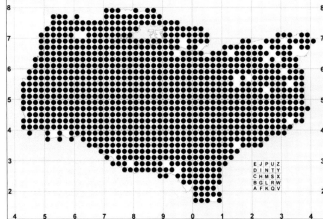

Native. Woodland rides, hedgerows, roadsides, waste and cultivated ground. Common throughout the county. **978** (994).

125

Potentilla sterilis (L.) Garcke   **Barren Strawberry**

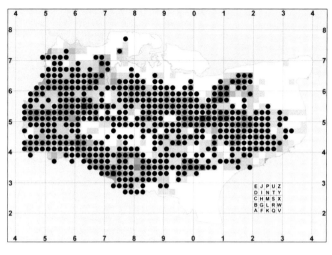

Native. Open woods, woodland margins and grassy roadside banks. It does not occur in marshy or coastal habitats. **517** (575).

Fragaria ananassa   **Garden Strawberry**
(Duchesne) Duchesne

Introduced (neophyte). Widely cultivated in farms, allotments and gardens, but probably under-recorded as only truly wild plants well away from cultivation have been mapped.   **12** (74).

Fragaria vesca L.   **Wild Strawberry**

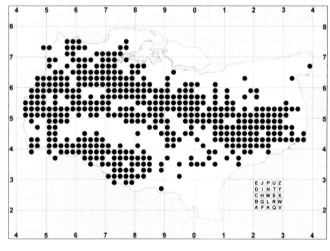

Native. Woods, scrub, chalk downland and roadside banks. Frequent except in coastal marshes and other wet areas. **466** (603).

Duchesnea indica   **Yellow-flowered Strawberry**
(Jacks.) Focke

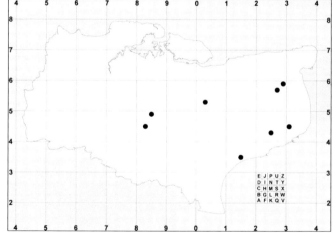

Introduced (neophyte). In churchyards and on waste ground. **8** (2).

Fragaria moschata   **Hautbois Strawberry**
(Duchesne) Weston

Introduced (neophyte). In the churchyard at Plaxtol TQ65B is the only record. There have been other casual records in the past. **1** (2).

Geum rivale L.   **Water Avens**

Native, extinct. Last recorded in 1777 from the Hothfield area. **0** (0).

Geum urbanum L. Wood Avens

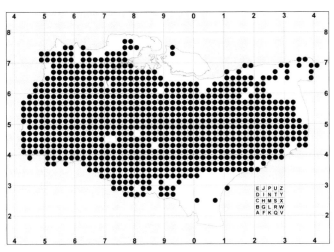

Native. In woods, scrub and shady roadside banks. It is also a regular inhabitant of gardens and other built-up areas where it can become a nuisance weed. **787** (795).

Geum quellyon Sweet Scarlet Avens

Introduced. A casual garden escape reported once in the past but there are no subsequent records. **0** (1).

Agrimonia eupatoria L. Agrimony

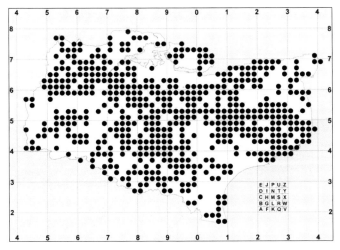

Native. Hedge banks, woodland margins, field borders and road-side verges. Widespread, but less frequent than in the past through loss or bad management of its habitats. **574** (827).

Agrimonia procera Wallr. Fragrant Agrimony

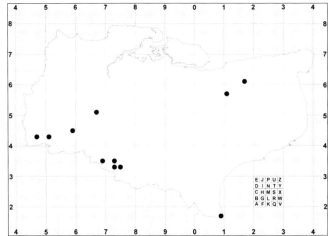

Native. Woodland margins and roadside verges. Rather local and in decline through loss of habitat. This species does not appear to be found on chalky soils. **11** (26).

Sanguisorba minor Scop. ssp. minor Salad Burnet

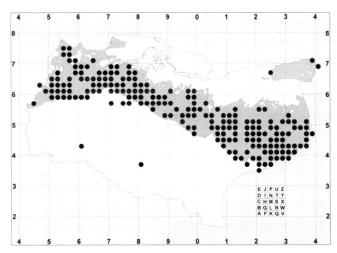

Native. On downland and roadside banks on the chalk. Plants off the chalk are casual introductions. **204** (275).

Sanguisorba minor Scop. ssp. muricata (Gremli) Briq. Fodder Burnet

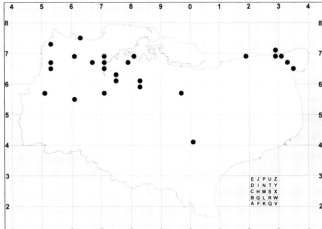

Introduced (neophyte). A relic of cultivation and sometimes introduced with seed mix sown on roadsides. On field edges and road verges; usually as a casual plant, although persistent in some localities. **26** (18).

Acaena novae-zelandiae Kirk   Pirri-pirri-bur

Introduced (neophyte). Well naturalised along woodland rides in
the Mereworth Woods area TQ65G, 65H & 65M where it has been
known for many years. Also found in woodland rides at Pembury
Walks TQ64B and Hartley Wood TQ66E. **5** (6).

Alchemilla xanthochlora   Intermediate Lady's-mantle
Rothm.

Native, although perhaps introduced with forestry work in Kent.
Found at the edge of a woodland ride in the Lyminge Forest in
1976 by R. Gorer, but repeated searches have failed to re-find this
plant. **0** (1).

Alchemilla filicaulis Buser   Lady's-mantle
ssp. vestita (Buser) M.E. Bradshaw

Native. Still just hanging on in a woodland ride in Great Wood,
Cobham TQ76E. **1** (2).

Alchemilla glabra Neygenf.   Smooth Lady's-mantle

Native. In a damp meadow (now gone) at Birling TQ66 in 1951 is
the sole record for the county. **0** (0).

Alchemilla mollis (Buser) Rothm.   Garden Lady's-mantle

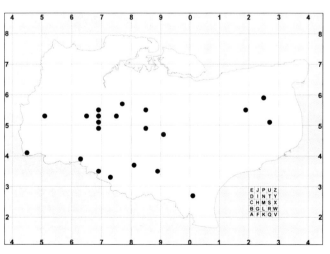

Introduced (neophyte). A common garden plant increasingly
found naturalised along woodland rides and roadside banks.
21 (1).

Aphanes arvensis L.   Parsley-piert

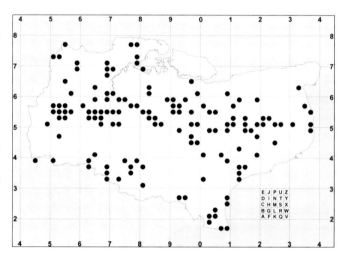

Native. Arable fields, woodland rides, heaths, gardens and waste
grassy areas, usually on well-drained soils. **271** (240).

Aphanes australis Rydb.   Slender Parsley-piert

Native. In similar habitats to the previous species, but usually on
more acidic or sandy soils. **139** (174).

Rosa multiflora Thunb.   **Many-flowered Rose**

Introduced (neophyte). A garden outcast found well established
in hedgerows or waste ground near Tonbridge TQ54T, Maidstone
TQ75N, Kemsley TQ96I and Wingham Well TR25I. **4** (8).

Rosa luciae   **Memorial Rose**
Franch. & Rochebr. ex Crép.

Introduced (neophyte). Plants referable to this group have been
recorded in the past, but the only ones seen during the present
survey were in strict cultivation. **0** (0).

Rosa arvensis Huds.   Field-rose

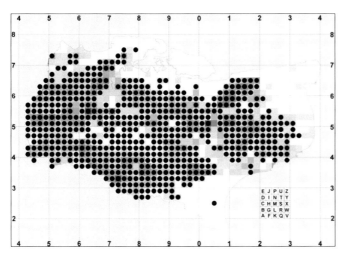

Native.   Woodland edges, hedgerows and roadside banks.
601 (675).

Rosa arvensis x *canina*
= *R.* x *irregularis* Déségl. & Guillon

Noted at Sevenoaks Weald TQ55F and from near Addisham TR25H, but probably over-looked elsewhere. **2** (2).

Rosa arvensis x *rubiginosa*
= *R.* x *gallicoides* (Baker) Déségl.

Once recorded from near Ryarsh in the past, but not seen during the present survey. **0** (0).

Rosa spinosissima L.   Burnet Rose

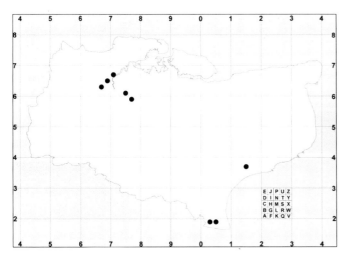

Native. On coastal sand-dunes and in chalk scrub. Very local and decreasing. **8** (13).

Rosa spinosissima x *canina*
= *R.* x *hibernica* Templeton

Recorded from Luddesdown in 1951 but not seen since. **0** (0).

Rosa spinosissima x *tomentosa*
= *R.* x *andrzejowskii* Boreau

Recorded in the distant past but there are no recent records. **0** (0).

Rosa spinosissima x *sherardii*
= *R.* x *involuta* Sm.

Recorded from West Kent in the past but there are no recent records. **0** (0).

Rosa spinosissima x *mollis*
= *R.* x *sabinii* Woods

Recorded from West Kent in the past but there are no recent records. **0** (0).

Rosa spinosissima x *rubiginosa*
= *R.* x *biturigensis* Boreau

Recorded from both East and West Kent in the past but was not found during the present survey. **0** (0).

Rosa rugosa Thunb.   Japanese Rose

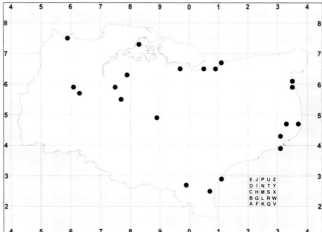

Introduced (neophyte). Well established in hedgerows, sand-dunes and waste places either as a garden throw-out or as a relic from original planting. **21** (22).

Rosa rugosa x *canina*
= *R.* x *praegeri* Wolley-Dod

One plant in a hedgebank at East Langdon TR34I growing near a good stand of *Rosa rugosa*. **1** (0).

Rosa 'Hollandica' hort., nom. nud.   Dutch Rose

Introduced (neophyte). A garden plant found naturalised in hedgerows at How Green TQ44T, near Egerton TQ84X, and Lenham TQ95B. **3** (0).

Rosa virginiana Herrm.   Virginian Rose

Introduced (neophyte). A relic of cultivation found at Capstone TQ76S and Kemsley TQ96C. **2** (0).

Rosa stylosa Desv.   Short-styled Field-rose

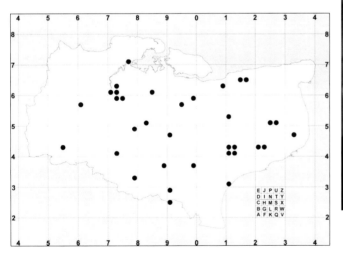

Native. Open woodland, scrub, hedgerows and disused quarries, usually on well-drained soil. **34** (80).

Rosa stylosa x *canina*
= *R.* x *andegavensis* Bastard

Recorded from Kent in the past but not found during the present survey. **0** (1).

Rosa canina L.   Dog-rose

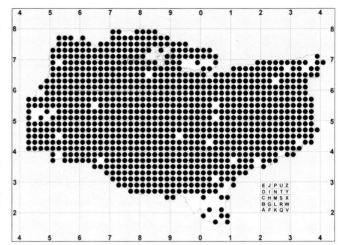

Native. Woodland, scrub, hedgerows and roadside banks. Much the commonest of the wild roses in the county. **947** (918).

Dog-rose *Rosa canina* © S. Smith

Rosa canina x *caesia* = *R.* x *dumalis* Bechst.

Recorded from West Kent in the past but not noted during the present survey. **0** (0).

Rosa canina x *obtusifolia* = *R.* x *dumetorum* Thuill.

On a roadside bank at Wittersham TQ92D. **1** (1).

Rosa canina x tomentosa
= R. x scabriuscula Sm.

In scrub on Bluebell Hill TQ76L, and in a roadside hedgerow at Bilsington TR03H. **2** (0).

Rosa canina x rubiginosa = R. x nitidula Besser

On open ground by Manston airport TR36I. **1** (0).

Rosa caesia Sm. ssp. vosagiaca   Glaucous Dog-rose
(N.H.F. Desp.) D.H. Kent

In a roadside hedgerow at Northfleet TQ67F where it had probably originally been planted. **1** (0).

Rosa obtusifolia Desv.   Round-leaved Dog-rose

Native.   Always a rare plant in Kent and not noted during the present survey. **0** (4).

Rosa tomentosa Sm.   Harsh Downy-rose

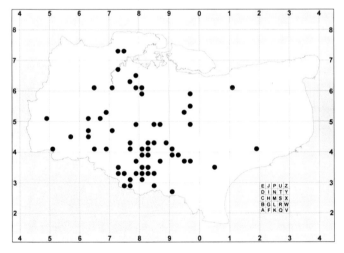

Native. Woodland edges and roadside hedgerows.   **62** (122).

Rosa sherardii Davies   Sherard's Downy-rose

Native.   Recorded in the past but there are no recent records. **0** (0).

Rosa mollis Sm.   Soft Downy-rose

Native, although not a rose one would expect to find in Kent. However, there are late 19th century specimens in the Natural History Museum collected from between Deal and Dover. Not found during the present survey. **0** (1).

Rosa rubiginosa L.   Sweet-briar

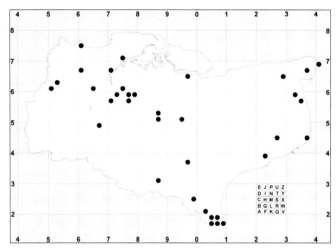

Native. In open scrub and in hedgerows on well-drained, non-acid soils. **35** (41).

Rosa rubiginosa x micrantha
= R. x bigeneris Duffort ex Rouy

Recorded in the past, but not found during the present survey. **0** (0).

Rosa micrantha   Small-flowered Sweet-briar
Borrer ex Sm.

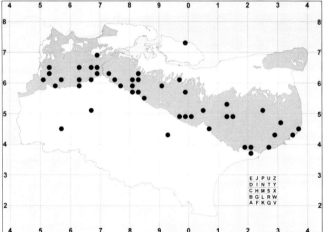

Native. Woodland edges, hedgerows and scrub, particularly on the chalk. **47** (83).

Rosa agrestis Savi   Small-leaved Sweet-briar

Native.   Always a rare plant in the county and the only present record is from the South Bank of Swale Nature Reserve TR06M. Nationally it is listed as 'Near Threatened'. **1** (0).

Prunus persica (L.) Batsch   Peach

Casual introduction. Recorded from rubbish-tips in West Kent in the past, but not noted during the present survey. **0** (7).

Prunus dulcis (Mill.) D.A. Webb   **Almond**

Casual introduction. Recorded from rubbish-tips in West Kent in the past, but not noted during the present survey. **0** (4).

Prunus cerasifera Ehrh.   Cherry Plum

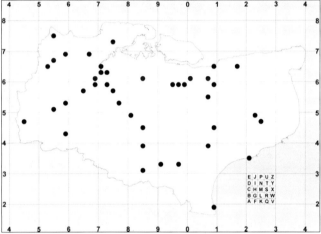

Introduced (neophyte). Woodland edges, hedgerows and roadsides. Often planted, but only trees that are not obviously planted or being tended have been recorded. **41** (94).

Prunus spinosa L.   Blackthorn

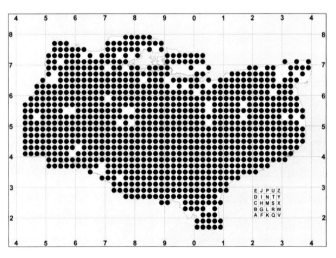

Native. Open woodland, scrub and hedgerows. A prostrate form, that grows true from seed, is to be found on the shingle beaches in the Dungeness area. **921** (953).

Prunus spinosa x *domestica*
= *P.* x *fruticans* Weihe

One bush, referable to this hybrid, was found on the Shorne Marshes TQ67R and another on scrub land at Great Chart TQ94W. It has probably been overlooked elsewhere. **2** (0).

Prunus domestica L.   Wild Plum

Introduced (archaeophyte). Woodland edges, hedgerows and scrub. Included here are subsp. *domestica* the true wild plum; subsp. *insititia* the bullace and damson, and subsp. *italica* the greengage, and all the various hybrids and clines between them. The most frequent is the damson. **607** (521).

Blackthorn *Prunus spinosa* © L. Manning

Prunus avium (L.) L.   Wild Cherry

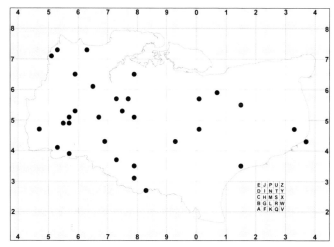

Native. Hedgerows, wood-borders and copses. It is also planted as a crop or for ornament, and some records might originate from suckering or seed from this source, but only non-cultivated plants have been recorded. **636** (614).

Prunus cerasus L.   Dwarf Cherry

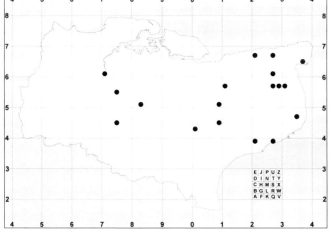

Introduced (neophyte). Wood borders and hedgerows. **18** (70).

Prunus mahaleb L.   St Lucie Cherry

Introduced. Well established on railway banks in the Longfield-Southfleet area TQ56Z & TQ67A, but has been in danger of being lost through high speed rail-related construction works. **2** (4).

Prunus padus L.   Bird Cherry

Introduced (neophyte). Free growing trees noted at Blue Bell Hill TQ76K, Newenden TQ82I and Elmstone Hole TQ84U. **3** (1).

Prunus serotina Ehrh.   Rum Cherry

Introduced (neophyte). One fine tree, plus a young seedling, in Joyden's Wood TQ57A is the only record in this survey. **1** (1).

Prunus lusitanica L.   Portugal Laurel

Introduced (neophyte). Frequently planted in parks, shelter belts and gardens and now well established in woods, scrub and waste ground. **31** (8).

Prunus laurocerasus L.   Cherry Laurel

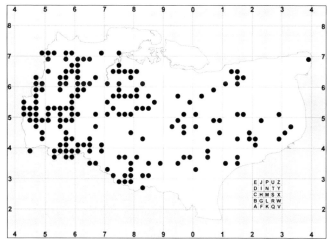

Introduced (neophyte). Much planted, particularly in the past, and now widely found in woods, hedgerows and scrub. It is regularly bird-sown and this is the source for it appearing in gardens and other new sites. **181** (74).

Cydonia oblonga Mill.   Quince

Introduced (neophyte). Formerly planted for its fruit and as a stock tree for pears, but less so in recent years. The only tree noted wild was in a hedgerow at West Malling TQ65Y. **1** (7).

Chaenomeles speciosa (Sweet) Nakai   Chinese Quince

Introduced (neophyte). Recorded in the past but not noted during the present survey. **0** (4).

Pyrus pyraster (L.) Burgsd.   Wild Pear

Introduced (archaeophyte), but the few plants seen have a good claim to be regarded as native. In hedgerows and woodland edge near Bough Beech TQ44T, Four Elms TQ44U and Ightham TQ55X. **3** (5).

Pyrus communis L.   Pear

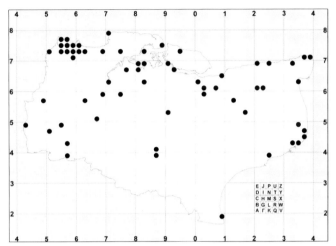

Introduced (archaeophyte). Scattered plants in woodland edges, railway banks, roadside verges and waste places, either as self-sown from discarded pears, or as relics from cultivation. **62** (80).

Malus sylvestris (L.) Mill.   Crab Apple

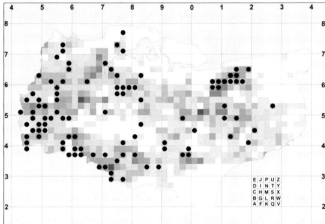

Native. In woodland and old hedgerows. Great care has been taken over the identification of the Crab Apple and only those that comply with all the required characters, (including completely glabrous leaves, pedicels and calyx) have been recorded as this species. **100** (163).

Darland Banks © S. Poyser

Malus pumila Mill.   Apple

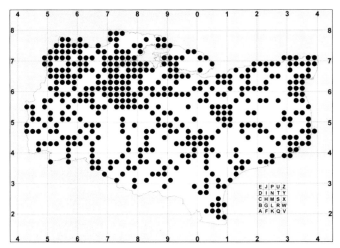

Introduced (archaeophyte). Woodland edges, hedgerows, scrub and waste land. Some plants are relics of cultivation, but many are self-sown from discarded apples. Included here are plants often intermediate between this species and *M. sylvestris,* or looking just like a true Crab Apple save that they have pubescent leaves. **465** (434).

Malus x purpurea (E. Barbier) Rehder   Purple Crab

Introduced (neophyte). One previous record of a seedling plant at Horns Cross in 1973. One mature, but wild unkept tree noted in a hedgerow near Egerton Forstal TQ84Y. **1** (1).

Sorbus aucuparia L.   Rowan

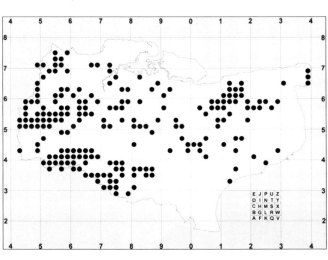

Native, also it can be bird-sown from planted trees. In woods, copses, scrub and in hedgerows. **208** (261).

Sorbus aucuparia x intermedia

has been found on occasion in the past with both parents in West Kent, but was not noted during the present survey. **0** (0).

Sorbus aucuparia x aria
= S. x thuringiaca (Ilse) Fritsch

The only record is from Knockholt Pound TQ45U, but has been recorded more widely in the past. **1** (4).

Sorbus hybrida L.   Swedish Service-tree

Introduced (neophyte). A record from Darenth Wood (Wild Fl. Mag. 414:13-14, 1989) was almost certainly of an originally planted tree. **0** (0).

Sorbus intermedia (Ehrh.) Pers.   Swedish Whitebeam

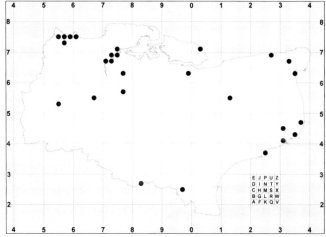

Introduced (neophyte). Widely planted as an ornamental tree and increasingly self-sown in copses, old quarries, hedgerows and waste ground. **27** (13).

Sorbus aria (L.) Crantz   Common Whitebeam

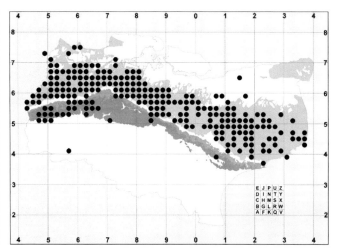

Native. In woods and hedgerows on the chalk and in places on the Folkestone/Hythe beds. **235** (237).

Sorbus aria x torminalis = S. x vagensis Wilmott

Native. Several trees, originally found by David Price in the Blean Woods TR15E & TR16A. **2** (0).

Sorbus torminalis (L.) Crantz — Wild Service-tree

Native. In old woods and hedgerows. Usually scattered trees and only locally frequent in a few areas within the Blean and the Weald. **127** (161).

Amelanchier lamarckii F.G. Schroed. — Juneberry

Introduced (neophyte). A delightful, slow growing tree surprisingly not more often planted out in gardens and parks. Appears to be naturalised and self-sowing in woods and hedgerows in the south west of the county and recorded at Hosey Common TQ45L, Tunbridge Wells Common TQ53U, Kilndown Wood TQ63X, Pembury Walks TQ64G and Hawkhurst TQ73Q. **5** (8).

Photinia davidiana (Decne.) Cardot — Stranvaesia

Introduced. Casual seedlings on waste ground near planted bushes were recorded in 1976, but none has been noted during the present survey. **0** (1).

In recent years various species of *Cotoneaster* have been widely planted in formal gardens around new commercial and housing developments and also along roadsides and on roundabouts with new road schemes. These plants set seed easily and some species are much favoured by birds and so the seed is spread. Plants that have obviously been planted and seedlings in gardens and formal cultivated areas have been ignored and only plants truly wild and established have been recorded. Included here are all species formally published, although some might not meet the strict limits set for the recording for this publication.

Cotoneaster monopyrenus — One-stoned Cotoneaster
(W.W. Sm.) Flinck & B. Hylmö

Introduced(neophyte). One mature bush and numerous seedlings on waste ground at Dartford TQ57L. **1** (0).

Cotoneaster insignis Pojark. — Lindley's Cotoneaster

Introduced (neophyte). Several plants at the edges of chalk quarries at Northfleet TQ67H. **1** (0).

Cotoneaster hissaricus — Circular-leaved Cotoneaster
Pojark.

Introduced (neophyte). Recorded from Dartford Heath in 1988 but not noted during the present survey. **0** (0).

Cotoneaster ignotus G. Klotz. — Black grape Cotoneaster

Introduced (neophyte). Has been recorded from West Kent. **0** (0).

Cotoneaster affinis Lindl. — Purpleberry Cotoneaster

Introduced (neophyte). Recorded from West Kent in the past but not noted during the present survey. **0** (5).

Cotoneaster obtusus — Dartford Cotoneaster
Wall. ex Lindl.

Introduced (neophyte). On waste land by Darford Heath TQ57B. **1** (0).

Cotoneaster bacillaris — Open-fruited Cotoneaster
Wall. ex Lindl.

Inrtoduced (neophyte). Has been recorded from Dartford Heath, but was not noted during the present survey. **0** (0).

Cotoneaster frigidus Wall. ex Lindl. — Tree Cotoneaster

Introduced (neophyte). In a disused chalk pit at Stone TQ57R in 1991 (now developed). **1** (2).

Cotoneaster x watereri Exell — Waterer's Cotoneaster

Introduced. Casual plants, probably relics of cultivation noted at Farningham TQ56N, Brooklands TQ57L, Dartford TQ57M, Swanscombe TQ67C, Northfleet TQ67H, and Lower Rainham TQ86D. **6** (0).

Cotoneaster salicifolius — Willow-leaved Cotoneaster
Franch.

Introduced (neophyte). Noted at Darenth Wood TQ57R and Greenhithe TQ57X. **2** (3).

Cotoneaster x suecicus G. Klotz — Swedish Cotoneaster

Introduced (neophyte). Noted at Swanscombe TQ67C and Maidstone TQ75S. **2** (0).

Cotoneaster conspicuus — Tibetan Cotoneaster
C. Marquand

Introduced (neophyte). Has been recorded from West Kent. **0** (0).

Cotoneaster pannosus Franch.   Silverleaf Cotoneaster

Introduced. Casual plants in the old hospital grounds at Dartford TQ57M. **1** (0).

Cotoneaster lacteus W.W. Sm.   Late Cotoneaster

Introduced (neophyte). Noted on roadside banks and waste land at Detling TQ75Z, Borstal TQ76I, and Rochester TQ76J. **3** (1).

Cotoneaster prostratus Baker   Procumbent Cotoneaster

Introduced (neophyte). Has been claimed as naturalised in West Kent but was not noted during the present survey. **0** (0).

Cotoneaster congestus Baker   Congested Cotoneaster

Introduced (neophyte). Has been recorded from West Kent. **0** (0).

Cotoneaster integrifolius   Entire-leaved Cotoneaster
(Roxb.) G. Klotz

Introduced (neophyte). On chalky soils at Swanscombe TQ67C, Dover TR34G, and Langdon Bay TR34L. **3** (0).

Cotoneaster linearifolius   Thyme-leaved Cotoneaster
(G. Klotz) G. Klotz

Introduced (neophyte). On waste ground at Tunbridge Wells TQ53Z. **1** (0).

Cotoneaster cashmirensis   Kashmir Cotoneaster
G. Klotz

Introduced (neophyte). Has been recorded from East Kent. **0** (0).

Cotoneaster hjelmqvistii   Hjelmqvist's Cotoneaster
Flinck & B. Hylmö

Introduced (neophyte). Recorded from South Darenth TQ56U, Dartford TQ57M, Leybourne TQ65Z, Eccles TQ76F, and Temple Marsh TQ76I. **5** (0).

Cotoneaster atropurpureus   Purple-flowered Cotoneaster
Flinck & B. Hylmö

Introduced (neophyte). Has been recorded from West Kent. **0** (0).

Cotoneaster adpressus Bois   Creeping Cotoneaster

Introduced (neophyte). Has been recorded from West Kent. **0** (0).

Cotoneaster nanshan   Dwarf Cotoneaster
M. Vilm. ex Mottet

Introduced (neophyte). Has been recorded from West Kent. **0** (0).

Cotoneaster divaricatus   Spreading Cotoneaster
Rehder & E.H. Wilson

Introduced (neophyte). Recorded in the past as seedlings from planted bushes at New Ash Green, but not seen during the present survey. **0** (1).

Cotoneaster nitens   Few-flowered Cotoneaster
Rehder & E.H. Wilson

Introduced (neophyte). Seedling from bush in nearby garden at edge of Darenth Wood TQ57Q. **1** (0).

Cotoneaster lucidus Schltdl.   Shiny Cotoneaster

Introduced (neophyte). Has been recorded from West Kent. **0** (0).

Cotoneaster horizontalis Decne.   Wall Cotoneaster

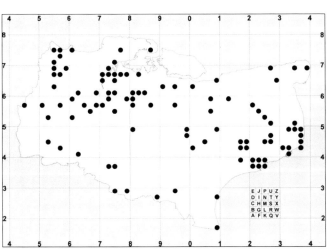

Introduced (neophyte). In quarries, roadside banks and cliffs, particularly on the chalk, and on old walls and buildings. **102** (57).

Cotoneaster simonsii Baker   Himalayan Cotoneaster

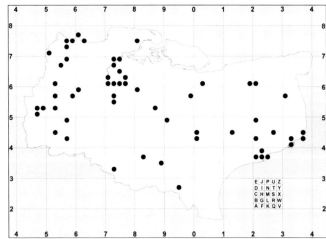

Introduced (neophyte). Woodland edges, hedgerows, roadside banks, quarries, cliffs, walls and in pavement cracks. The berries are much favoured by birds and the seed distributed widely. **58** (29).

Cotoneaster bullatus Bois   Hollyberry Cotoneaster

Introduced (neophyte). Recorded at South Darenth TQ56U, Darenth Wood TQ57R, and Dartford TQ57S. **3** (1).

Cotoneaster rehderi Pojark.   Bullate Cotoneaster

Introduced (neophyte). Recorded from West Kingsdown TQ56R, Dartford TQ57M, Leybourne TQ65Z, near Thurnham TQ85E, near Petham TR15A and from Folkestone TR23I. **6** (0).

Cotoneaster dielsianus   Diels' Cotoneaster
E. Pritz. ex Diels

Introduced (neophyte). Recorded from Sutton-at-Hone TQ56P, South Darenth TQ56U, Longfield TQ56Z, Dartford TQ57M, Darenth Wood TQ57R, Eccles TQ76F, and Rochester TQ76J. **7** (0).

Cotoneaster splendens   Showy Cotoneaster
Flinck & B. Hylmö

Introduced (neophyte). Has been recorded from West Kent. **0** (0).

Cotoneaster franchetii Bois   Franchet's Cotoneaster

Introduced (neophyte). Recorded from Eccles TQ76F, Rochester TQ76J, and Brook TR04S. **3** (3).

Cotoneaster sternianus (Turrill)   Stern's Cotoneaster

Introduced (neophyte). Recorded from South Darenth TQ56U, Darenth Wood TQ57R, and Swanscombe TQ67C. **3** (0)

Cotoneaster amoenus   Beautiful Cotoneaster
E.H. Wilson

Introduced (neophyte). Has been recorded from East Kent in the past. **0** (0).

Cotoneaster zabelii C.K. Schneid.   Cherryred Cotoneaster

Introduced (neophyte). Was established on an old wall at Gravesend, but the wall and plants have now gone. **0** (1).

Cotoneaster calocarpus (Rehder   Sikang Cotoneaster
& E.H. Wilson) Flinck & B. Hylmö

Introduced (neophyte). Has been recorded from West Kent. **0** (0).

Cotoneaster cochleatus   Yunnan Cotoneaster
(Franch.) G. Klotz

Introduced (neophyte). Has been recorded from East Kent. **0** (0).

Cotoneaster perpusillus   Slender Cotoneaster
(C.K. Schneid.) Flinck & B. Hylmö

Introduced (neophyte). Has been recorded from West Kent. **0**

Cotoneaster serotinus Hutch.   Yuletide Cotoneaster

Introduced (neophyte). Has been reported from West Kent. **0** (0).

Pyracantha coccinea M. Roem.   Firethorn

Introduced (neophyte). Noted on waste ground at Maidstone TQ75M and Faversham TR06F. **2** (5).

Pyracantha rogersiana   Orange Firethorn
(A.B. Jacks.) Coltm.-Rog.

Introduced (neophyte). Recorded from Dartford TQ57M and Milton Regis TQ96C. It has now gone from a former site at Aylesford. **2** (1).

Mespilus germanica L.   Medlar

Introduced (archaeophyte). Always a scarce plant in the county and although especially searched for, it could not be found during the present survey. **0** (2).

Crataegus submollis Sarg.   Hairy Cockspurthorn

Introduced. A previous casual record from West Kent. **0** (0).

Crataegus coccinioides   Large-flowered Cockspurthorn
Ashe

Introduced (neophyte). There are previous records from West Kent. **0** (1).

Crataegus coccinea L.   Pear-fruited Cockspurthorn

Introduced. A previous casual record from West Kent. **0** (0).

Crataegus crus-galli L.   Cockspurthorn

Introduced (neophyte). A few trees in the former hospital grounds at Dartford TQ57N. **1** (0).

Crataegus persimilis   Broad-leaved Cockspurthorn
Sarg.

Introduced. A previous casual record from West Kent. **0** (0).

Crataegus monogyna Jacq.   Hawthorn

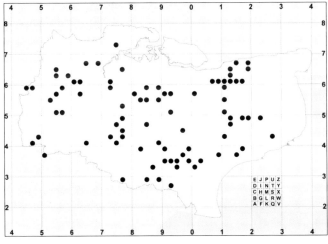

Native. In wood-borders, hedgerows and scrub, whilst odd bushes can often persist in open grazing or coastal marshes. **1012** (1015).

Crataegus monogyna x laevigata = C. x media Bechst.

In woods, hedgerows and scrub, usually with both parents present, but occasionally in the absence of *C. laevigata*. **83** (55).

Crataegus laevigata (Poir.) DC.   Midland Hawthorn

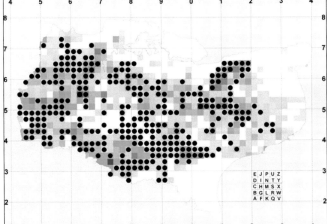

Native. In ancient woodland, wood-borders and old hedgerows. **313** (354).

Crataegus orientalis Pall. ex M. Bieb.   Oriental Hawthorn

Introduced (neophyte). Has been recorded in the past from West Kent. **0** (0).

CAESALPINIACEAE

Senna occidentalis (L.) Link.   Coffee Senna

Introduced. Casual records from where oil-seed waste had been deposited near Dartford in the 1970s, but with no subsequent records. **0** (1).

FABACEAE

Robinia pseudoacacia L.   False-acacia

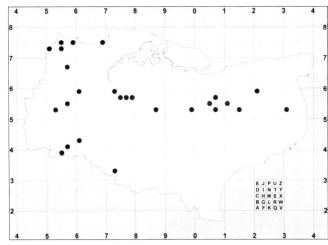

Introduced (neophyte). Occasionally planted in gardens and woodlands, but now well naturalised and spreading by suckering and by seed in open woodlands, quarries, roadsides and waste land. **26** (54).

Phaseolus vulgaris L.   French Bean

Introduced. Casual plants noted on a rubbish-tip in the past, but not recorded during the present survey. **0** (1).

Phaseolus coccineus L.   Runner Bean

Introduced. Casual plants have been recorded on rubbish-tips in the past, but not seen during the present survey. **0** (5).

Phaseolus lunatus L.   Butter Bean

Introduced. Odd casual plants on a rubbish-tip in the past, but not recorded during the present survey. **0** (1).

Vigna radiata (L.) Wilczek   Mung-bean

Introduced.   Casual plants noted on a rubbish-tip in the past but not recorded during the present survey.   **0** (1).

Colutea arborescens x *orientalis*   Orange Bladder-senna
= *C.* x *media* Willd.

Recorded from West Kent in the past, but not noted during the present survey.   **0** (5).

Glycine max (L.) Merr.   Soyabean

Introduced (neophyte).   Recorded from rubbish-tips and waste ground where oil-seed waste had been dumped in north-west Kent in the 1970s, but not recorded since.   **0** (3).

Astragalus glycyphyllos L.   Wild Liquorice

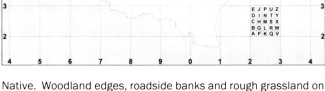

Galega officinalis L.   Goat's-rue

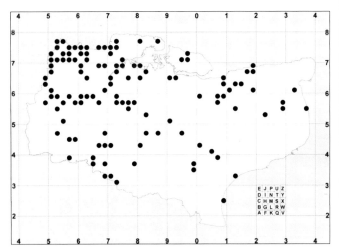

Native. Woodland edges, roadside banks and rough grassland on well-drained soils.   A species much in decline through loss of habitat.   **14** (28).

Introduced (neophyte).   A garden escape now well naturalised in old quarries, roadsides and waste places.   **119** (93).

Onobrychis viciifolia Scop.   Sainfoin

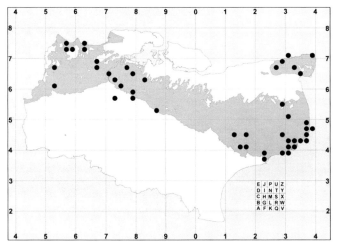

Colutea arborescens L.   Bladder-senna

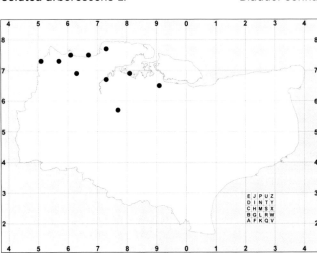

Introduced (neophyte).   Naturalised on railway banks, roadsides and in rough grassland.   **10** (20).

Native, although some records may be relics from cultivation.   On unimproved chalk grassland and roadside banks and verges on the chalk.   Appears to be in decline through loss of habitat and in the Red List is placed in the 'Near Threatened' category. **46** (85).

Anthyllis vulneraria L.   Kidney Vetch

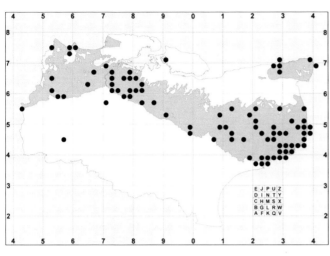

Native. On chalk grassland, cliffs and roadside banks and verges. The native plant is subsp. *vulneraria* which is in decline. The species is frequently sown on roadside verges and this nearly always turns out to be the alien subsp. *carpatica* or subsp. *polyphylla.* **87** (156).

Dorycnium hirsutum (L.) Ser.   Canary Clover

Introduced (neophyte). A garden plant well established on the verge of the A2 near Bishopsbourne TR15W. **1** (0).

Dorycnium pentaphyllum Scop.

Introduced. A casual garden escape, recorded in the past, but not noted during the present survey. **0** (1).

Lotus tenuis   Narrow-leaved Bird's-foot-trefoil
Waldst. & Kit. ex Willd.

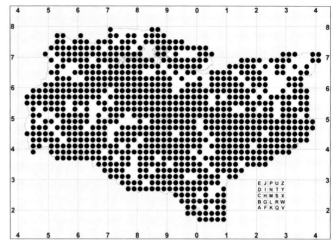

Native. On coastal grazing marshes and sea-walls, and occasionally inland on roadside verges and rough grassland. **124** (84).

Lotus corniculatus L.   Common Bird's-foot-trefoil

Native. In fields, road verges, waste ground and rough grassland. **856** (990).

Lotus pedunculatus Cav.   Greater Bird's-foot-trefoil

Native. Wet meadows, marshes, ditches and margins of lakes and rivers. **355** (486).

Lotus angustissimus L.   Slender Bird's-foot-trefoil

Native. A rare plant ('Near Threatened' in the Red List) of sandy areas. Repeated visits to its former sites in East Kent have failed to find this plant, but it might still linger on. **0** (3).

Tetragonolobus maritimus (L.) Roth   Dragon's-teeth

Introduced (neophyte). Naturalised in great quantity on the cliffs at Warden Point in Sheppey TQ97W & TR07B. Other plants, probably from seed carried from the Warden Point colony, at Minster TQ97M, Warden Bay TR07F and Sandwich Bay TR35P. A casual plant was noted inland in rough grassland at Detling TQ75Z. **6** (8).

Ornithopus compressus L.   Yellow Serradella

Introduced (neophyte). Well established on a grassy roadside bank at Swanley (just inside the Kent boundary) in TQ46Z. **1** (0).

Ornithopus perpusillus L.   Bird's-foot

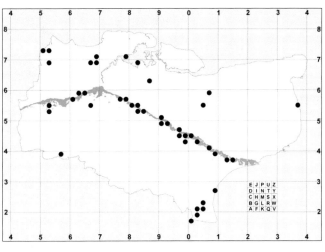

Native. In open, dry , grassy areas on sand or gravel. Rather local. **44** (52).

Ornithopus pinnatus (Mill.) Druce   Orange Bird's-foot

Introduced (neophyte). A specimen was collected from Folkestone Warren in 1897 but there are no subsequent records. **0** (0).

Hippocrepis emerus (L.) Lassen   Scorpion Senna

Introduced (neophyte). On the top of the cliffs at Kingsdown TR34Y. **1** (0).

Hippocrepis comosa L.   Horseshoe Vetch

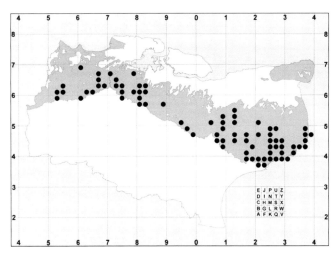

Native. On open downland and banks and roadside verges with little or no other vegetation, usually on the chalk. It has been lost from a number of former sites. **79** (96).

Securigera varia (L.) Lassen   Crown Vetch

Introduced. Casual plants on a roadside bank at Cobham TQ66U constitute the only recent record. **1** (2).

Scorpiurus muricatus L.   Caterpillar-plant

Introduced. A casual plant recorded with wool shoddy or oil-seed waste in the past, but not seen during the present survey. **0** (2).

Vicia cracca L.   Tufted Vetch

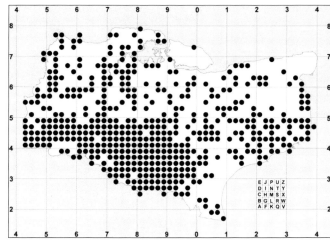

Native. Roadside banks, wood-borders and rough grassy areas. **502** (714).

Vicia cassubica L.   Danzig Vetch

Introduced (neophyte). Was naturalised at one site in West Kent from 1931 until last seen in 1963. Not recorded since. **0** (0).

Vicia tenuifolia Roth   Fine-leaved Vetch

Introduced. Casual plants in the past but not seen during the present survey. **0** (2).

Vicia sylvatica L.   Wood Vetch

Native. Always a rare plant in Kent, this plant appears to have declined even further in recent years and was only recorded from woodland edges at Atchester Wood TR14T and Covert Wood TR14U. **2** (9).

Vicia villosa Roth   Fodder Vetch

Introduced (neophyte). A casual plant of roadside banks, rough grassland and waste ground, although quite common over the Swanscombe Marshes. **12** (11).

Vicia hirsuta (L.) Gray — Hairy Tare

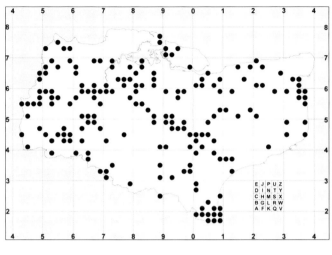

Native. Roadside banks, hedgerows, scrubby grassland and consolidated shingle beaches. **187** (351).

Vicia sepium L. — Bush Vetch

Native. In woodland, scrub and hedgerows. **582** (701).

Vicia parviflora Cav. — Slender Tare

Native. Always a rare plant in Kent (in the Red List Category, 'Vulnerable') and not recorded during the present survey. **0** (1).

Vicia pannonica Crantz — Hungarian Vetch

Introduced (neophyte). Still present on roadside verges on the approach road to the Dartford Crossing TQ57L, but could not be found elsewhere. **1** (2).

Vicia tetrasperma (L.) Schreb. — Smooth Tare

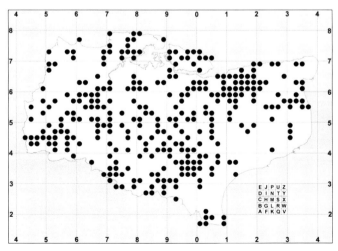

Native. In hedgerows, wood borders, rough grassland and disturbed waste ground. **313** (352).

Vicia sativa L. ssp. nigra (L.) Ehrh. — Narrow-leaved Vetch

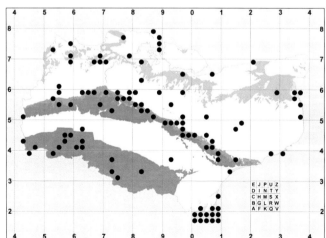

Native. On coastal sand-dunes and consolidated shingle beaches, and on dry sandy grazing fields, roadside banks and heaths inland. **104** (210).

Vicia sativa L. ssp. *segetalis*   Common Vetch
(Thuill.) Gaudin

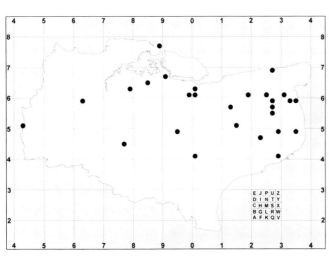

Introduced (neophyte). In fields, roadside banks and rough grassy areas. **729** (909).

Vicia sativa L. ssp. *sativa*   Common Fodder Vetch

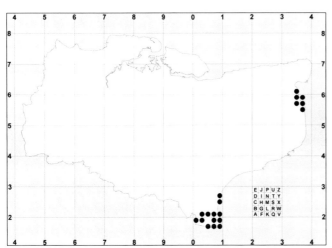

Introduced (neophyte). Widely scattered records of casual plants on roadside banks and field borders, usually as an escape from cultivation. **27** (19).

Vicia lathyroides L.   Spring Vetch

Native. On dry short grassland on coastal sand-dunes and consolidated shingle beaches. **19** (22).

Vicia lutea L.   Yellow-vetch

Native. Always a rare plant in Kent (Red List Category 'Near Threatened'), and only now recorded from a few plants in grassy areas over the shingle at Dungeness TR01Y. **1** (9).

Vicia bithynica (L.) L.   Bithynian Vetch

Native. A rare plant on a grassy bank at Stone TQ57S, and on coastal cliffs at Minster TQ97R and Warden TR07F. In the Red List Category, 'Vulnerable'. **3** (8).

Vicia faba L.   Broad Bean

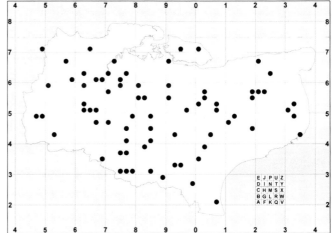

Introduced (neophyte). Casual plants, usually as an escape from cultivation, on field borders, roadside verges and waste places. **74** (25).

Vicia narbonensis L.   Narbonne Vetch

Introduced (neophyte). Past records from West Kent but not seen during the present survey. **0** (0).

Lens culinaris Medik.   Lentil

Introduced. A few casual plants on waste ground where refuse had been tipped at Swanscombe TQ67C constitute the only recent record. **1** (3).

Lathyrus niger (L.) Bernh.   Black Pea

Introduced (neophyte). Appears to have gone from its former locality at Tunbridge Wells and there are no other records. **0** (1).

Lathyrus japonicus Willd.   Sea Pea

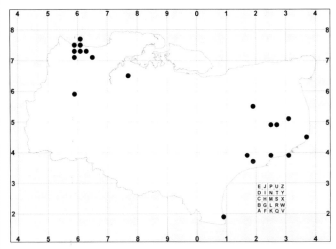

Native. On shingle beaches just above the high tide mark. Our plant is subspecies *maritimus*. **9** (8).

Lathyrus linifolius (Reichard)   Bitter-vetch

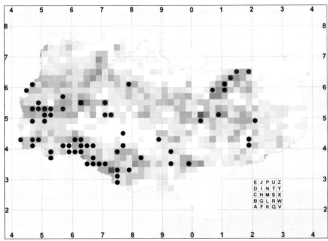

Native. Woodland edges and rides, and on sheltered roadside banks, particularly on the more acidic soils. **62** (167).

Lathyrus pratensis L.   Meadow Vetchling

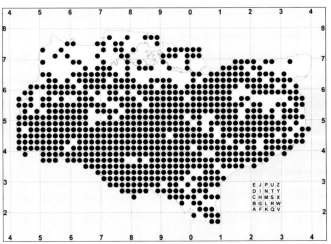

Native. In meadows, rough grassland, scrub and roadside verges. **755** (941).

Lathyrus tuberosus L.   Tuberous Pea

Introduced (neophyte). A garden plant occasionally naturalised, but with no recent records. **0** (1).

Lathyrus grandiflorus Sm.   Two-flowered Everlasting-pea

Introduced (neophyte). Several plants on disturbed waste ground at New Hythe TQ76A. **1** (1).

Lathyrus sylvestris L.   Narrow-leaved Everlasting-pea

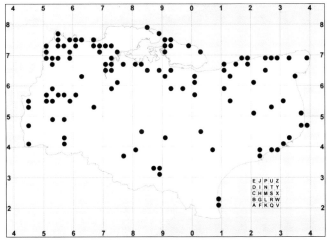

Native. Wood borders, scrub, rough grassland and roadside banks. **20** (46).

Lathyrus latifolius L.   Broad-leaved Everlasting-pea

Introduced (neophyte). A garden plant now well naturalised on railway banks, roadside verges, scrub and rough grassland. **109** (146).

Lathyrus hirsutus L.   Hairy Vetchling

Introduced (neophyte). Well established in rough grassland at Warden Bay TR07F - the only locality noted during the present survey. **1** (1).

Lathyrus nissolia L.   Grass Vetchling

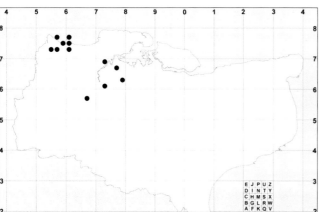

Native.   Meadows, wood-borders, rough grassland and roadside verges.   **188** (300).

Lathyrus aphaca L.   Yellow Vetchling

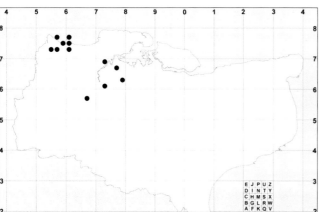

Native.   On sea-walls, roadside banks and rough grassland, usually on the chalk or near the coast.   Noted in the Red List as 'Vulnerable'.   **12** (20).

Lathyrus annuus L.   Fodder Pea

Introduced. Noted in the past as a casual bird seed alien but with no recent records.   **0** (1).

Lathyrus odoratus L.   Sweet Pea

Introduced.   A casual garden escape on a disturbed roadside verge at Maidstone TQ75T.   **1** (2).

Lathyrus clymenum L.

Introduced.   Casual records in the past but not seen during the present survey.   **0** (1).

Pisum sativum L.   Garden Pea

Introduced. Casual plants as an escape from cultivation noted at Goudhurst TQ73I, Woodchurch TQ93G and Leysdown TR07A. **3** (11).

Cicer arietinum L.   Chick Pea

Introduced. Casual records from rubbish-tips during the 1970s, but not seen since.   **0** (2).

Ononis spinosa L.   Spiny Restharrow

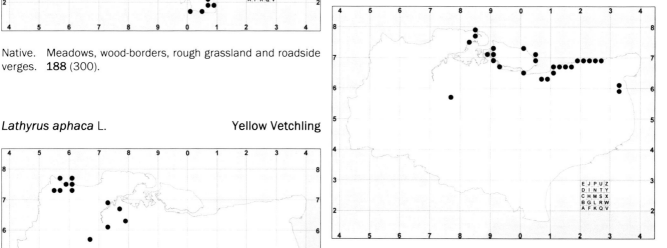

Native. On coastal grazing marshes and on sea-walls. The occasional plant has been noted elsewhere where a wildflower seed mix has been sown.   **27** (53).

Ononis repens L.   Common Restharrow

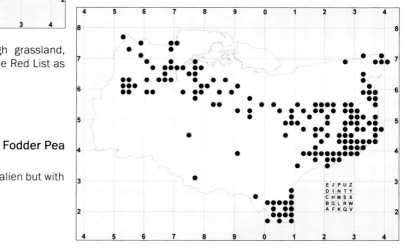

Native. On sand-dunes and shingle beaches on the coast, and on downland and rough grassland on the chalk.   It is also occasionally found on grazing meadows and roadside banks elsewhere.   **165** (230).

Ononis alopecuroides L.   Salzmann's Restharrow

Introduced.   A casual plant on a rubbish-tip at Dartford in 1976, but with no subsequent records.   **0** (1).

Ononis baetica Clemente   Andalucian Restharrow

Introduced. A single plant was recorded at Sandwich in 1957, but with no subsequent records. **0** (0).

Ononis mitissima L.   Mediterranean Restharrow

Introduced. There were casual records in the past for this bird seed alien in West Kent. **0** (0).

Melilotus altissimus Thuill.   Tall Melilot

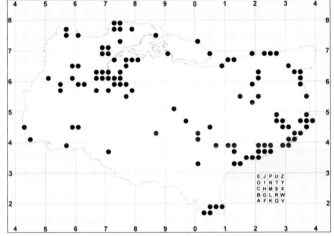

Introduced (archaeophyte). Roadsides, field borders and waste places, particularly on recently disturbed ground. Although it is usually regarded as a casual plant, the present distribution shows very little change from that of the 1971-80 mapping. **112** (104).

Melilotus albus Medik.   White Melilot

Introduced (neophyte). Roadsides, field borders and waste ground, particularly on recently disturbed soil. **174** (198).

Melilotus officinalis (L.) Pall.   Ribbed Melilot

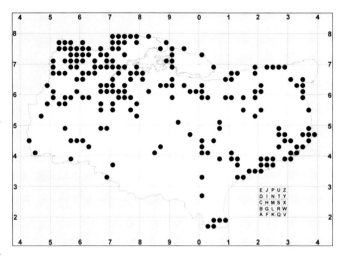

Introduced (neophyte). On disturbed soil on roadsides, old quarries and waste places. **129** (214).

Melilotus indicus (L.) All.   Small Melilot

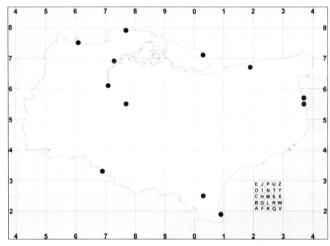

Introduced. A casual plant of cultivated fields, rubbish-tips and waste ground, particularly in sandy areas. **12** (29).

Melilotus sulcatus Desf.   Furrowed Melilot

Introduced. A casual plant in a garden at Eynsford in 1973, but with no subsequent records. **0** (1).

Trigonella corniculata (L.) L.   Sickle-fruited Fenugreek

Introduced. Casual plants on a rubbish-tip at Northfleet in 1978, but with no subsequent records. **0** (1).

Trigonella foenum-graecum L.   Fenugreek

Introduced. Casual records from rubbish-tips and waste ground in West Kent in the past, but with no recent records. **0** (4).

Medicago lupulina L.   Black Medick

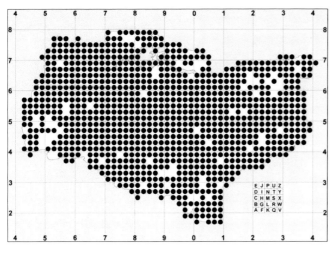

Native. On roadside verges, dry grassland, cultivated and waste land. **950** (983).

Medicago sativa L. ssp. *falcata*   Sickle Medick
(L.) Arcang.

Introduced. A casual plant on disturbed waste ground at Gillingham TQ76T. **1** (3).

Medicago sativa L. ssp. *varia*   Sand Lucerne
(Martyn) Arcang.

Introduced. Casual plants noted on Swanscombe Marshes TQ67D, Strood TQ76I, Stoke TQ87H, Murston TQ96H and Dover TR34G. **5** (13).

Medicago sativa L. ssp. *sativa*   Lucerne

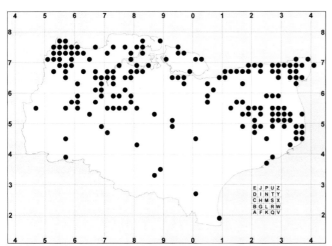

Introduced (neophyte). A relic from cultivation on roadside verges and field margins. Noticeably much less frequent in recent years. **174** (324).

Medicago minima (L.) Bartal.   Bur Medick

Native. On sandy or gravelly places on the coast. It is no longer found as a wool shoddy alien inland and in the Red List is categorised as 'Vulnerable'. **11** (25).

Medicago polymorpha L.   Toothed Medick

Native. On sandy and gravelly habitats on or near the coast. No longer to be found as a wool shoddy alien inland. **15** (32).

Medicago littoralis Rohde ex Loisel.   Shore Medick

Introduced (neophyte). About 20 plants on the beach at Whitstable TR16D in 2001 constituted the first record for Kent. **1** (0).

Medicago arabica (L.) Huds.   Spotted Medick

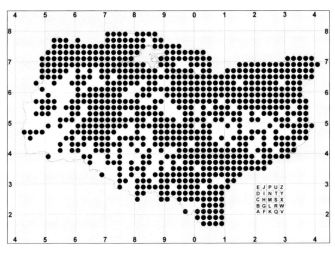

Native. In grassy places, especially on sandy or gravelly soils.
Common, particularly near the coast. **780** (646).

Medicago intertexta (L.) Mill.   Hedgehog Medick

Introduced. One 1978 record as a wool shoddy casual, but with
no subsequent records. **0** (1).

Medicago laciniata (L.) Mill.   Tattered Medick

Introduced. Formerly as a wool shoddy casual, but with no recent
records. **0** (5).

Medicago praecox DC.   Early Medick

Introduced. Past records as a wool shoddy casual, the last in
1960. **0** (0).

Medicago truncatula Gaertn.   Strong-spined Medick

Introduced. Recorded as a wool shoddy casual in the past, but
with no recent records. **0** (2).

Trifolium ornithopodioides L.   Bird's-foot Clover

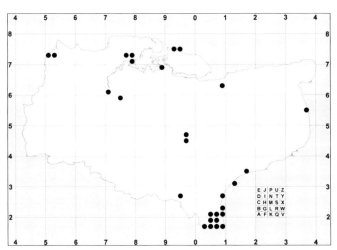

Native. On sand, gravel or compacted shingle, in areas with only
very little other short vegetation. **28** (22).

Trifolium repens L.   White Clover

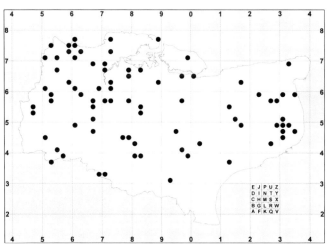

Native. In meadows, lawns, roadside verges, waste ground and
grassy places in general. **1006** (1030).

Trifolium hybridum L.   Alsike Clover

Introduced (neophyte). Formerly grown as a fodder crop and now
found on field borders, roadside verges and waste disturbed
ground. **80** (247).

Trifolium cernuum Brot.   Nodding Clover

Introduced. A casual wool shoddy alien, last recorded from West
Kent in 1960. **0** (0).

Trifolium glomeratum L.   Clustered Clover

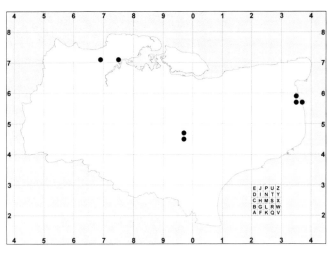

Native. A rare plant of dry sandy heaths and dunes, on compacted soil with little or no other vegetation. **7** (16).

Trifolium suffocatum L.   Suffocated Clover

Native. A scarce plant found on firm sand or sandy shingle on the coast. Inland on sandy heathland at Shorne TQ67V and Hothfield Common TQ94T. **23** (17).

Hop Trefoil   *Trifolium campestre* © D. Mills

Trifolium fragiferum L.   Strawberry Clover

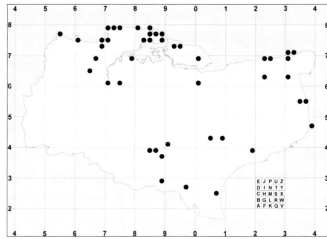

Native. In old meadows and coastal grazing marshes, practically always on clay soils. There appears to be a decline in the number of records through loss of habitat, either through 'improvement' or ploughing up of old pastures, or through housing developments. **45** (107).

Trifolium resupinatum L.   Reversed Clover

Introduced. Has been recorded in the past, either as a casual contaminant in crop seed or introduced with wool shoddy, but last seen in 1985. **0** (0).

Trifolium tomentosum L.   Woolly Clover

Introduced. A shoddy wool casual, last recorded in the county in 1960. **0** (0).

Trifolium aureum Pollich   Large Trefoil

Introduced. Noted as a casual in arable fields in the past, but not recorded during the present survey. **0** (2).

Trifolium campestre Schreb.   Hop Trefoil

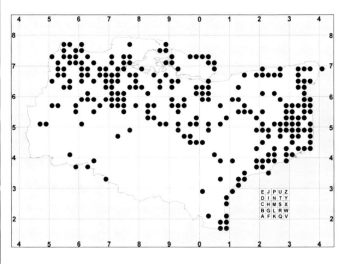

Native. On roadside verges, disturbed grassland and waste ground. **254** (397).

Trifolium dubium Sibth.   Lesser Trefoil

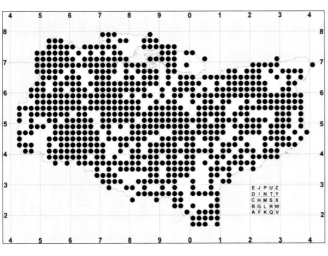

Native. In meadows, lawns, woodland rides, cultivated land and disturbed waste places. **738** (909).

Trifolium medium L.   Zigzag Clover

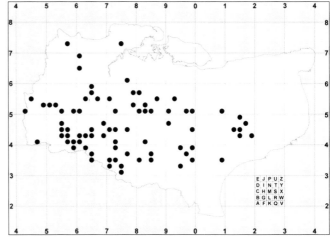

Native. Roadside banks and wood borders, particularly on heavier soils. There appears to be some decline, mainly due to modern roadside verge management. **80** (216).

Trifolium micranthum Viv.   Slender Trefoil

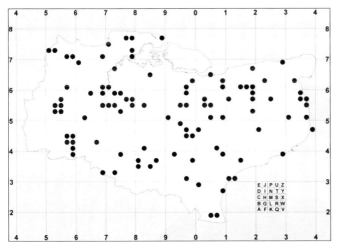

Native. On open sandy or gravelly short grassland, particularly on lawns, roadside verges and coastal banks. **102** (164).

Trifolium incarnatum L.   Crimson Clover

Introduced. Casual records in the past, but not seen during the present survey. **0** (4).

Trifolium pratense L.   Red Clover

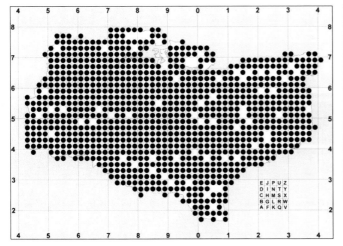

Native. Grassy places, waste and rough ground. Generally common. The var. *sativum* is occasionally found as a relic from cultivation. **938** (1019).

Trifolium striatum L.   Knotted Clover

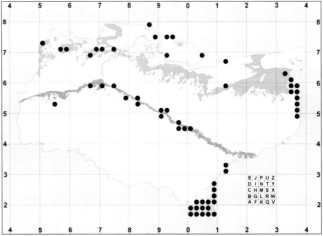

Native. In short grassland and open spaces on sandy soils, especially near the coast. **57** (73).

Trifolium scabrum L.   Rough Clover   *Trifolium squamosum* L.   Sea Clover

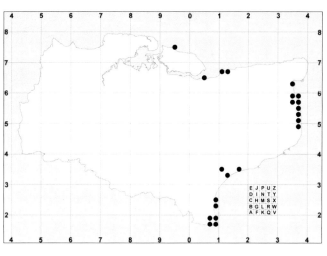 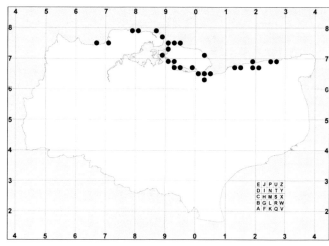

Native. In short grassland and open spaces on sandy, or firm   Native. On sea-walls and brackish grassland on the coast.
shingle soils on the coast. **22** (20).   **28** (30).

Trifolium hirtum All.   Rose Clover   *Trifolium alexandrinum* L.   Egyptian Clover

Introduced. A wool shoddy casual with past records from West   Introduced (neophyte). Well established in grassland by the
Kent (the last in 1979), but not seen during the present survey. sea-wall near Deal TR35S. **1** (0).
0 (2).

Trifolium arvense L.   Hare's-foot Clover   *Trifolium subterraneum* L.   Subterranean Clover

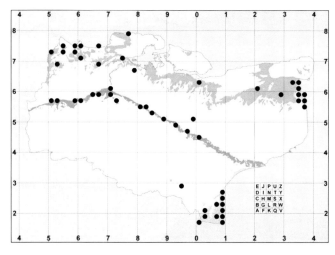 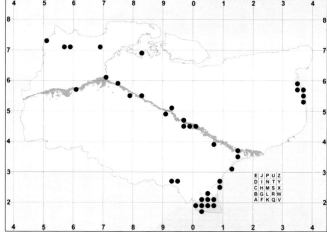

Native. On open or disturbed ground on sandy soils. **53** (108).   Native. In grassy areas on sandy or gravelly soils, particularly on
                                                                    the Folkestone Sands and near the coast. **38** (50).

Trifolium angustifolium L.   Narrow Clover

Introduced. Recorded as a wool shoddy casual in the past, but
not seen during the present survey. **0** (3).

Lupinus arboreus Sims   Tree Lupin

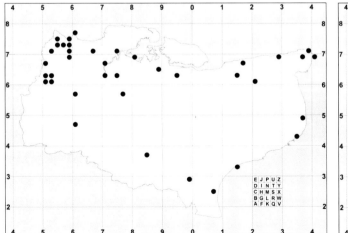

Introduced (neophyte). Sometimes planted to stabilise sand-dunes or introduced with seed sown on roadside verges. Now well naturalised and spreading by seed in these habitats. **14** (24).

Lupinus arboreus x polyphyllus   Russell Lupin
= L. x regalis Bergmans

Introduced (neophyte). Escapes from cultivation noted on roadside banks and waste ground at Crockenhill TQ56D, Hothfield TQ94T, Naccolt TR04M and Canterbury TR15J. **4** (1).

Lupinus polyphyllus Lindl.   Garden Lupin

Introduced (neophyte). Although recorded in the past, this garden plant was not noted growing wild during the present survey. **0** (21).

Laburnum anagyroides Medik.   Laburnum

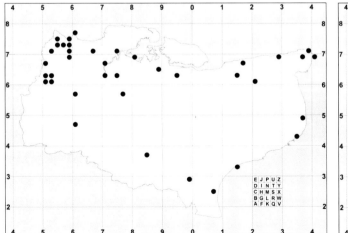

Introduced (neophyte). Commonly planted and now widely naturalised and reproducing itself by seed in old quarries, roadsides and waste places. **38** (99).

Cytisus nigricans L.   Black Broom

Introduced (neophyte). Now gone from its locality at Aylesford and not found elsewhere. **0** (1).

Cytisus striatus (Hill) Rothm.   Hairy-fruited Broom

Introduced (neophyte). Well established on sandy banks by a quarry at Addington TQ65P. **1** (0).

Cytisus scoparius (L.) Link   Broom

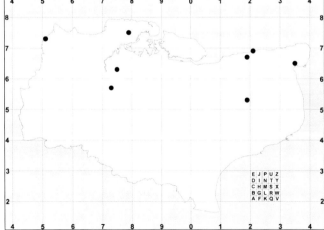

Native. On heathland, roadside banks, open woodland and rough ground, usually on sandy soils. **464** (569).

Spartium junceum L.   Spanish Broom

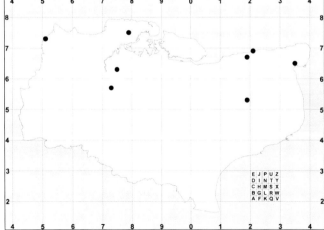

Introduced (neophyte). Occasionally planted on roadside banks, particularly along motorways, and now becoming established and reproducing by seed. **8** (9).

Genista monspessulana   Montpellier Broom
(L.) L.A.S. Johnson

Introduced (neophyte). Past records from West Kent, but not noted during the present survey. **0** (4).

Genista tinctoria L.   Dyer's Greenweed

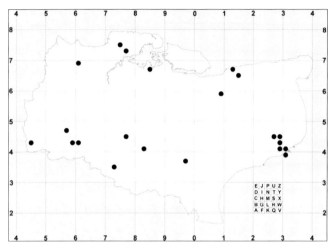

Native. Rough pastures, old meadows, open downland and grassy roadside banks. There is an apparent decline through loss of habitat. **21** (45).

Genista pilosa L.   Hairy Greenweed

Native, extinct. Was recorded from Wrotham Heath at some date before 1899 but has not been seen since. **0** (0).

Genista anglica L.   Petty Whin

Native. A rare plant of heathland. Now only found on Dartford Heath TQ57B & 57G, and at Gibbin's Brook TR13E, and is listed as 'Near Threatened'. **3** (4).

Genista hispanica L.   Spanish Gorse

Introduced (neophyte). A garden plant well naturalised in Darenth Wood TQ57R and on a roadside bank near Eyhorne Street. A former site at Maidstone was destroyed through road widening. **2** (2).

Genista aetnensis   Mount Etna Broom
(Raf. ex Biv.) DC.

Introduced. A past casual record from West Kent, but not seen during the present survey. **0** (0).

Ulex europaeus L.   Gorse

Native. On roadside banks, open scrub, shingle beaches, woodland rides and field borders on sandy or mildly acid soils. **420** (559).

Ulex gallii Planch.   Western Gorse

Native. A scarce plant in Kent and recorded from Causton Wood TQ83I, Hothfield Common TQ94S, Aldington Frith TR03N, Stelling Minnis TR14N, Clowes Wood TR16G and near Swingfield Minnis TR24H. **6** (3).

Ulex minor Roth   Dwarf Gorse

Native. On heathland and acid woodland, but becoming rather scarce in the county. **11** (22).

Arachis hypogaea L.   Peanut

Introduced. Casual plants recorded on a rubbish-tip in West Kent in the past. Apart from casual plants in my garden at Aylesford TQ75J from peanuts buried by Grey Squirrels there are no other records. **1** (1).

Ceratonia siliqua L.   Locust Tree

Introduced. Casual seedlings on an industrial dump at Greenhithe in 1979 did not persist. There are no other records. **0** (1).

Cercis siliquastrum L.   Judas Tree

Introduced (neophyte). A tree reported as naturalised at Hythe in 1973 could not be re-found. There are no other records. **0** (1).

Lablab purpureus (L.) Sweet   Lablab-bean

Introduced. Casual plants on a rubbish-tip in West Kent in the past, but there are no recent records. **0** (1).

Sesbania exaltata (Raf.) Cory   Colorado River-hemp

Introduced. Casual plants where oil-seed waste had been dumped in the 1970s, but no subsequent records. **0** (2).

ELAEAGNACEAE

Hippophae rhamnoides L.   Sea-buckthorn

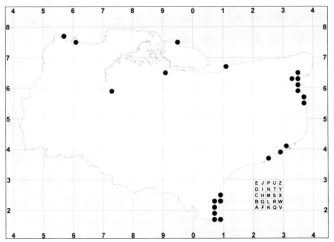

Native on fixed sand-dunes and waste places on the coast. Occasionally planted as an amenity shrub inland and at times can become established (neophyte) and reproduce itself on roadside verges or waste land. **23** (18).

Eleagnus umbellata Thunb.   Spreading Oleaster

Introduced. A few casual records of this garden escape from West Kent in the past but with no recent records. **0** (3).

HALORAGACEAE

Myriophyllum verticillatum L.   Whorled Water-milfoil

Native. Always a rather scarce plant in the county, this plant appears to have declined even further and is now only recorded from the Dartford Marshes TQ57I & 57N, and from the Worth Marshes TR35M. Noted as 'Vulnerable' in the Red List. **3** (9).

Myriophyllum aquaticum (Vell.) Verdc.   Parrot's-feather

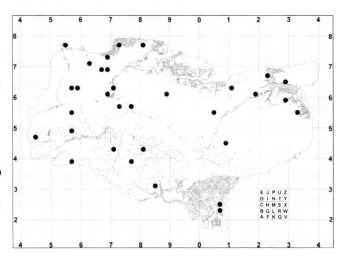

Introduced (neophyte). A native of South America, this plant is grown in water gardens and is still on sale at aquatic garden centres. It was first recorded growing wild in Kent on the Chistlet Marshes in 1989 and is now quite widespread in ponds and dykes in scattered localities throughout the county. It reproduces quickly and can soon smother out any other native vegetation and so should not be planted out in the wild. **32** (0).

Myriophyllum spicatum L.   Spiked Water-milfoil

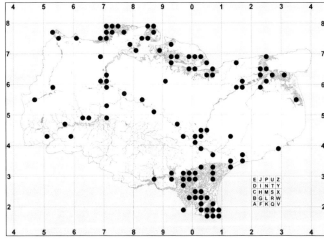

Native. In rivers, ponds, marsh dykes and flooded quarries. **108** (142).

Myriophyllum alterniflorum DC.   Alternate Water-milfoil

Native. Very few previous records for the county and not found during the present survey. **0** (2).

LYTHRACEAE

Lythrum salicaria L. — Purple-loosestrife

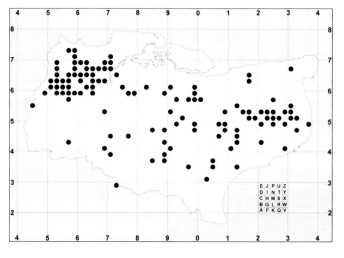

Native. By rivers, streams, ponds, ditches, flooded gravel-pits and in marshes. **195** (252).

Lythrum junceum Banks & Sol. — False Grass-poly

Introduced. Casual plants from wool shoddy or bird seed recorded in the past, but not seen during the present survey. **0** (2).

Lythrum hyssopifolia L. — Grass-poly

Native, or perhaps a long established introduction (archaeophyte). Casual records in the past, but last recorded in 1913 and now considered extinct. **0** (0).

Lythrum portula (L.) D.A. Webb — Water-purslane

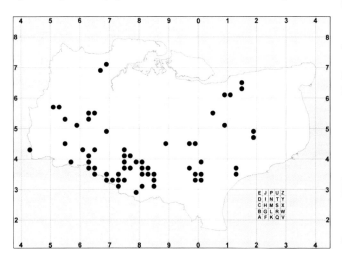

Native. In temporarily flooded areas such as rutted tracks and woodland rides, and occasionally in damp areas in disused sand-quarries. **63** (56).

THYMELAEACEAE

Daphne mezereum L. — Mezereon

A rare native plant although probably always introduced as a garden escape in Kent (neophyte). One plant persisted in the Yockletts Bank nature reserve during the early part of this survey (in the 1990s) but has now gone. **1** (1).

Daphne laureola L. — Spurge-laurel

Native. In deciduous woodland and scrub, often growing in deep shade. Although with a preference for the chalk, it is not confined by soil type. **119** (141).

MYRTACEAE

Eucalyptus gunnii Hook. f. — Cider Gum

Introduced (neophyte). Has been reported from West Kent but not seen during the present survey. **0** (0).

PUNICACEAE

Punica granatum L. — Pomegranate

Introduced (neophyte). Many seedlings were seen growing on fields near Dartford that had been spread with fertilizer (ex sewage waste) in 1980, but they did not persist. **0** (0).

ONAGRACEAE

The species of *Epilobium*, when growing close together, are very much prone to produce hybrids. These hybrids have not been specifically searched for but have been recorded when found, and in all cases both parents have been found nearby. It is almost certain that if searched for, these hybrids would be more widely recorded than as listed here.

Epilobium hirsutum x *palustre*
= *Epilobium* x *waterfallii* E.S. Marshall

Has been recorded from East Kent in the past but was not found during the present survey. **0** (0).

Epilobium hirsutum L.   Great Willowherb

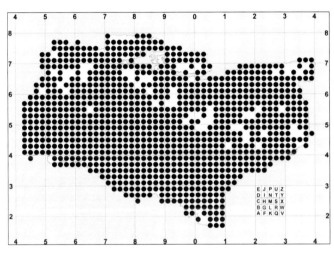

Native. A common plant of the edges of rivers, lakes and ponds, in ditches, marshes and other wet habitats. It also occurs on roadside banks, scrub and as a street weed, but is less frequent on chalky soils. **944** (909).

Epilobium parviflorum Schreb.   Hoary Willowherb

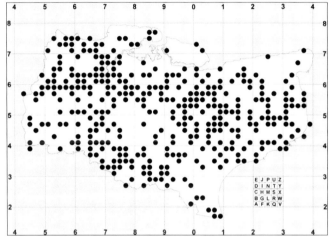

Native. In marshes, ditches and other wet places, and also in dry habitats such as quarries, dry waste ground and as a street weed. **366** (287).

Epilobium hirsutum x *parviflorum*
= *E.* x *subhirsutum* Gennari

Recorded on rough ground near Otford TQ55E. **1** (1).

Epilobium parviflorum x *montanum*
= *E.* x *limosum* Schur

Recorded from near Otford TQ55E and Vigo Village TQ66F. **2** (0).

Epilobium hirsutum x *montanum*
= *E.* x *erroneum* Hausskn.

Recorded from a woodland ride in Denge Wood TR15A. **1** (0).

Epilobium parviflorum x *tetragonum*
= *E.* x *palatinum* F.W. Schultz

Recorded from Beacon Woods TQ57V, Hook Green TQ63M, Yalding TQ64Z, Swanscombe Marshes TQ67C, Snodland TQ76B and Teynham TQ96L. **6** (0).

Epilobium hirsutum x *tetragonum*
= *E.* x *brevipilum* Hausskn.

Recorded from disturbed ground near Cooling TQ77M, and from field borders at Teynham TQ96L & 96S. **3** (0).

Epilobium parviflorum x *obscurum*
= *E.* x *dacicum* Borbás

Recorded from East and West Kent in the past but not found during the present survey. **0** (0).

Epilobium hirsutum x *ciliatum*
= *E.* x *novae-civitatis* Smejkal

Recorded from Joyden's Wood TQ57A. **1** (0).

Epilobium parviflorum x *roseum*
= *E.* x *persicinum* Rchb.

Has been recorded on a few occasions in the past but was not seen during the present survey. **0** (0).

Epilobium parviflorum x *ciliatum*
= *E.* x *floridulum* Smejkal

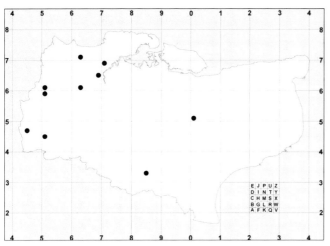

A frequent hybrid where both parents grow together.   **11** (1).

Epilobium montanum x *obscurum*
= *E.* x *aggregatum* Celak.

Has been recorded from East and West Kent in the past but was not found during the present survey.   **0** (0).

Epilobium montanum x *roseum*
= *E.* x *heterocaule* Borbás

Has been recorded from West Kent in the past but there are no recent sightings.   **0** (0).

Epilobium montanum x *ciliatum*
= *E.* x *interjectum* Smejkal

Recorded from Edenbridge TQ44N, Tunbridge Wells TQ53Z, Stone Street TQ55S, near Paddock Wood TQ64T, Vigo Village TQ66F, Holly Hill TQ66R, Great Chart TQ94Q and Rodmersham Green TQ96A.   **8** (1).

Epilobium montanum L.   Broad-leaved Willowherb

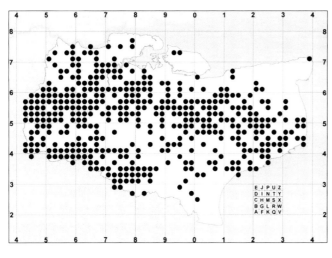

Native.   In woods, hedgerows, gardens and waste land.   **441** (518).

Epilobium lanceolatum   Spear-leaved Willowherb
Sebast. & Mauri

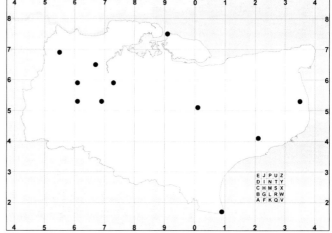

Native. Open woodland, roadside banks and gardens. Has always been a rather scarce plant in the county.   **11** (18).

Epilobium montanum x *lanceolatum*
= *E.* x *neogradense* Borbás

A 19th century record from West Kent but not found during the present survey.   **0** (0).

Epilobium lanceolatum x *obscurum*
= *E.* x *lamotteanum* Hausskn.

Has been rarely recorded from the county in the past but was not found during survey.   **0** (0).

Epilobium montanum x *tetragonum*
= *E.* x *haussknechtianum* Borbás

Has been recorded from West Kent but was not found during the present survey.   **0** (0).

Epilobium lanceolatum x *ciliatum*

Has been recorded from West Kent but was not found during the present survey.   **0** (0).

Epilobium tetragonum L.   Square-stalked Willowherb

Native. Open woodland, roadside banks, gardens, and cultivated and waste ground. **385** (210).

Epilobium tetragonum x roseum
= *E.* x *borbasianum* Hausskn.

Has been recorded from West Kent in the past but there are no recent records. **0** (0).

Epilobium tetragonum x ciliatum
= *E.* x *mentiens* Smejkal

Recorded from Polhill TQ56A, Vigo Village TQ66F and Teynham TQ96L. **3** (0).

Epilobium tetragonum x palustre
= *E.* x *laschianum* Hausskn.

Was recorded from near Dungeness in 1913, but there have been no subsequent sightings. **0** (0).

Epilobium obscurum Schreb.   Short-fruited Willowherb

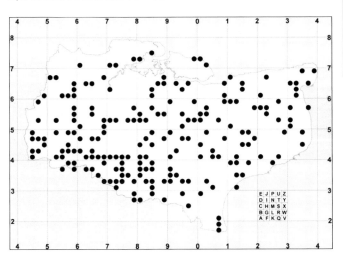

Native. In marshes and by wet ditches and stream-sides, and also on cultivated and waste ground. **206** (109).

Epilobium obscurum x roseum
= *E.* x *brachiatum* Celak.

Has been recorded from West Kent in the past, but there are no recent sightings. **0** (0).

Epilobium obscurum x ciliatum
= *E.* x *vicinum* Smejkal

Recorded in Denge Wood TR16A. **1** (0).

Epilobium obscurum x palustre
= *E.* x *schmidtianum* Rostk.

Recorded rarely in the past but there are no recent records. **0** (0).

Epilobium roseum Schreb.   Pale Willowherb

Native. Recorded only from Ryarsh TQ66Q, Denge Wood TR15A, and Worth Minnis TR35M. There appears to have been a dramatic decline in the occurrence of this plant in the county. **3** (54).

Epilobium ciliatum Raf.   American Willowherb

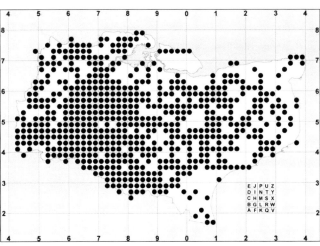

Introduced (neophyte). First recorded in the county in 1928, this is now the most frequent willowherb in Kent. It occurs in open woodland, gardens, field borders and other disturbed ground. It is also a frequent plant in built-up areas such as in pavement cracks and on walls. **635** (781).

Epilobium palustre L.   Marsh Willowherb

Native. In bogs, marshes and other wet acidic sites. Only recorded from Hothfield Common TQ94S & 94T, Hatch Park TR04Q and Gibbin's Brook. **4** (29).

159

Epilobium brunnescens
(Cockayne) Raven & Engelhorn   New Zealand Willowherb

Introduced (neophyte). A garden plant with the only recent record of it being as well naturalised in a churchyard at Thurnham TQ85D. **1** (4).

Chamerion angustifolium   Rosebay Willowherb
(L.) Holub

Native. Woodland rides and clearings, and on roadsides, railway banks and waste ground, particularly on burnt ground. **736** (852).

Ludwigia palustris x repens   False Hampshire-purslane
= **L. x kentiana** E.J. Clement

Introduced (neophyte). By a garden pond at Tonbridge 1989 and 1990, probably introduced with aquatic plants from a garden centre. Not seen during the present survey. **0** (0).

Oenothera glazioviana   Large-flowered Evening-primrose
P. Micheli

Introduced (neophyte). Roadsides, railway banks, disused quarries and neglected cultivated areas. **101** (110).

Oenothera glazioviana x biennis
= **O. x fallax** Renner

Introduced (neophyte). Recorded from roadside banks near Sissinghurst TQ73Y, Newington TQ86S, Egerton TQ94D, and West Hougham TR24Q. **4** (0).

Oenothera biennis L.   Common Evening-primrose

Introduced (neophyte). A scarce plant on disturbed soil on roadside banks, old quarries and neglected cultivated areas. It is much less frequent in recent years and now only recorded from Green Street Green TQ57V, Bewl Water TQ63W, Gravesend TQ67S, Aylesford TQ75J and Strood TQ76E. **5** (42).

Oenothera cambrica   Small-flowered Evening-primrose
Rostański

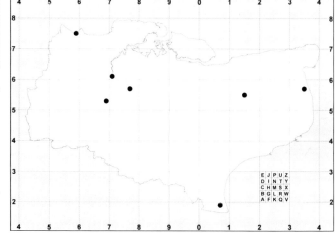

Introduced (neophyte). Roadside verges, sand-dunes and waste sandy areas. **7** (4).

Oenothera stricta   Fragrant Evening-primrose
Ledeb. ex Link

Introduced (neophyte). Long established on fixed sand-dunes at Littlestone TR02X and in the Sandwich Bay area TR35N, 35P, 35T & TR36K. **5** (3).

Oenothera perangusta R.R. Gates

Introduced. A casual plant in a quarry at Stone in 1974 is the sole record. **0** (1).

Clarkia unguiculata Lindl.   Clarkia

Introduced. A casual garden escape recorded in the past, but not seen during the present survey. **0** (1).

Clarkia amoena (Lehm.) A. Nelson & J.F. Macbr.   Godetia

Introduced. Recorded as a casual from tipped garden rubbish in the past, but not seen during the present survey. **0** (2).

Cornus sericea L.   Red-osier Dogwood

Introduced (neophyte). Much planted on roadside banks and parkland and will certainly be recorded more widely in the future. Considered naturalised at Eccles TQ76F, Borstal TQ76I and Denge Wood TR05W & TR15B. **4** (4).

Fuchsia magellanica Lam.   Fuchsia

Introduced (neophyte). Noted as garden escapes 1971-80, but with no recent records. **0** (2).

Cornus alba L.   White Dogwood

Introduced (neophyte). Another shrub now much planted on roadsides and in amenity plantings. The only plants noted as fully naturalised were in Denge Wood TR05W, but one would expect it to be more widely recorded in the future. **1** (0).

Circaea lutetiana L.   Enchanter's-nightshade

Cornus mas L.

Introduced (neophyte). Although recorded from West Kent in the past, all the specimens of this fine shrub seen during the present survey had obviously been planted. **0** (2).

Aucuba japonica Thunb.

Introduced (neophyte). Naturalised plants noted at Fordcombe TQ54F, Dartford Heath TQ57G and Maidstone TQ75T. **3** (1).

SANTALACEAE

Native. In woods, shady roadside and river banks, and as a weed in gardens and other cultivated areas. **468** (535).

Thesium humifusum DC.   Bastard-toadflax

Native, extinct. A plant of chalk grassland, last recorded in the county in 1963. **0** (0).

CORNACEAE

VISCACEAE

Cornus sanguinea L.   Dogwood

Viscum album L.   Mistletoe

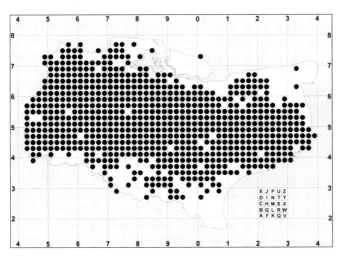

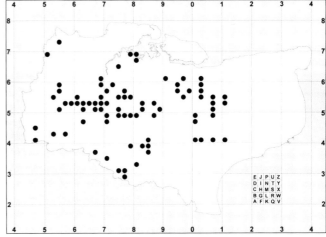

Native. In woods, scrub and hedgerows, being particularly common on the chalk. **725** (767).

Native. A hemiparasite on a wide range of trees in hedgerows, parkland, gardens and orchards. **81** (64).

CELASTRACEAE

AQUIFOLIACEAE

Euonymus europaeus L.   Spindle

Ilex aquifolium L.   Holly

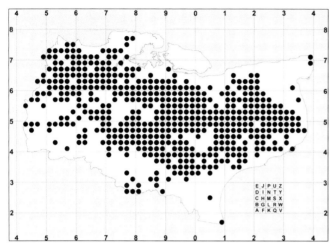

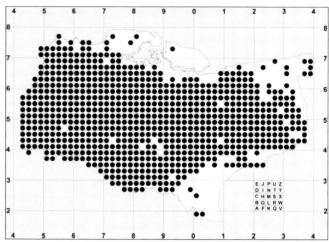

Native. In hedgerows, open woodland and scrub, particularly on chalky soils. **512** (586).

Native. In woods, hedgerows, parkland and scrub. **773** (779).

Ilex aquifolium x *perado*   **Highclere Holly**
= *I.* x *altaclerensis* (hort. ex Loudon) Dallim.

Introduced (neophyte). A plant of cultivation that has been recorded from West Kent in the past but not noted during the present mapping. **0** (0).

Euonymus latifolius (L.) Mill.   **Large-leaved Spindle**

Introduced (neophyte). A garden plant reported from West Kent in the past but not seen during the present mapping. **0** (0).

Euonymus japonicus Thunb.   **Evergreen Spindle**

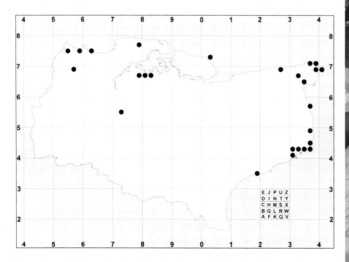

Introduced (neophyte). Much planted for hedging and now frequently naturalised or bird-sown, particularly in coastal areas. **26** (11).

Spindle *Euonymus europaeus* © L. Rooney

162

Ilex crenata Thunb.

Introduced. A casual garden escape noted in a hedgerow near Sevenoaks TQ55S. **1** (0).

BUXACEAE

Buxus sempervirens L.   Box

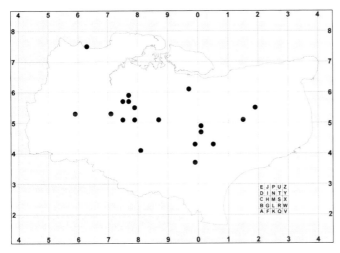

Perhaps native at Boxley (after which the village had been named, and certainly known there since at least 1695), and in a few other localities on the chalk. Elsewhere it occurs as a naturalised introduction (neophyte) in hedgerows, scrub and churchyards. **19** (20).

EUPHORBIACEAE

Mercurialis perennis L.   Dog's Mercury

Native. In woodlands and shaded hedgerows. Although widespread, it does not appear to colonize new ground such as in new plantations. **682** (734).

Mercurialis annua L.   Annual Mercury

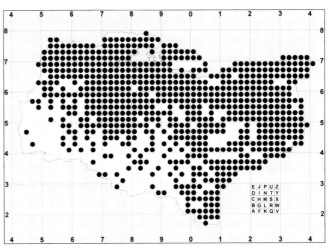

Listed as an archaeophyte, but possibly native, certainly in the Thanet area. In cultivated ground in gardens, allotments and field borders, and on disturbed soil on roadsides, rubbish-tips and waste ground. **718** (749).

Ricinus communis L.   Castor-oil-plant

Introduced. Casual records from rubbish and industrial dumps in the Stone-Greenhithe area 1973-79, but with no subsequent sightings. **0** (2).

Euphorbia platyphyllos L.   Broad-leaved Spurge

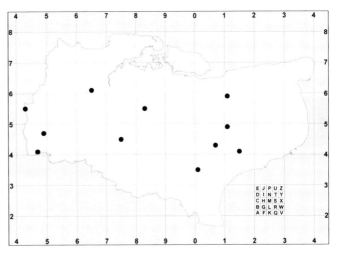

Introduced (archaeophyte). At the margins of arable fields and occasionally on roadside verges. Formerly a frequent cornfield weed. **11** (12).

Euphorbia serrulata Thuill.　　　　　　　　　Upright Spurge

Introduced (neophyte). In fair quantity on waste ground (former gravel pits that had been filled many years previously) at Yalding TQ64Z in 2000. **1** (0).

Euphorbia exigua L.　　　　　　　　　　　Dwarf Spurge

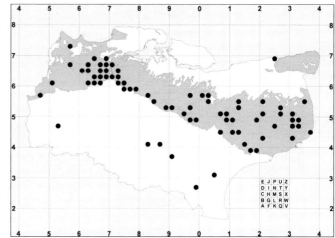

Introduced (archaeophyte). In arable fields, especially cornfields, particularly on the chalk. This plant continues to decline through the intensification of agriculture, especially through the use of herbicides. This decline is relevant to its Red List category of 'Near Threatened'. **74** (200).

Euphorbia helioscopia L.　　　　　　　　　Sun Spurge

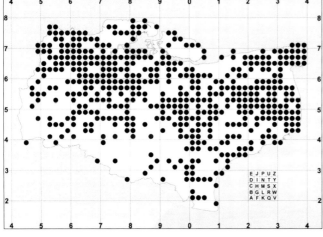

Introduced (archaeophyte), although it behaves as native. On disturbed soils in arable fields, gardens and waste ground. **506** (686).

Euphorbia peplus L.　　　　　　　　　　Petty Spurge

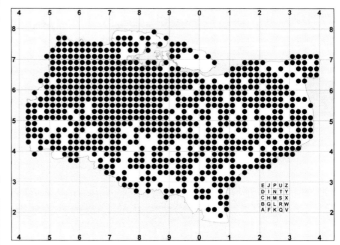

Introduced (archaeophyte). In gardens, allotments and other cultivated or disturbed soil. It also occurs as a street weed in built-up areas. **760** (770).

Euphorbia lathyris L.　　　　　　　　　Caper Spurge

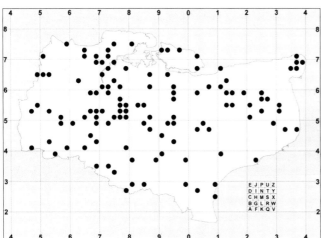

Introduced (archaeophyte). In woods, roadsides and disturbed soil in waste places. Although rarely cultivated nowadays, it appears to have become more frequent in recent years. **121** (57).

Euphorbia paralias L.　　　　　　　　　　Sea Spurge

Native. On sandy sea-shores and mobile dunes at Shellness, Sheppey TR06P, Sandwich-Pegwell Bay TR35T, 36K & 36L, and Greatstone TR02W. **5** (3).

Euphorbia esula x waldsteinii   Twiggy Spurge
= *E.* x *pseudovirgata* (Schur) Soó

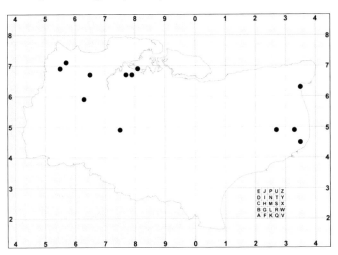

Introduced (neophyte). On roadside verges and waste grassy areas. Appears to have become less frequent in recent years, perhaps through building developments on former sites. **12** (31).

Euphorbia cyparissias L.   Cypress Spurge

Introduced (neophyte). However, it looks very native on the chalk at Darland Banks TQ76X, and near Dover at TR24V & TR34A. Also found as a garden escape well established on roadside verges at Lade TR02V and at Martin Mill TR34I. **5** (11).

Euphorbia amygdaloides L.   Wood Spurge

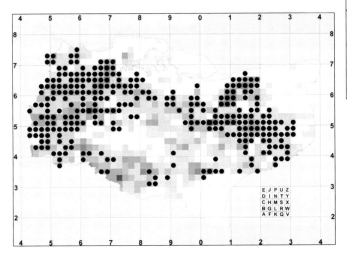

Native. In woods, particularly those that are regularly coppiced, and in shaded hedgerows. It also occurs on open chalk grassland and cliffs on the coast. **296** (360).

Euphorbia characias L.   Mediterranean Spurge

Introduced. Casual plants have been reported from West Kent in the past but it was not found during the present mapping. **0** (0).

Rhamnus cathartica L.   Buckthorn

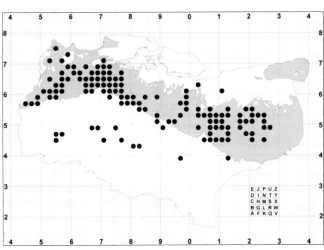

Native. In woods, scrub and hedgerows, particularly on the chalk. **133** (186).

Frangula alnus Mill.   Alder Buckthorn

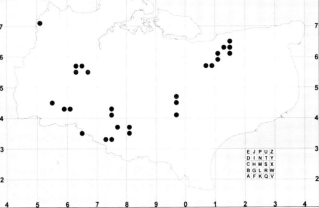

Native. In woods, heaths, scrub and hedgerows on damp peaty or sandy soils. **27** (81).

VITACEAE

Vitis vinifera L.   Grape-vine

Introduced. A casual plant of river-banks, rubbish-tips and waste ground. In the present mapping only noted on waste ground near Rochester TQ76E, but recorded more widely in the past. **1** (14).

Parthenocissus quinquefolia　　　　Virginia-creeper
(L.) Planch.

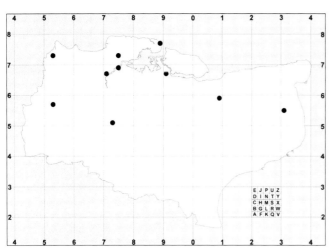

Introduced (neophyte). Occasionally established on old buildings and waste ground. **10** (3).

Linum bienne Mill.　　　　Pale Flax

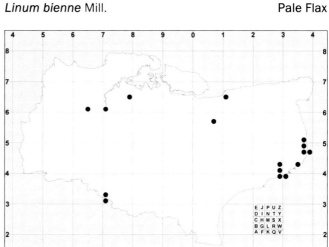

Native. In dry grassy places and open scrub, particularly near the coast. Appears to have become much scarcer in recent years. **16** (29).

Parthenocissus inserta　　　　False Virginia-creeper
(A. Kern.) Fritsch

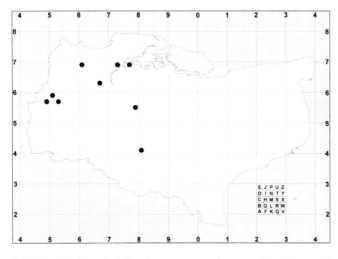

Introduced (neophyte). An escape from cultivation and occasionally naturalised on old buildings, scrub and waste land. **9** (14).

Linum usitatissimum L.　　　　Flax

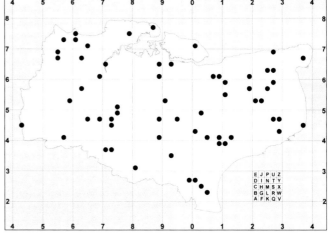

Introduced (neophyte). In recent years much planted for oil-seed production and now increasingly found as a casual plant on road verges and waste ground. **62** (25).

Parthenocissus tricuspidata　　　　Boston-ivy
(Siebold & Zucc.) Planch.

Introduced (neophyte). Growing over a demolished building at Sandwich Bay TR35T. **1** (0).

Linum perenne L.　　　　Perennial Flax

Ssp. *anglicum* (Mill.) Ockendon. Native, but now extinct. There are a few very old casual records from the past. **0** (0).
Ssp. *montanum* (Schleich. ex DC.) Ockendon.　　Introduced (neophyte). In open chalk scrub near Darenth Wood in 1976, but has not persisted. **0** (1).

Linum austriacum L.

Introduced (neophyte). A fine clump of this European flax turned up on a lay-by near Barham TR25A in 1982 and persisted for a few years, but now appears to have gone. **1** (0).

Linum catharticum L.   Fairy Flax

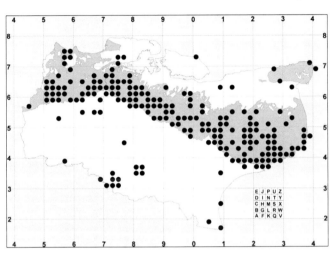

Native. A plant of open downland and grassy roadside banks on the chalk. It also occurs more sparingly on heaths, acid woodland rides and coastal dunes. **202** (302).

Linum narbonense L.

Introduced. Recorded as a casual garden weed at Womenswold in 1973, but there are no subsequent records. **0** (1).

Radiola linoides Roth   Allseed

Native. In damp woodland rides. Rather uncertain in its appearance as it will disappear from known sites when the surrounding trees produce too much shade. Very local and listed as 'Near Threatened'. **9** (6).

POLYGALACEAE

Polygala vulgaris L.   Common Milkwort

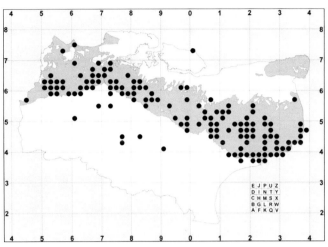

Native. In open grassland, particularly, but not exclusively, on the chalk. **140** (216).

Polygala vulgaris x calcarea

There is a past record from near Sevenoaks, but there are no recent sightings. **0** (0).

Polygala vulgaris x amarella

A past record, growing with both parents, from near Wye, but there are no subsequent records. **0** (0).

Polygala serpyllifolia Hosé   Heath Milkwort

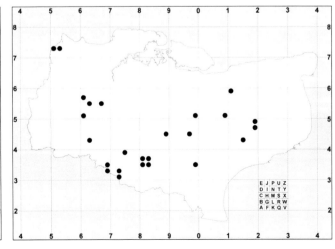

Native. On heaths and woodland rides on acid sandy or gravelly soils. **25** (75).

Polygala calcarea F.W. Schultz   Chalk Milkwort

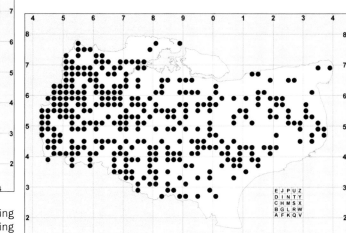

Native. In short grassland on the chalk, usually on south-facing slopes. Has been lost from some sites through either being ploughed or through scrub invasion. **21** (32).

Polygala amarella Crantz   Dwarf or Kentish Milkwort

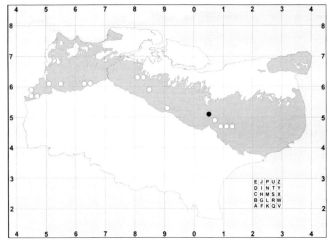

Native. On disturbed chalk downland. Although all the previous sites (marked with open circles) have been searched it was only found on downland at Godmersham TR05K. Seed can lay dormant for years and it is hoped that it will appear at other sites in the future. **1** (8).

STAPHYLEACEAE

Staphylea pinnata L.   Bladdernut

Introduced (neophyte). Naturalised in a copse near Otford TQ55J. **1** (1).

HIPPOCASTANACEAE

Aesculus hippocastanum L.   Horse-chestnut

Introduced (neophyte). This tree is frequently planted in parks and roadsides, and is now widely self-sown and naturalised. A small moth *Cameraria ohridella*, first found in the county in 2001 and which can completely defoliate the tree, could threaten the future status of this tree. **353** (433).

Dwarf or Kentish Milkwort *Polygala amarella* © A. Gay

Aesculus carnea J. Zeyh. Red Horse-chestnut

Introduced (neophyte). A few trees naturalised on Dartford Heath TQ75B. **1** (0).

ACERACEAE

Acer platanoides L. Norway Maple

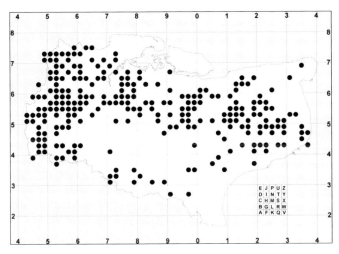

Introduced (neophyte). Planted in large gardens, parks, shelter-belts and along road sides. Now widely naturalised and spreading into woods, hedgerows and waste places. **255** (186).

Acer cappadocicum Gled. Cappadocian Maple

Introduced. Casual trees noted naturalised at Penshurst TQ54G and Maidstone TQ75T. **2** (0).

Acer campestre L. Field Maple

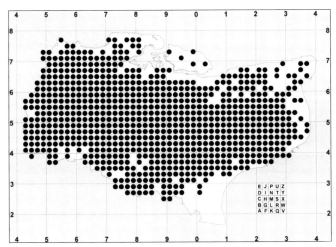

Native in woodland, scrub and old hedgerows. It is now often planted in amenity areas and roadsides and railway banks but these plants are mostly ssp. *leiocarpum* and not the native plant. **790** (816).

Acer pseudoplatanus L. Sycamore

Introduced (neophyte). Formerly widely planted in parks, large gardens and amenity areas. Now completely and widely naturalised, and setting seed freely, in a wide range of natural and man-made habitats in all but the most acid or water-logged soils. **887** (905).

Acer saccharinum L. Silver Maple

Introduced. Casual naturalised small trees noted in Bedgebury Forest TQ73G & 73L, Maidstone TQ75R and Littlebourne TR25D. **4** (1).

Acer negundo L. Ashleaf Maple

Introduced (neophyte). Frequently planted in town parks, streets and car parks. Hundreds of plants, from fresh self-sown seedlings to well-grown trees, noted as a street weed and on waste ground at Swanley TQ56E, all originating from such plantings. **1** (1).

ANACARDIACEAE

Rhus typhina L. Stag's-horn Sumach

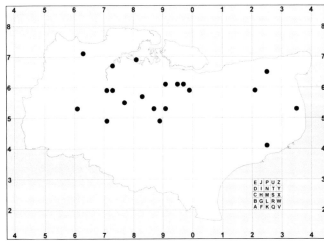

Introduced (neophyte). A garden escape or throw-out found on roadsides, railway banks and waste ground, now well naturalised and spreading in many places. **20** (17).

SIMAROUBACEAE

Ailanthus altissima (Mill.) Swingle   Tree-of-heaven

Introduced (neophyte). A large tree occasionally planted in streets and parks in urban areas. Only noted naturalised at Wrotham Heath TQ65J, Maidstone TQ75N and Little Mongeham TR35F. **3** (23).

RUTACEAE

Citrus spp.   Orange, Lemon, Grapefruit etc.

Introduced. Casual self-sown seedlings noted in the past, mainly on rubbish-tips, but none recorded during the present mapping. **0** (5).

Choisya ternata Kunth   Mexican Orange

Introduced (neophyte). Plants noted at Darenth Wood TQ57R and Maidstone TQ75T, both in areas of former cultivation. **2** (1).

Ruta graveolens L.   Rue

Introduced. A casual garden out-cast reported from Northfleet in the 1970s, but with no subsequent records. **0** (1).

OXALIDACEAE

Oxalis corniculata L.   Procumbent Yellow-sorrel

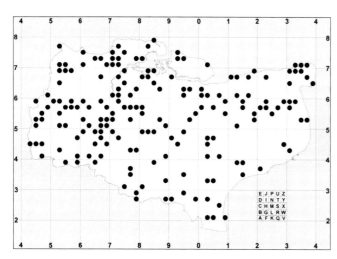

Introduced (neophyte). In gardens, churchyards, and as a street weed in towns and other built-up areas, growing in cracks between pavement stones or walls. **185** (78).

Oxalis exilis A. Cunn.   Least Yellow-sorrel

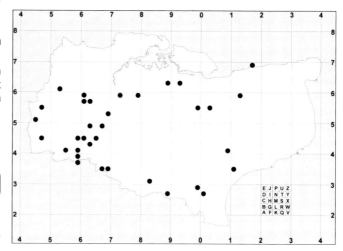

Introduced (neophyte). First recorded wild in Kent in 1975 and now with scattered plants in churchyards, old walls, gardens, and roadside verges and other rough grassland that is regularly mown. **34** (5).

Oxalis stricta L.   Upright Yellow-sorrel

Introduced (neophyte). On disturbed soil in gardens and waste places at Borough Green TQ65D, Chainhurst TQ74I, Teston TQ75B, Aylesford TQ75J and Maidstone TQ75S. **5** (12).

Oxalis articulata Savigny   Pink-sorrel

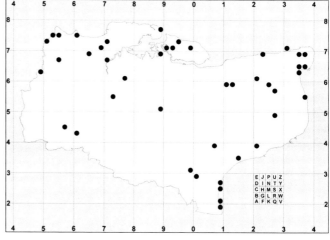

Introduced (neophyte). A garden plant now naturalised on road-sides, waste ground and sea-shores. **44** (62).

Oxalis acetosella L.   Wood-sorrel

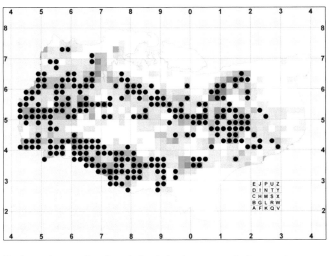

Native. In woodland and shady hedgerows. It does not appear to colonize disturbed or open ground. **269** (384).

Oxalis debilis Kunth   Large-flowered Pink-sorrel

Introduced. A casual garden escape noted in the Lydd-Greatstone area TR02L, 02R & 02W, and at Shepherdswell TR24U. **4** (0).

Oxalis latifolia Kunth   Garden Pink-sorrel

Introduced. A casual garden escape, recorded from West Kent in the past, but not seen during the present mapping. **0** (9).

Oxalis incarnata L.   Pale Pink-sorrel

Introduced. A casual garden escape and only noted on a road-side bank near Horsmonden TQ63Z. **1** (2).

GERANIACEAE

Geranium endressii J. Gay   French Crane's-bill

Introduced. A casual garden escape noted on roadside banks near Putt Wood TQ96U and at Ripple TR34P. **2** (6).

Geranium endressii x *versicolor*   Druce's Crane's-bill
= *G.* x *oxonianum* Yeo

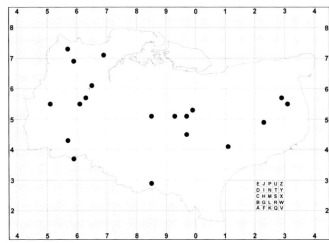

Introduced (neophyte). Much grown in gardens and increasingly found naturalised on roadside banks and waste ground. **19** (11).

Geranium versicolor L.   Pencilled Crane's-bill

Introduced (neophyte). A garden escape found naturalised on roadside banks at High Halden TQ93D, Smeeth TR03U, Hawkinge TR03E and near Ash TR25Y. **4** (6).

Geranium rotundifolium L.   Round-leaved Crane's-bill

Native. On roadside verges, waste ground and between pavement cracks as a street weed. **75** (45).

171

Geranium pratense L.   Meadow Crane's-bill

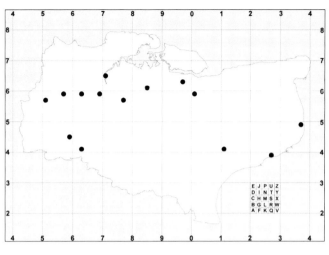

Native, although most present records are probably through introductions with grass-seed mixes. On roadside banks and occasionally in amenity grassland. **14** (39).

Geranium dissectum L.   Cut-leaved Crane's-bill

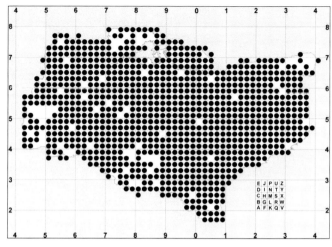

Introduced (archaeophyte). Long established and behaving as a native plant. On cultivated and disturbed ground. **932** (918).

Geranium sanguineum L.   Bloody Crane's-bill

Introduced (neophyte). A garden escape found established on rough sandy ground at Barming TQ75H, New Hythe TQ76A, Lydd-on-Sea TR01Z, Greatstone TR02W and Littlestone TR02X. **5** (12).

Geranium ibericum x **platypetalum**   Purple Crane's-bill
= **G.** x **magnificum** Hyl.

Introduced (neophyte). A garden plant found naturalised on waste ground at Chevening TQ45Y. **1** (4).

Geranium columbinum L.   Long-stalked Crane's-bill

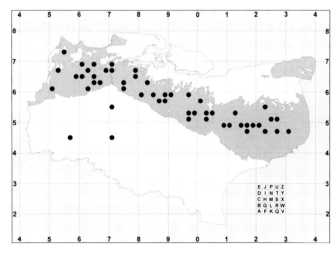

Native. Roadside banks, hedgerows and light scrub, usually on the chalk. **51** (88).

Geranium pyrenaicum Burm. f.   Hedgerow Crane's-bill

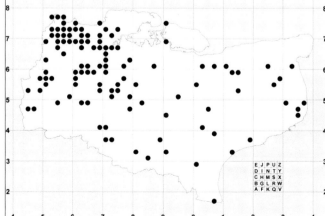

Introduced (neophyte). Roadsides, field margins, rough grassy areas and waste places, most often near human habitation. **113** (129).

Geranium pusillum L.　　　　　Small-flowered Crane's-bill

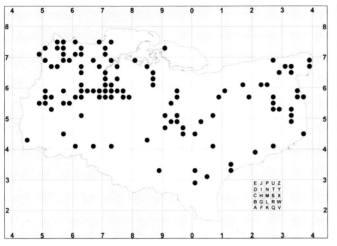

Native.　On cultivated land, roadside verges and waste places, particularly on light sandy soils. **115** (92).

Geranium lucidum L.　　　　　Shining Crane's-bill

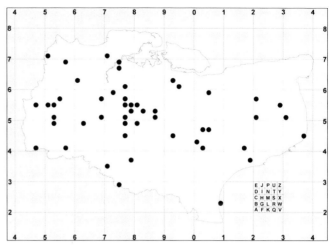

Native. Roadside banks, churchyards, old walls and occasionally as a garden weed. **50** (17).

Geranium molle L.　　　　　Dove's-foot Crane's-bill

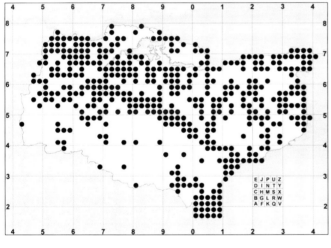

Native.　Roadside verges, dry grassland including lawns, sand-dunes, cultivated and waste ground.　Although still widespread, this plant appears to be less frequent than formerly. **452** (576).

Geranium robertianum L.　　　　　Herb-Robert

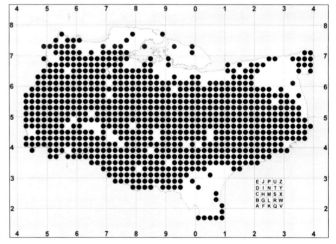

Native.　In woods, hedgerows, shaded banks and on old walls. The subspecies *maritimum* is found on shingle beaches between Dungeness and Deal. **779** (822).

Geranium macrorrhizum L.　　　　　Rock Crane's-bill

Introduced (neophyte).　On a waste sandy area at Sandwich Bay TR35T. **1** (0).

Geranium purpureum Vill.　　　　　Little-Robin

Native. After mapping had been finished and the final text for this Atlas just about completed, Sue Buckingham reported a possible plant in June 2007, which was confirmed the following day, on a railway bridge near Tonbridge TQ54T. This constitutes the first genuinely wild record of this plant for the county. **1** (0).

Geranium phaeum L.   Dusky Crane's-bill

Introduced (neophyte). A garden plant found naturalised on roadside banks at Otford TQ55J and Loose TQ75L. **2** (5).

Erodium lebelii Jord.   Sticky Stork's-bill

Native. Has been recorded from fixed sand-dunes in the Deal - Sandwich Bay area in the past, but could not be found during the present mapping. **0** (0).

Erodium maritimum (L.) L'Hér.   Sea Stork's-bill

Native. First recorded in Kent on sandy ground at Deal in 1777 and then at Sandgate some time before 1802. It was not seen again in the county until 1996 when it was found on sandy tracks on the RSPB reserve at Dungeness TR01U. It remains there and appears to have spread, but as yet has not reached out of that one tetrad. **1** (0).

Erodium botrys (Cav.) Bertol.   Mediterranean Stork's-bill

Introduced. Casual plants recorded in the past where wool shoddy had been used, but not seen during the present mapping. **0** (5).

Erodium moschatum (L.) L'Hér.   Musk Stork's-bill

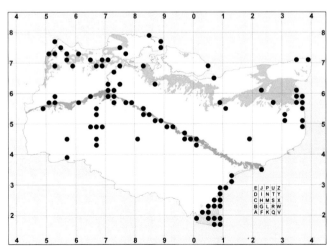

Introduced (archaeophyte). In arable fields and on waste land, perhaps as a relic from when wool shoddy was used. **9** (12).

Erodium brachycarpum (Godr.) Thell.   Hairy-pitted Stork's-bill

Introduced. Past casual records from where wool shoddy had been used, but not seen during the present mapping. **0** (2).

Erodium crinitum Carolin   Eastern Stork's-bill

Introduced. Previous records of casual plants from where wool shoddy had been used, but not seen during the present mapping. **0** (2).

Erodium manescavii Coss.   Garden Stork's-bill

Introduced. A casual garden escape, recorded from waste ground in West Kent in the past, but not seen during the present mapping. **0** (0).

Erodium cicutarium (L.) L'Hér.   Common Stork's-bill

Pelargonium x hybridum Aiton   Scarlet Geranium

Introduced. A casual garden outcast, recorded in the past, but not seen wild during the present mapping. **0** (2).

LIMNANTHACEAE

Limnanthes douglasii R. Br.   Meadow-foam

Native. On coastal fixed sand-dunes, and inland on heaths, arable fields, roadside verges and waste ground on sandy soils. **98** (119).

Introduced (neophyte). A garden escape found well naturalised on grassy banks at Newenden TQ82I and on a roadside near West Hougham. TR23U. **2** (0).

TROPAEOLACEAE

Tropaeolum majus L.   Nasturtium

Introduced (neophyte). A garden escape noted growing on waste land at New Hythe TQ76A and near Pluckley TQ94C.   **2** (13).

BALSAMINACEAE

Impatiens capensis Meerb.   Orange Balsam

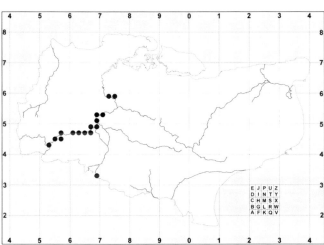

Introduced (neophyte). First recorded in Kent in 1864 and now well naturalised on river banks, marshes and ditches along the Medway Valley. The population now appears stabilised and there is no longer any aggressive spread. **16** (23).

Impatiens glandulifera Royle   Indian Balsam

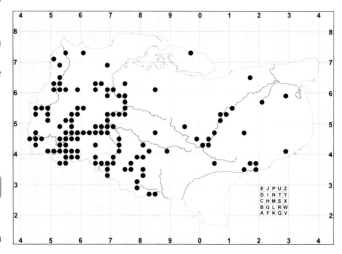

Introduced (neophyte). First recorded in the county in 1904 and now well established along the banks of the rivers Darent, Eden, Teise and Medway, and along parts of the River Great Stour. It is still grown as a garden plant and some records elsewhere might be the result of escapes from cultivation. **125** (141).

ARALIACEAE

Hedera colchica (K. Koch) K. Koch   Persian Ivy

Introduced (neophyte). Planted in gardens, particularly around hotels and large country houses, and now established in parts of the county, spreading vegetatively or by seed. Recorded from Farningham TQ56N, Plaxtol TQ65C, Basted TQ56D, Maidstone TQ75N, near Tenterden TQ93B, Faversham TR06F, St. Margaret's at Cliffe TR34L & 34S, and at Betteshanger TR35B.   **9** (3).

Impatiens parviflora DC.   Small Balsam

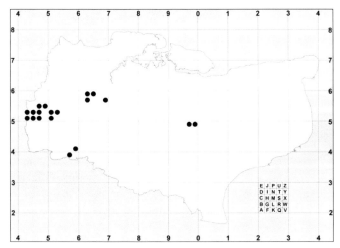

Introduced (neophyte). First recorded in the county in 1895 and now an established alien in woods, shady roadside verges and damp waste places, particularly in parts of West Kent. **19** (36).

Hedera helix L. ssp. *helix*   Common Ivy

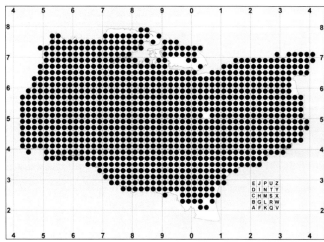

Native. In woods, scrub, hedgerows, and also about old buildings and walls. **981** (965).

Hedera hibernica (G. Kirch.) Bean   Atlantic Ivy

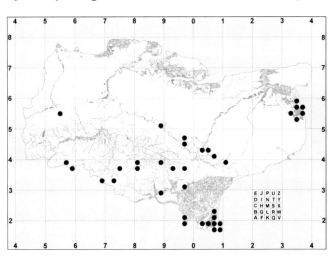

Introduced (neophyte). Established in built-up areas or around old buildings. Scattered records, but probably over-looked and under-recorded. **15** (2).

Hedera algeriensis Hibberd   Algerian Ivy

Introduced. Casual records in the past, but not found during the present mapping. **0** (0).

Aralia chinensis L.   Chinese Angelica-tree

Introduced. Casual records from West Kent in the past, but it was not seen during the present mapping. **0** (0).

APIACEAE

Hydrocotyle vulgaris L.   Marsh Pennywort

Native. In marshes, bogs and fens, and in damp areas amongst dune-slacks and stabilised shingle. **36** (58).

Hydrocotyle moschata G. Forst.   Hairy Pennywort

Introduced (neophyte). Was established on a lawn at Tunbridge Wells between 1960 and 1975, but there are no subsequent records. **0** (1).

Hydrocotyle ranunculoides L. f.   Floating Pennywort

Introduced (neophyte). First recorded in the county from Claygate TQ74C in 1977 where it had completely choked out a pond and the small surrounding field, and is still present there. It has since been found near Paddock Wood TQ64T and near Woodchurch TQ93M, in each case beginning to completely cover quite large water bodies. Unfortunately, it has also been observed in a few garden ponds where it is being tended and kept under control, but there is a fear that it could become more widespread in the countryside ponds and other waterways and completely smother our native flora. **3** (0).

Sanicula europaea L.   Sanicle

Native. In deciduous woodland, usually of Beech or Oak, on well drained soils. **171** (314).

Astrantia major L.   Astrantia

Introduced. A garden escape with a few casual records in the past, but not seen during the present survey. **0** (0).

Eryngium planum L.   Blue Eryngo

Introduced (neophyte). Still well established on fixed sand-dunes at Littlestone-on-Sea TR02X, where it has been known for over fifty years. A few casual plants also found on waste ground in a built-up area at Northfleet TQ67H. **2** (2).

Eryngium maritimum L.   Sea-holly

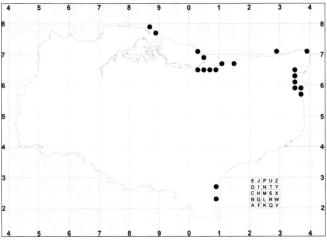

Native. On sand and shingle beaches. Appears to be doing well and is now more widespread and numerous than ever recorded before. **20** (12).

Eryngium campestre L.   Field Eryngo

Listed as introduced (archaeophyte), but possibly native in Kent, it being particularly common just over the Channel in the Pas-de-Calais area. Now only found on the chalk at Darenth TQ57R, Chatham TQ76S and near Bredhurst TQ86A, and with only a few plants in each locality. With few populations in southern England, this species is regarded nationally as 'Critically Endangered'. **3** (2).

Eryngium tripartitum Desf.

Introduced. A casual garden escape found on sandy ground at Sandwich Bay in 1971 but with no subsequent records. **0** (1).

Echinophora spinosa L.

A possible native plant, last recorded before 1746, and now extinct. **0** (0).

Chaerophyllum temulum L.   Rough Chervil

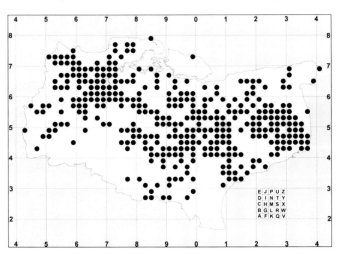

Native. Roadside verges, hedgerows and wood-borders. **367** (573).

Anthriscus sylvestris (L.) Hoffm.   Cow Parsley

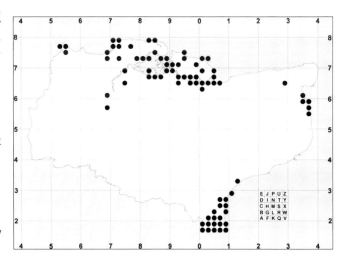

Native. Roadside verges and hedgerows; the modern 'management' of county lanes appears to favour this plant. It also occurs in woodland rides, railway banks and neglected pastures. **1000** (1010).

Anthriscus caucalis M. Bieb.   Bur Chervil

Native. On sea-walls, hedge banks and neglected grassy places in coastal areas, and occasionally inland on field borders and hedgerows. **79** (106).

Anthriscus cerefolium (L.) Hoffm.   Garden Chervil

Introduced. A casual escape from cultivation, last recorded in the county in 1949. **0** (0).

Scandix pecten-veneris L.   Shepherd's-needle

Introduced (archaeophyte). A long established weed of arable fields, particularly on chalky soils. Now only recorded, in the present survey, from near Longfield TQ56Z, Marden TQ74S and Dungenesss TR01U. Noted as 'Critically Endangered' in the Red List. **3** (7).

Osmorhiza chilensis Hook. & Arn.

Introduced. Past casual plants where wool shoddy had been used, last recorded in 1968. **0** (0).

Myrrhis odorata (L.) Scop.   Sweet Cicely

Introduced. A casual garden escape in the past, but not seen during the present mapping. **0** (0).

Coriandrum sativum L.   Coriander

Introduced. A casual plant found in arable fields and on waste ground. Noted at Hextable TQ57F, Darenth TQ57R, and Swanscombe TQ67C. **3** (22).

Smyrnium olusatrum L.   Alexanders

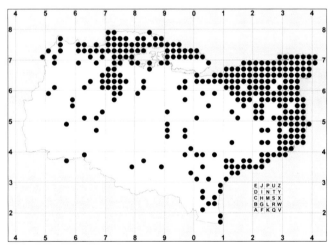

Introduced (archaeophyte). Formerly cultivated, but now long and well established. On roadside verges, hedge banks and waste ground; common on the coast and slowly spreading inland. Once established on a roadside verge, or other limited area, it will suppress the usually ubiquitous *Anthriscus sylvestris*. **322** (222).

Smyrnium perfoliatum L.   Perfoliate Alexanders

Introduced. A casual escape from cultivation, and noted on waste ground near Bearsted TQ85C. **1** (0).

Conopodium majus (Gouan) Loret   Pignut

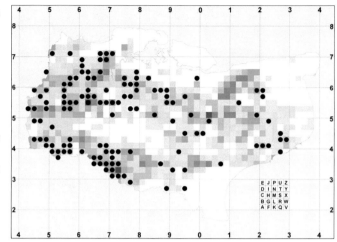

Native. In woods and occasionally in meadows, but does not like disturbed soils. **128** (235).

Pimpinella major (L.) Huds.   Greater Burnet-saxifrage

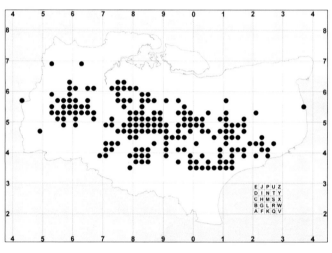

Native. On roadside banks, hedgerows and woodland edges. **189** (336).

Pimpinella saxifraga L.   Burnet-saxifrage

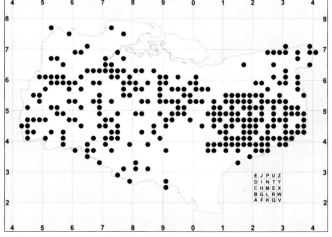

Native. In meadows, churchyards, roadside banks and dry grassy areas on chalk downland. **296** (487).

Aegopodium podagraria L.   Ground-elder

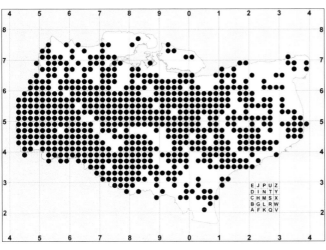

Introduced (archaeophyte). In gardens and in hedgerows, woodland or waste ground near human habitation. One of the most persistent, and difficult to eradicate, garden weeds. **663** (749).

Berula erecta (Huds.) Coville   Lesser Water-parsnip

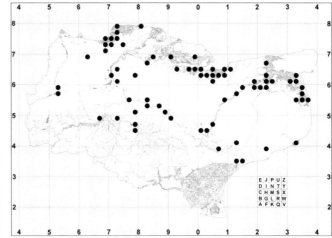

Native. At the edge of dykes, ponds and streams. Appears to have been lost from some former sites. **73** (99).

Crithmum maritimum L.   Rock Samphire

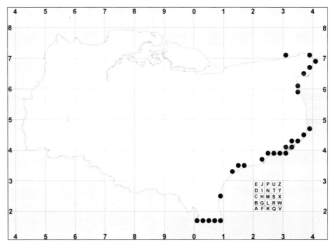

Native. On sea-cliffs, sea-walls and stabilised shingle on the coast. **27** (22).

Greater Water-parsnip *Sium latifolium* © D. Mills

Sium latifolium L.   Greater Water-parsnip

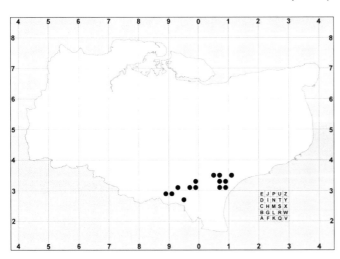

Native. In ditches and other wet habitats in the Romney Marsh area. In spite of some conservation measures this plant still appears to be in decline. In the Red List, categorised as 'Endangered'. **14** (25).

Oenanthe fistulosa L.   Tubular Water-dropwort

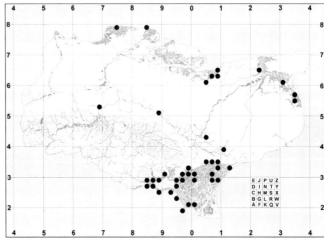

Native. In emergent and fringing vegetation in marsh dykes near the coast, and occasionally in similar habitats by ponds and rivers further inland. Listed as 'Vulnerable'. **42** (104).

179

Oenanthe silaifolia   Narrow-leaved Water-dropwort
M. Bieb.

Native. In damp meadows that usually flood in the winter months. Recorded from the Medway Valley near Tonbridge in TQ54M, 54N & 54T, and on a damp grazing marsh at Seasalter TR06X. Rare and decreasing, and listed as 'Near Threatened'. 4 (7).

Oenanthe pimpinelloides L.   Corky-fruited Water-dropwort

Native. On a grassy roadside at Halstead TQ46V, a chalky bank at Lullingstone Country Park TQ56H, a damp meadow at Cross-at-Hand TQ74Y, and a grassy bank at Swalecliffe TR16I. 4 (3).

Oenanthe fluviatilis   River Water-dropwort
(Bab.) Coleman

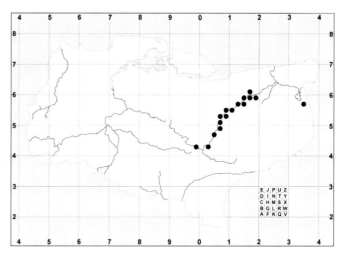

Native. In rivers and streams along the Stour Valley. 16 (21).

Oenanthe lachenalii   Parsley Water-dropwort
C.C. Gmel.

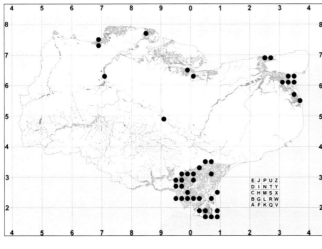

Native. In marshes, damp meadows and ditch-sides in both fresh and brackish water, particularly near the coast. 42 (71).

Oenanthe aquatica   Fine-leaved Water-dropwort
(L.) Poir.

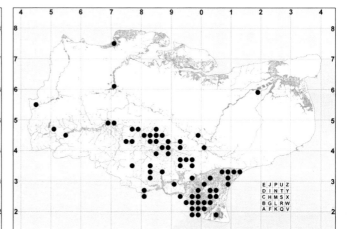

Native. In ponds, ditches and in other still or slow-moving water bodies, usually on clayey soils. 69 (128).

Oenanthe crocata L.   Hemlock Water-dropwort

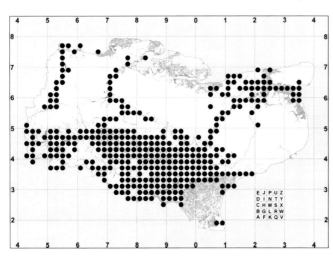

Native. On the banks of rivers, streams, lakes and ponds, and in shallow water in ditches, wet woodland and marshes. 362 (369).

Aethusa cynapium L.   Fool's Parsley

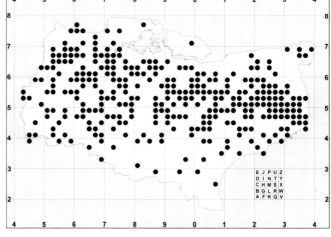

Native. In gardens, arable fields and other disturbed soils. 328 (564).

Foeniculum vulgare Mill.   Fennel

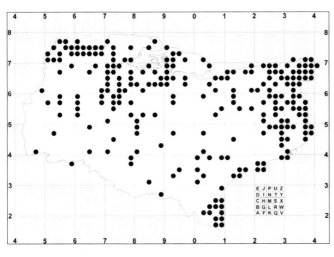

Introduced (archaeophyte). On roadsides and waste ground, particularly in coastal areas. **242** (222).

Anethum graveolens L.   Dill

Introduced. Casual plants on waste ground in the Dartford-Gravesend area during the 1970s, but there are no recent records. **0** (4).

Silaum silaus (L.) Schinz & Thell.   Pepper-saxifrage

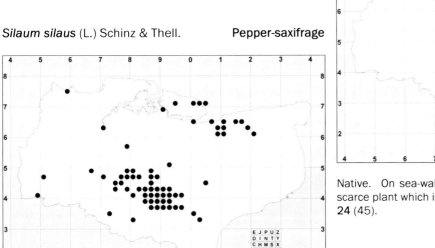

Native. In hay-meadows and species-rich pastures and roadside verges. Appears to have declined through loss of habitat and detrimental roadside management. **68** (165).

Conium maculatum L.   Hemlock

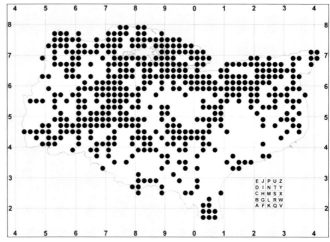

Probably native, although listed as an archaeophyte. On river banks, roadside verges, rough grassland and waste ground. Appears to have extended its range in recent years and has definitely occurred on sites from where it had not previously been recorded. **504** (377).

Bupleurum fruticosum L.   Shrubby Hare's-ear

Introduced (neophyte). Well naturalised on a railway bank at South Darenth TQ56U where it has been known since at least 1937. **1** (1).

Bupleurum tenuissimum L.   Slender Hare's-ear

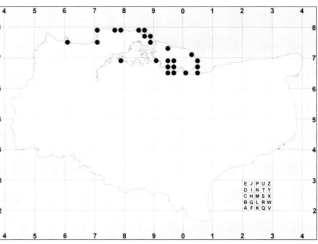

Native. On sea-walls and other grassy banks on the coast. A scarce plant which is noted in the Red List Category, 'Vulnerable'. **24** (45).

Bupleurum subovatum
Link ex Spreng.   False Thorow-wax

Introduced. A casual plant of gardens and waste ground, but not seen during the present mapping. **0** (4).

Bupleurum rotundifolium L.   Thorow-wax

Introduced (neophyte). Formerly a weed of cornfields and other cultivated land, mainly on the chalk. First recorded in 1629, and last recorded somewhere between 1883 and 1899. **0** (0).

Petroselinum crispum   Garden Parsley
(Mill.) Nyman ex A.W. Hill

Introduced. A casual escape from cultivation. Noted on disturbed waste ground at Bough Beech TQ44V and Dungeness TR01Z. **2** (20).

Apium graveolens L.   Wild Celery

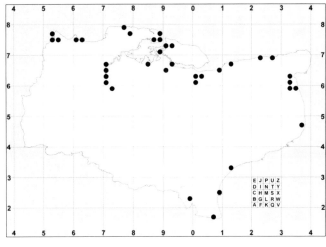

Native. By rivers, ditches and by sea-walls in coastal areas. There appears to have been a serious decline of this species in recent years. **37** (85).

Petroselinum segetum (L.) W.D.J. Koch   Corn Parsley

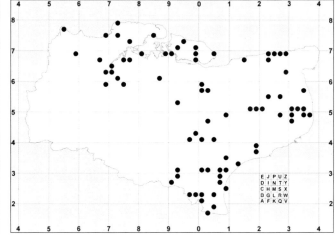

Native. On arable field margins, sea-walls and disturbed roadside verges. **78** (132).

Apium nodiflorum (L.) Lag.   Fool's Water-cress

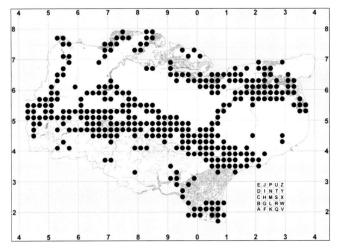

Native. In shallow water in ditches, swamps and marshes, and on the edges of streams, rivers, ponds and lakes. **354** (393).

Ridolfia segetum (Guss.) Moris   False Fennel

Introduced. A few casual plants in a cornfield at Crockham Hill TQ45F. **1** (0).

Sison amomum L.   Stone Parsley

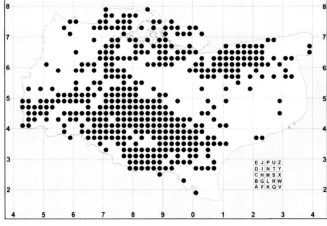

Apium inundatum (L.) Rchb. f.   Lesser Marshwort

Native. A rare and elusive plant, and now only found in a pond at Lenham TQ85V and a shallow pond at Hinxhill TR04L. **2** (3).

Trachyspermum ammi (L.) Sprague   Ajowan

Introduced. Recorded as casual on rubbish-tips 1972-77, but with no subsequent records. **0** (3).

Native. Roadside banks, hedgerows, scrubby grassland and disturbed waste ground. **440** (440).

Ammi majus L.   Bullwort

Introduced. Casual plants have been recorded in the past, but none were noted during the present mapping. **0** (3).

Ammi visnaga (L.) Lam.   Toothpick-plant

Introduced. Past records of casual plants from rubbish-tips and from wool shoddy, but not seen during the present survey. **0** (1).

Falcaria vulgaris Bernh.   Longleaf

Introduced (neophyte). On disturbed ground at Sharp's Green TQ85V, and the long-known plants persist on chalky ground at North Foreland TR37V. **2** (1).

Carum carvi L.   Caraway

Introduced (archaeophyte). Casual records in the past, but not recorded during the present mapping. **0** (3).

Angelica sylvestris L.   Wild Angelica

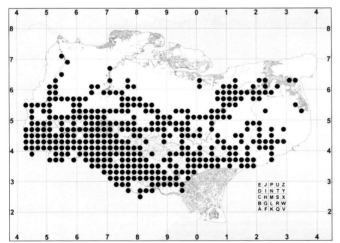

Native. In damp meadows and wet woods, and by ponds and streams. **394** (457).

Angelica archangelica L.   Garden Angelica

Introduced. Casual plants along the Thames shore-line in the past, but not seen during the present mapping. **0** (6).

Ferula communis L.   Giant Fennel

Introduced (neophyte). A fine plant on the banks of the M25 near Swanley TQ56J, originally found by R.M. Burton in 2006 outside the survey period, but included here as it is likely to spread along further roadside banks in the future. **1** (0).

Peucedanum officinale L.   Hog's Fennel

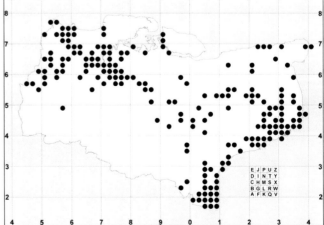

Native. In salt-marshes, on the banks of creeks and on sea-walls in the Whitstable area where it has been known since 1597. **7** (4).

Pastinaca sativa L.   Wild Parsnip

Native. Roadsides, railway banks and rough grassland, particularly on the chalk. Appears to have decreased in numbers and range in recent years. **195** (456).

Heracleum sphondylium L.   Hogweed

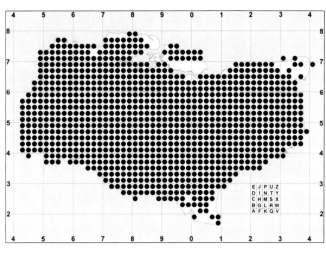

Native. On rough or disturbed grassland, particularly on roadsides woodland rides, river banks and neglected ground. **962** (994).

Heracleum sphondylium x *mantegazzianum*

This hybrid was found growing with both parents at Platt in 1972, but there are no subsequent records. **0** (1).

Heracleum mantegazzianum   Giant Hogweed
Sommier & Levier

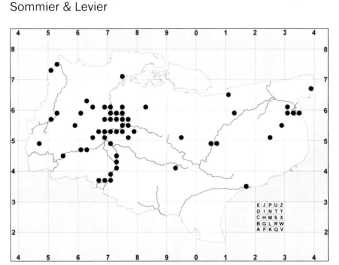

Introduced (neophyte). A garden plant now naturalised and spreading along river and stream banks, and occasionally along road verges. **58** (44).

Torilis japonica (Houtt.) DC.   Upright Hedge-parsley

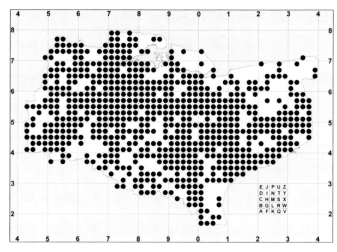

Native.   Roadside, hedge banks and rough grassy areas. **700** (807).

Torilis arvensis (Huds.) Link   Spreading Hedge-parsley

Introduced (archaeophyte). Formerly a widespread plant of cultivated and waste ground, but with no recent records and now probably extinct in the county. It is listed nationally as 'Endangered'. **0** (2)

Torilis nodosa (L.) Gaertn.   Knotted Hedge-parsley

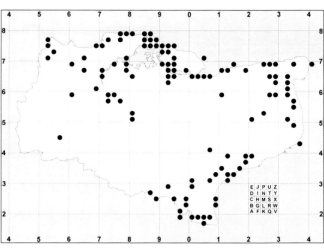

Native. On dry banks such as sea-walls, and on other grassy areas near the sea.   In recent years there has been slow spread inland, particularly on mown grass verges. **113** (99).

Caucalis platycarpos L.   Small Bur-parsley

Introduced (neophyte), but now long extinct. First recorded in 1680 and last seen in the county in the mid-19th century. **0** (0).

Daucus carota L. ssp. *carota*   Wild Carrot

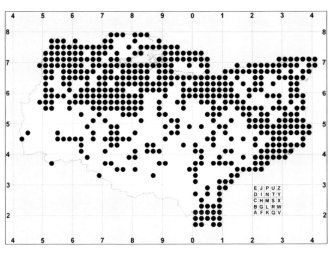

Native. On dry pastures, roadsides and rough grassland, particularly on chalky soils. **534** (620).

Daucus carota L. ssp. *gummifer*   Sea Carrot
(Syme) Hook. f.

Native. On chalk cliffs on the coast between Folkestone and Deal. Noted at TR23U, TR34A & TR34L. **3** (-).

GENTIANACEAE

Centaurium scilloides (L. f.) Samp.   Perennial Centaury

Introduced (neophyte). Well established on a lawn at Southborough in 1974, but not recorded since. **0** (1).

Centaurium erythraea Rafn   Common Centaury

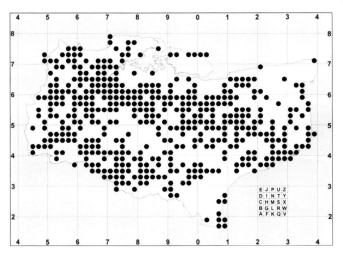

Native. Dry grassland, heathland, sand-dunes and woodland rides on well-drained soils. **464** (494).

Centaurium pulchellum (Sw.) Druce   Lesser Centaury

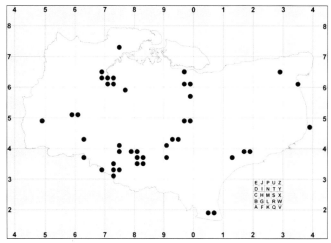

Native. In dry open grassland and heaths, in woodland rides, and on coastal sand-dunes. **44** (11).

Blackstonia perfoliata (L.) Huds.   Yellow-wort

Native. On grassland, roadside banks, cliffs and quarries on the chalk, on coastal sand-dunes and clay cliffs, and occasionally on well-drained roadside verges. **157** (186).

Gentianella germanica x amarella
= G. x *pamplinii* (Druce) E.F. Warb.

Native. There are specimens collected at Lyminge in 1885, and at Deal 1902, but it has not been found subsequently. (McVeigh, Carey & Rich, 2005). **0** (0).

Gentianella amarella (L.) Börner   Autumn Gentian

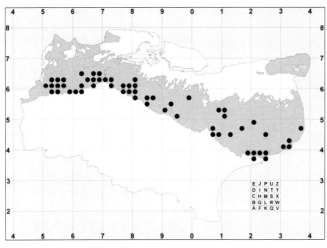

Native. On open downland, quarries and roadside banks on the chalk. **58** (97).

Autumn Gentian *Gentianella amarella* © A. Witts

Gentianella anglica   Early Gentian
(Pugsley) E.F. Warb.

Native. Recorded on chalk downland near Shoreham TQ56A, 56F & 56G, and Wrotham TQ66F. However, it is the writer's considered opinion that this is not a good species, but merely an early flowering form of the Autumn Gentian. The reasons for this are that it rarely ever appears in the same place in subsequent years, and it only occurs at known Autumn Gentian sites. At the Wrotham site mentioned above good *G. anglica* was found flowering in early May. Dr Tim Rich was informed of these plants as he was then involved in a national survey of this species, but he could not attend the site until mid-June. His verdict, after careful study, was that all the plants then in flower were hybrids between the two species. The author then returned later in the year and all the plants in flower were then good *G. amarella*. It appears that in some years a few seeds germinate earlier than normal. **4** (3) + **1** (0) hybrid.

Gentiana pneumonanthe L.   Marsh Gentian

Native, now extinct. Last recorded in the county in 1896. **0** (0).

Gentiana cruciata L.   Cross Gentian

Introduced (neophyte). Recorded naturalised near Snodland in 1911 (specimen in **MNE**), but there are no subsequent records. **0** (0).

APOCYNACEAE

Vinca minor L.   Lesser Periwinkle

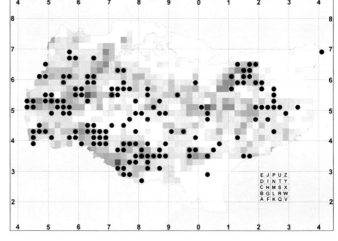

Introduced (archaeophyte). In deciduous woodland where it looks very native, and also in hedgerows and on roadside banks. **153** (150).

Vinca difformis Pourr.   Intermediate Periwinkle

Introduced (neophyte). Has been recorded from West Kent in the past, but was not seen during the present mapping. **0** (0).

Vinca major L.   Greater Periwinkle

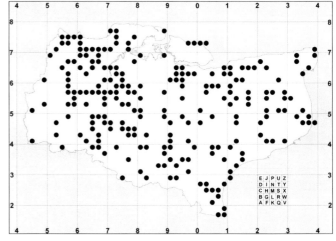

Introduced (neophyte). Roadside banks and woodland edges, either as an escape from gardens, or from dumped garden refuse. Widely dispersed throughout the county. **230** (206).

SOLANACEAE

Nicandra physalodes (L.) Gaertn. Apple-of-Peru

Introduced. A casual plant on cultivated and waste land. **14** (10).

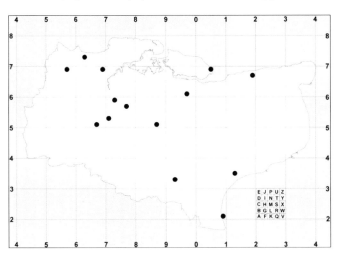
Deadly Nightshade *Atropa belladonna* © P. Gay

Lycium barbarum L. Duke of Argyll's Teaplant

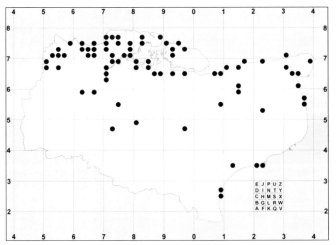

Introduced (neophyte). Well naturalised in hedgerows, on old walls and on waste ground, particularly near the coast. All plants checked when in flower have proved to be this species and no plants of *L. chinense* have as yet been found. **76** (97).

Atropa belladonna L. Deadly Nightshade

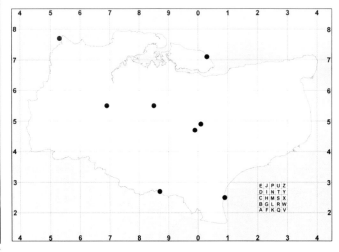

Native. At the edge of woods and in scrub on the chalk, and occasionally elsewhere on calcareous soils. **74** (81).

Hyoscyamus niger L. Henbane

Introduced (archaeophyte). Long established and looking native on chalky banks and coastal sandhills. It is usually found on disturbed soils such as are found about rabbit warrens, but appears to have decreased in recent years, probably through more efficient farming practice. Nationally, it is listed as 'Vulnerable'. **8** (28).

Salpichroa origanifolia (Lam.) Thell. Cock's-eggs

Introduced. A casual record from near Dover in the past, but there are no recent records. **0** (1).

Physalis ixocarpa Brot. ex Hornem. Tomatillo

Introduced. Casual plants with wool shoddy in the past and last recorded in 1960. **0** (0).

187

Physalis alkekengi L.   Japanese-lantern

Introduced (neophyte).   A garden escape with scattered records in the past, but only found on waste ground at Staple TR25T during the present mapping.   **1** (8).

Physalis peruviana L.   Cape-gooseberry

Introduced. Casual plants on disturbed waste ground at Dartford TQ57M and Gravesend TQ67M.   **2** (6)

Physalis acutifolia   Wright's Ground-cherry
(Miers) Sandwith

Introduced.   A casual wool shoddy alien, last recorded in 1979.   **0** (2).

Physalis philadelphica Lam.   Large-flowered Tomatillo

Introduced.   Casual plants in sewage sludge on Dartford marshes in 1978, but with no subsequent records.   **0** (1).

Capsicum annuum L.   Sweet Pepper

Introduced. Casual plants on a disused rubbish-tip at Wouldham TQ76C is the only record during the present survey.   **1** (4).

Lycopersicon esculentum Mill.   Tomato

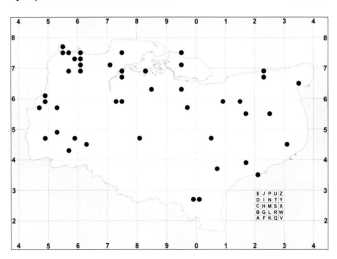

Introduced (neophyte). On cultivated land, disturbed waste ground, rubbish-tips and sewage waste.   **45** (44).

Solanum nigrum L. ssp. *nigrum*   Black Nightshade

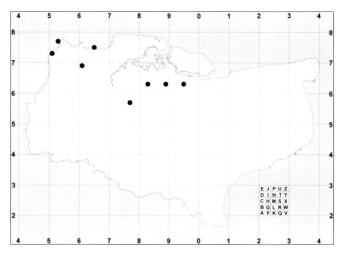

Native.   A weed of cultivated and disturbed waste land.   **641** (845).

Solanum nigrum L. **ssp. *schultesii*** (Opiz) Wessely

Introduced (neophyte).   On disturbed waste ground, rubbish-tips and occasionally along the shore-line.   **8** (6).

Solanum nigrum x *physalifolium*
= *S.* x *procurrens* A.C. Leslie

With both parents near Springhead TQ67B in 1984.   **0** (1).

Solanum villosum Mill. **ssp. *miniatum***
(Bernh. ex Willd.) Edmonds

Introduced. Recorded as a casual wool shoddy alien at Wateringbury in 1979, but with no subsequent records.   **0** (1).

Solanum chenopodioides Lam.   Tall Nightshade

Introduced (neophyte).   On disturbed soil at Sutton-at-Hone TQ56P in 2003 is the only record during the survey. **1** (0).

Solanum physalifolium Rusby   Green Nightshade

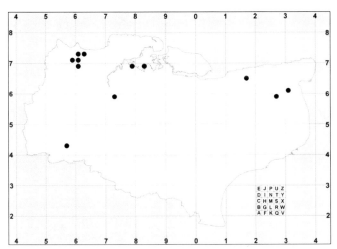

Introduced (neophyte). Casual plants on cultivated fields, waste land and refuse tips, although well established and regular in some fields in the north-west of the county. **12** (4).

Solanum pseudocapsicum L.   Winter-cherries

Introduced. Casual records from the Dartford marshes where sewage manure had been used in 1978, but with no subsequent records. **0** (2).

Solanum dulcamara L.   Bittersweet

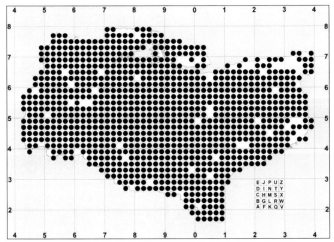

Native. Woodlands, scrub, hedgerows and marshy ground. The var. *marinum* occurs on shingle beaches on the coast. **948** (999).

Solanum tuberosum L.   Potato

Introduced. Casual plants, usually relics from cultivation, in arable fields and waste ground. **41** (91).

Solanum carolinense L.   Horse-nettle

Introduced. Casual plants where soya-waste had been dumped in the 1970s, but there are no recent records. **0** (2).

Solanum sisymbriifolium Lam.   Red Buffalo-bur

Introduced (neophyte). One specimen on a rubbish-tip in 1976 is the only record. **0** (1).

Solanum rostratum Dunal   Buffalo-bur

Introduced (neophyte). In arable fields and hop-gardens where wool shoddy had been used, and on waste ground where oil-seed waste had been tipped in the past. However, these activities have now ceased and there are no recent records. **0** (2).

Datura stramonium L.   Thorn-apple

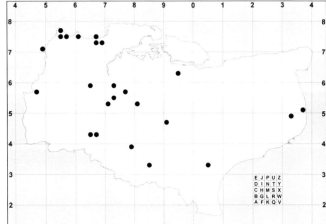

Introduced (neophyte). In arable fields, particularly where potatoes are grown, and also in gardens and on waste ground and refuse tips. **24** (57).

Datura ferox L.   Angels'-trumpets

Introduced. Casual records in the past where wool shoddy had been used, but not seen during the present mapping. **0** (1).

Nicotiana rustica L.   Wild Tobacco

Introduced (neophyte). A garden outcast last recorded growing wild in 1953. **0** (0).

Nicotiana alata Link & Otto   Sweet Tobacco

Introduced. Casual records in the past, but not seen during the present mapping. **0** (8).

Nicotiana alata x *forgetiana*
= *N.* x *sanderae* W. Watson

Introduced. Casual plants as garden escapes noted at Dartford TQ57M, Stone TQ57S, Maidstone TQ75T, Murston TQ86H, Old Wives Lees TR05S, Bekesbourne TR25C and Sutton TR34J. **7** (2).

Petunia axillaris x *integrifolia*   Petunia
= *P.* x *hybrida* (Hook.) Vilm.

Introduced. A casual escape from cultivation noted on roadside verges and waste land at Beltring TQ64T, Gravesend TQ67M, Leeds TQ85B and Greatstone-on-Sea TR02W. **4** (5).

CONVOLVULACEAE

Convolvulus arvensis L.   Field Bindweed

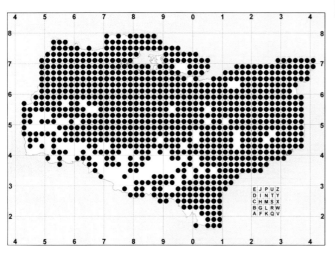

Native. In cultivated fields, gardens, hedgerows, sand-dunes and waste ground. Less frequent on the more acid soils. **876** (992).

Calystegia soldanella (L.) R. Br.   Sea Bindweed

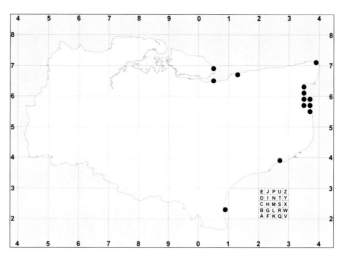

Native. On sand-dunes, and above the strand-line on sand and shingle beaches. **13** (8).

Calystegia sepium (L.) R. Br.   Hedge Bindweed

Native. Hedgerows, woodland edges and scrub and as a garden weed, but also found at the edges of ponds, rivers and in other marshy areas. **789** (915).

Calystegia sepium x *pulchra*
= *C.* x *scanica* Brummitt

Has been recorded from West Kent in the past, but was not found during the present mapping. **0** (0).

Calystegia sepium x silvatica
= C. x *lucana* (Ten.) G. Don

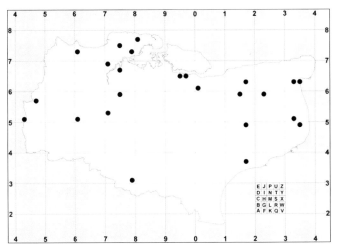

Scattered records in hedgerows, along fence lines, and on waste land. **24** (9).

Calystegia pulchra
Brummitt & Heywood   Hairy Bindweed

Introduced (neophyte). Only recorded from a hedge bank at Dover TR34A. **1** (21).

Calystegia pulchra x silvatica
= C. x *howittiorum* Brummitt

Has been recorded from the Kent Weald (Stace, 1975), but there are no recent sightings. **0** (0).

Calystegia silvatica (Kit.) Griseb.   Large Bindweed

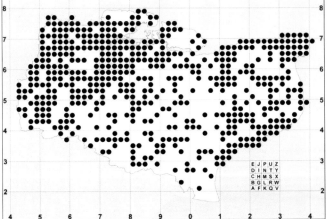

Introduced (neophyte). Hedgerows, fences, gardens and waste ground. **547** (477).

Ipomoea hederacea Jacq.   Ivy-leaved Morning-glory

Introduced. A casual garden escape found growing on disturbed ground near Borstal TQ76I. **1** (3).

Ipomoea lacunosa L.   White Morning-glory

Introduced. Casual plants noted in the 1970s where oil-seed waste had been tipped. **0** (3).

Ipomoea purpurea Roth   Common Morning-glory

Introduced. Casual plants on a recently disturbed roadside verge on the outskirts of Maidstone TQ75T in 2005. **1** (4).

Ipomoea cf. trichocarpa Elliott

Recorded from a rubbish-tip near Dartford where oil-seed waste had been dumped in 1975, but not subsequently. **0** (1).

CUSCUTACEAE

Cuscuta campestris Yunck.   Yellow Dodder

Introduced. Casual records from cultivated fields and gardens in the past, usually introduced with cultivated plants or seed, especially carrot. Last recorded in 1982. **0** (0).

Cuscuta europaea L.   Greater Dodder

Native, now extinct. A few records from the past, the last positive one being in 1864. **0** (0).

Cuscuta epilinum Weihe   Flax Dodder

Introduced. One casual record before 1899. **0** (0).

Cuscuta epithymum (L.) L.   Dodder

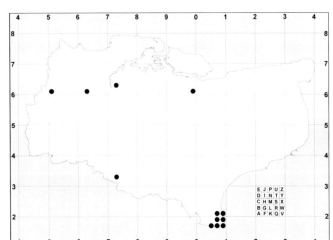

Native. A parasitic plant on a wide range of plants, particularly *Teucrium scorodonia* and *Ulex europaeus*. A scarce and declining species through loss of habitat, giving relevance to its national listing as 'Vulnerable'. **12** (22).

MENYANTHACEAE

Menyanthes trifoliata L.   Bogbean

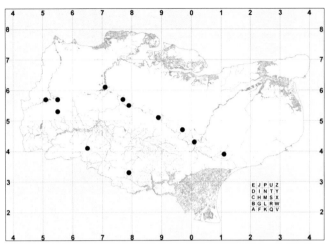

Native, although there is a chance that it could have been originally introduced at some localities. At the shallow edge of lakes, pools or slow-flowing rivers, and in bogs and swamps. **12** (8).

Nymphoides peltata Kuntze   Fringed Water-lily

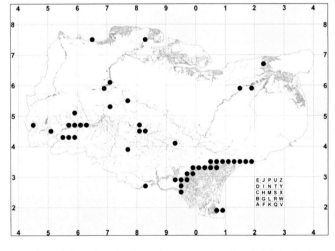

Introduced (neophyte). Long known and well established along the Royal Military Canal, and increasingly found on other water bodies, particularly lakes where it has been deliberately, or accidentally, introduced by man, or naturally dispersed by birds. **47** (17).

POLEMONIACEAE

Polemonium caeruleum L.   Jacob's-ladder

Introduced. A casual garden escape noted on disturbed soil near Hythe TR13M. **1** (1).

Polemonium foliosissimum (A. Gray) A. Gray

Introduced (neophyte). Persistent in an area of a former garden (not tended for at least fifty years) in Vinters Park L.N.R. Maidstone TQ75T. **1** (0).

Gilia tricolor Benth.   Bird's-eyes

Introduced. One casual plant on bare disturbed ground near Deal TR35L in 1995. **1** (0).

Phlox paniculata L.   Phlox

Introduced. Casual garden outcasts in the past, but not noted during the present mapping. **0** (5).

HYDROPHYLLACEAE

Phacelia tanacetifolia Benth.   Phacelia

Introduced (neophyte). Grown in gardens for ornament and in fields as source for nectar for beneficial insects. Occasional plants in arable field edges and on disturbed waste ground. **13** (1).

BORAGINACEAE

Lithospermum purpureocaeruleum L.   Purple Gromwell

Introduced. A few casual records from areas of chalk scrub in the past, the last from near Ospringe in 1959. **0** (0).

Lithospermum officinale L.   Common Gromwell

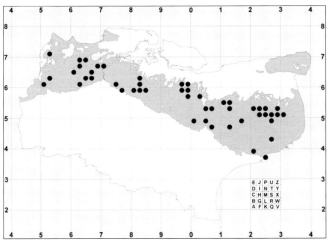

Native. On grassy banks and light scrub on chalky soils.
49 (53).

Echium vulgare L.   Viper's-bugloss

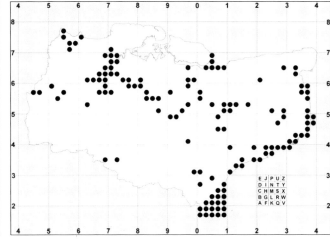

Native. On well drained soils such as shingle beaches, chalk cliffs
and sand-dunes on the coast, and grassy banks, roadside verges,
quarries and neglected ground on chalk or sand inland.
136 (178).

Viper's-bugloss *Echium vulgare* © S. Poyser

Echium plantagineum L.   Purple Viper's-bugloss

Introduced. Casual plants in arable fields at Longfield TQ66E and
Goudhurst TQ73J. **2** (4).

Lithospermum arvense L.   Field Gromwell

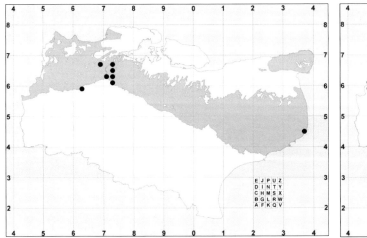

Introduced (archaeophyte). First recorded in the county in 1597,
and long known as a frequent cornfield weed. Like so many other
cornfield weeds, this plant has become very scarce in recent years
and is recorded in the Red List as 'Endangered'. **8** (12).

Pulmonaria officinalis L.   Lungwort

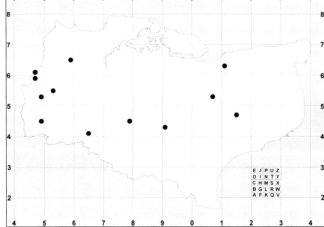

Introduced (neophyte). A garden plant now locally well naturalised
at woodland edges, hedgerows and roadside banks.   **12** (13).

Symphytum officinale L.   Common Comfrey

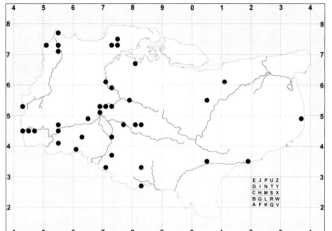

Native. On the banks of rivers, streams, roadside ditches, and other damp marshy areas. **38** (102).

Symphytum officinale x *asperum*   Russian Comfrey
= S. x *uplandicum* Nyman

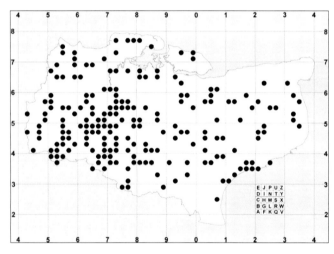

Introduced (neophyte). At the sides of arable fields, woodland edges, on roadside banks and waste ground. **203** (266).

Symphytum officinale x *asperum* x   Hidcote Comfrey
grandiflorum = S. 'Hidcote Blue'
hort. ex G. Thomas

Introduced (neophyte). A garden escape found established on roadside banks at Cowden TQ44K, Offham TQ65N, East Malling TQ65X, Leeds TQ85G and Smeeth TR03U. **5** (0).

Symphytum asperum Lepech.   Rough Comfrey

Introduced. Casual records in the past, but not seen during the present mapping. **0** (1).

Symphytum tuberosum L.   Tuberous Comfrey

Introduced. Casual plants at Tunbridge Wells TQ54Q and Eyhorne Street TQ85H. **2** (5).

Symphytum grandiflorum DC.   Creeping Comfrey

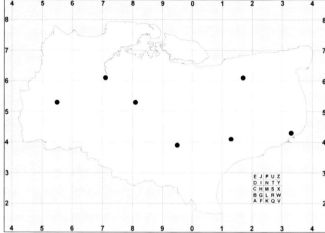

Introduced (neophyte). A ground-cover plant used in gardens, churchyards and parks and now found established on a few scattered roadside verges and banks. **7** (6).

Symphytum orientale L.   White Comfrey

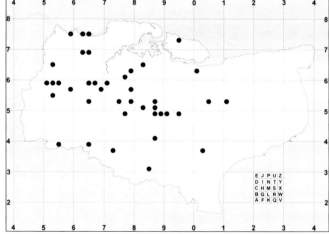

Introduced (neophyte). On roadside verges and banks, and on waste ground near buildings. Well established and persistent at some sites. **40** (35).

Symphytum caucasicum M. Bieb.   Caucasian Comfrey

Introduced (neophyte). A small colony on a roadside bank near Goathurst Common TQ55B, but not refound near Farningham Wood where it was recorded in 1977. **1** (1).

Brunnera macrophylla
(Adams) I.M. Johnst.

Great Forget-me-not

Introduced (neophyte). Established on roadside banks at Ulcombe TQ84P, Hogben's Hill TRO5I and Alkham TR24L. **3** (2).

Anchusa ochroleuca M. Bieb.

Yellow Alkanet

Introduced (neophyte). Once recorded from East Kent but there are no recent sightings. **0** (0).

Anchusa officinalis L.

Alkanet

Introduced (neophyte). A 19th century sighting in a cornfield near Gravesend (if correctly identified) is the only record. **0** (0).

Anchusa arvensis (L.) M. Bieb.

Bugloss

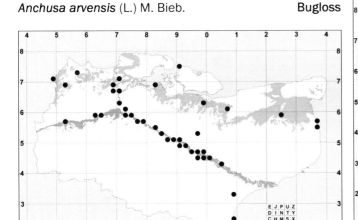

Introduced (archaeophyte). First recorded in 1629 and long regarded as a native plant. On well-drained soils in arable fields, heaths, dunes and disturbed waste ground, particularly in sandy areas. **41** (68).

Pentaglottis sempervirens
(L.) Tausch ex. L.H. Bailey

Green Alkanet

Introduced (neophyte). A garden plant now well established and spreading on roadside-banks, hedgerows, scrub and woodland edges, particularly near human habitation. **231** (145).

Borago officinalis L.

Borage

Introduced (neophyte). An occasional plant of roadsides, field edges and waste ground as an escape or relic from cultivation, or as a bird seed alien. **31** (18).

Cynoglottis barrelieri
(All.) Vural & Kit Tan

False Alkanet

Introduced (neophyte). A garden escape, discovered by T. Miller on a rubbish-tip in a chalk quarry at Folkestone in 1982, but not seen during the present mapping. **0** (0).

Trachystemon orientalis
(L.) G. Don

Abraham-Isaac-Jacob

Introduced (neophyte). An escape from cultivation, long and well established at Knockholt Pound TQ45U, Penshurst TQ54G, Allington TQ75P and in woods at Walderslade TQ76K & 76L. Surprisingly there are not more records for this very vigorous and invasive garden plant. **5** (5).

Amsinkia micrantha Suksd. **Common Fiddleneck**

Introduced (neophyte). On disturbed ground by footpaths at Teston TQ75B and Hythe TR13S. **2** (1).

Asperugo procumbens L. **Madwort**

Introduced (neophyte). Casual 19th century records, but none since. **0** (0).

Myosotis scorpioides L. **Water Forget-me-not**

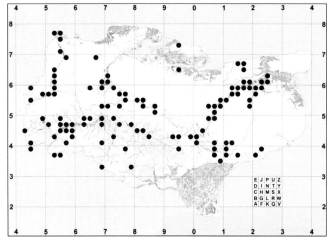

Native. At the edge of lakes, ponds, rivers and streams, and in other wet habitats. **112** (246).

Myosotis secunda Al. Murray **Creeping Forget-me-not**

Native. At the edge of ponds and streams, and in marshy flushes on acid peaty soils. Recorded only at Bough Beech TQ44Z, Bewl Water TQ63W, Roundshill Park Wood TQ83E and Hothfield Common TQ94S & 94T. **5** (9).

Myosotis laxa Lehm. **Tufted Forget-me-not**

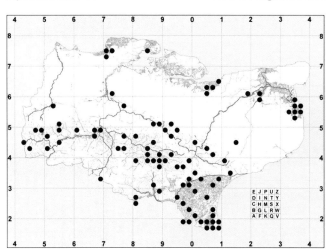

Native. At the edge of ponds and streams, and in other marshy places, particularly where there has been some soil disturbance. **93** (184).

Myosotis sylvatica Ehrh. ex Hoffm. **Wood Forget-me-not**

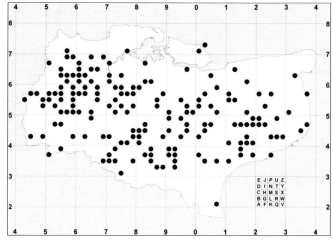

Native, although some records must refer to garden escapes. In woodland, and also on roadside verges and disturbed waste ground. **175** (220).

Myosotis arvensis (L.) Hill **Field Forget-me-not**

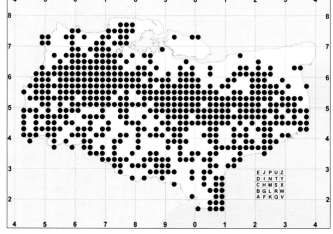

Introduced (archaeophyte). Long established on cultivated fields, woodland edges, open grassland, hedgerows and roadside verges. **579** (667).

Myosotis ramosissima Rochel **Early Forget-me-not**

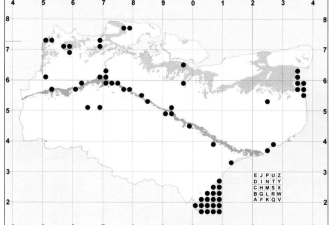

Native. On shallow well-drained soils, particularly in coastal dunes and on disturbed sandy areas inland. **62** (90).

Myosotis discolor Pers.   Changing Forget-me-not

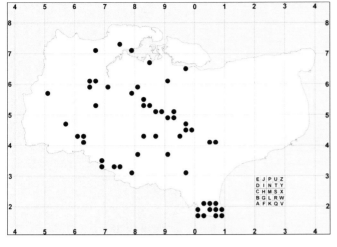

Native. In open grassland, cultivated fields and disturbed waste ground. **53** (57).

Lappula squarrosa (Retz.) Dumort   **Bur Forget-me-not**

Introduced. Casual plants introduced with grass-seed or bird seed, the last in 1979, and not seen during the present mapping. **0** (2).

Omphalodes verna Moench   **Blue-eyed-Mary**

Introduced (neophyte). Has been recorded from West Kent in the past but was not seen during the present survey. **0** (0).

Cynoglossum officinale L.   **Hound's-tongue**

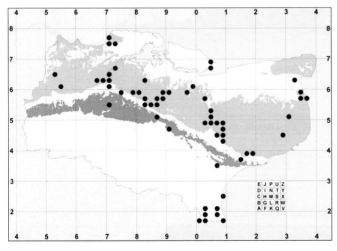

Native. On sand and gravel areas on the coast, and in rough-grassy and disturbed areas on the chalk, particularly near rabbit warrens. It is listed as 'Near Threatened' in the Red List. **59** (55).

Cynoglossum germanicum   **Green Hound's-tongue**
Jacq.

Native, now extinct as such.   However it still persists in one spot along the Pilgrims Way near Ryarsh TQ66K where seed was sown in 1958. **1** (0).

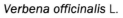

VERBENACEAE

Verbena officinalis L.   Vervain

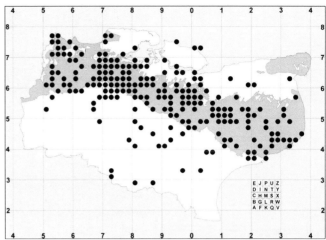

Introduced (archaeophyte). Completely naturalised on rough grassland, scrub and roadside verges on well drained soils, particularly on the chalk. **222** (222).

Verbena bonariensis L.   Argentinian Vervain

Introduced (neophyte). A frequent garden plant found well established on old ragstone walls at Otham TQ75W. **1** (0).

Verbena rigida Spreng.   Slender Vervain

Introduced. A casual garden escape, but with no recent records. **0** (1).

LAMIACEAE

Stachys officinalis (L.) Trevis.   Betony

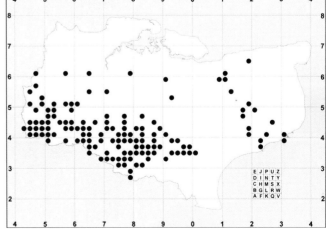

Native. Woodland rides and margins, heaths and roadside banks. **137** (268).

Stachys byzantina K. Koch   Lamb's-ear

Introduced (neophyte). A garden escape found well established on roadside banks and waste ground near Hook Green TQ63N, Tonbridge TQ64D, Yalding TQ64Z, Hunton TQ74E, Linton TQ75K, Greatstone-on-Sea TR02V and Whitstable TR15D. **7** (3).

Stachys germanica L.   Downy Woundwort

Native, but now extinct. Last recorded by Darenth Wood in 1857. **0** (0).

Stachys sylvatica L.   Hedge Woundwort

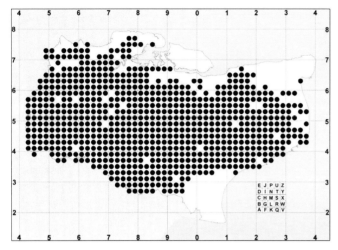

Native. In woods, hedgerows, banks of rivers and streams, and in rough grassland and waste places. **749** (824).

Stachys sylvatica x **palustris**   Hybrid Woundwort
= S. x **ambigua** Sm.

Found growing with both parents on roadside verges at Dundale Farm TQ63J and Covert Wood TR14Z. **2** (7).

Stachys palustris L.   Marsh Woundwort

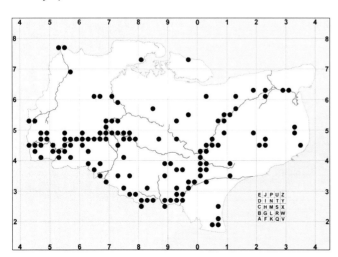

Native. By rivers, streams, ponds and other wet habitats, and occasionally in hedgerows and field-borders on well-drained soils. **130** (230).

Stachys arvensis (L.) L.   Field Woundwort

Introduced (archaeophyte). A long known weed of arable fields, first recorded in the county in 1632. Now becoming a scarce plant because of modern farming practices, and noted in the Red List Category, 'Near Threatened'. **23** (108).

Stachys annua (L.) L.   Annual Yellow-woundwort

Introduced. A casual plant of arable fields and waste ground, but with no recent confirmed records. **0** (0).

Ballota nigra L.   Black Horehound

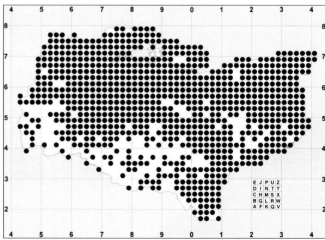

Introduced (archaeophyte), but behaving completely as a native plant. Roadsides, hedgerows, field-borders, gardens and waste ground. Scarce or absent from parts of the Weald. Our plant is subsp. *meridionalis* (Bég.) Bég. **836** (830).

Leonurus cardiaca L. Motherwort

Introduced (neophyte). Spontaneous in a garden at Slade TQ95H in 1996 is the only record during this survey. **1** (0).

Lamiastrum galeobdolon (L.) Ehrend. & Polatschek **ssp.** *montanum* (Pers.) Ehrend. & Polatschek Yellow Archangel

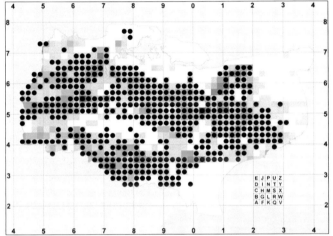

Native. In woods, hedgerows and shady roadside banks. **480** (487).

Lamiastrum galeobdolon (L.) Ehrend. & Polatschek **ssp.** *argentatum* (Smejkal) Stace Garden Yellow Archangel

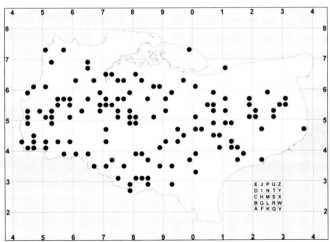

Introduced (neophyte). Much grown in gardens and often escaping, or tipped out with garden rubbish, and now well established and spreading in woodland edges, roadside verges and on waste land. **132** (0).

Lamium album L. White Dead-nettle

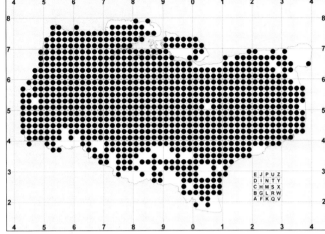

Introduced (archaeophyte). Long established in woodland edges, hedgerows, roadside verges and waste ground. **879** (906).

Lamium maculatum (L.) L. Spotted Dead-nettle

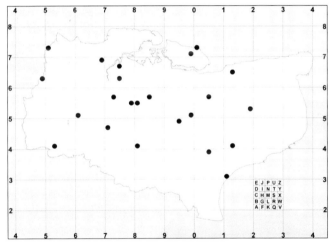

Introduced (neophyte). A plant of cultivation, and frequently found on roadside verges, woodland edges and waste ground, particularly where garden rubbish has been tipped. **23** (22).

Lamium purpureum L. Red Dead-nettle

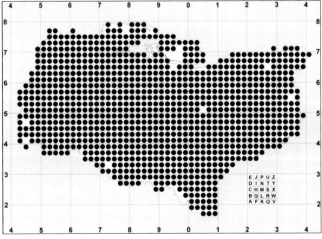

Introduced (archaeophyte). On cultivated and disturbed ground, and found in practically every type of habitat except dense woodland and very wet marshland. **987** (987).

Lamium hybridum Vill. Cut-leaved Dead-nettle

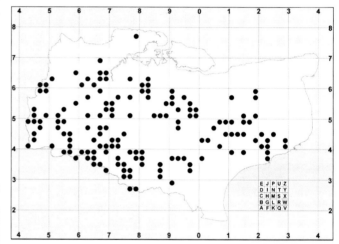

Introduced (archaeophyte). Formerly common on cultivated and disturbed soils, but its range has slowly declined over the past fifty years or so, and this decline continues at the present. **27** (38).

Lamium amplexicaule L. Henbit Dead-nettle

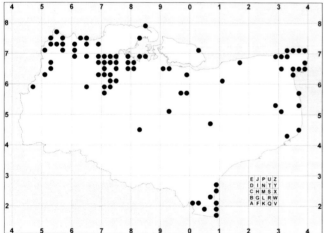

Introduced (archaeophyte). In open cultivated and waste ground, particularly in built-up areas. **87** (163).

Galeopsis segetum Neck. Downy Hemp-nettle

Introduced (archaeophyte). A scarce plant, last recorded in the county in 1836 and now considered extinct. **0** (0).

Galeopsis angustifolia Red Hemp-nettle
Ehrh. ex Hoffm.

Introduced (archaeophyte). Formerly a frequent plant of cornfields, shingle beaches and open downland. Now restricted to shingle beaches in the Dungeness area in TR01I, 01Y, 01Z and TR02V. Nationally listed as 'Critically Endangered'. **4** (17).

Galeopsis speciosa Mill. Large-flowered Hemp-nettle

Introduced (archaeophyte). Casual plants recorded during the 1971-80 survey at two sites, but not seen since. **0** (2).

Galeopsis tetrahit agg Common Hemp-nettles

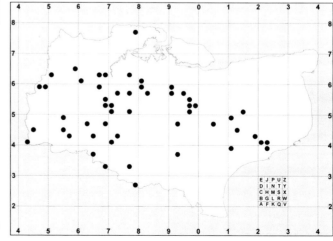

Galeopsis tetrahit and *G. bifida* have been much confused in the past and can only be reliably identified when in flower. All records for the two separate species have been carefully checked when the plants were in flower, but included here are all the records of these two species plus plants found at other times of the year that could not be positively identified. **150** (314).

Galeopsis tetrahit L. Common Hemp-nettle

Native. Woodland edges, hedgerows, edges of arable fields and drier parts of marshland. **52** (308).

Galeopsis bifida Boenn.   **Bifid Hemp-nettle**

Scutellaria galericulata L.   **Skullcap**

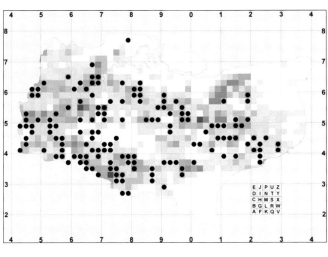
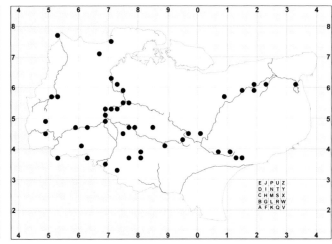

Native. In arable, waste and cultivated land, and occasionally along ditches and woodland edges. Careful recording has proved this species to be more frequent than was formerly suggested. **54** (19).

Native. At the edges of rivers, streams and ponds and in other damp habitats. **45** (81).

Phlomis fruticosa L.   **Jerusalem Sage**

Scutellaria galericulata x *minor*
= *S.* x *hybrida* Strail

Introduced (neophyte). A garden plant long established at Toy's Hill TQ45Q, and casual plants found at Woodnesborough TR35D. **2** (1).

Has been recorded in West Kent in the past, the last in 1954. **0** (0).

Melittis melissophyllum L.   **Bastard Balm**

Native. A rare plant of South-west England and last recorded in Kent in 1879. In the Red List Category, 'Vulnerable'. **0** (0).

Scutellaria minor Huds.   **Lesser Skullcap**

Marrubium vulgare L.   **White Horehound**

Introduced (neophyte). Recorded from the Cliffe Marshes TQ77E and from near Lydd TR01J. **2** (2).

Scutellaria altissima L.   **Somerset Skullcap**

Introduced (neophyte). Several plants on a roadside verge at Boughton Street TR05U in 2003. **1** (0).

Native. On damp woodland rides, usually on the more acid soils, and in bogs and marshes. **34** (31).

Teucrium scorodonia L.   Wood Sage

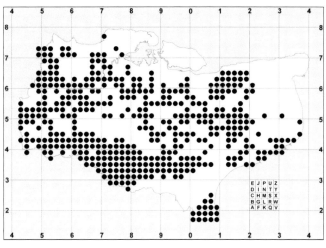

Native. On well-drained soils in woodlands, hedgerows, heaths and shingle beaches. **457** (485).

Teucrium chamaedrys L.   Wall Germander

Introduced (neophyte). Established on an old wall at East Malling TQ75D where it has been known since at least 1956. **1** (1).

Teucrium botrys L.   Cut-leaved Germander

Native. A rare plant of bare ground in open chalk grassland. A few plants still exist in a chalk quarry at Upper Halling TQ66X where it has been known since 1894. However it is now in imminent danger of becoming extinct because the area is being allowed to tree- and scrub-up. **1** (1).

Ajuga reptans L.   Bugle

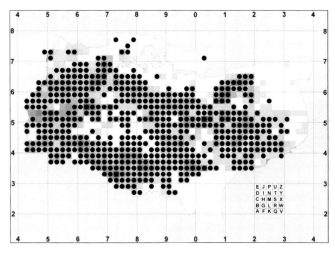

Native. In damp deciduous woods and woodland rides, and occasionally in shaded areas in unimproved grassland. **545** (637).

Ajuga chamaepitys (L.) Schreb.   Ground-pine

Native. In arable fields on the chalk, and on chalk downland where the soil has been disturbed by rabbits or scrub clearance. Has been specifically looked for in most of its former sites and not always re-found. In the Red List Category, 'Endangered'. **11** (13).

Ground-pine *Ajuga chamaepitys* © J. Shorter

Nepeta cataria L.   Cat-mint

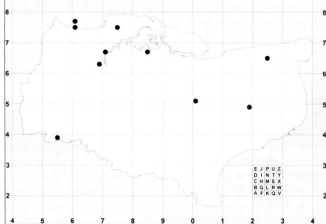

Introduced (archaeophyte). Hedgerows, roadside banks and rough ground, usually on the chalk. In the Red List Category, 'Vulnerable'. **10** (19).

Nepeta x *faassenii*   Garden Cat-mint
Bergmans ex Stearn

Introduced. Casual plants have been recorded in the past, but no wild-growing plants were noted during the present mapping. **0** (3).

Prunella laciniata (L.) L.   Cut-leaved Selfheal

Introduced (neophyte). On chalk downland at Trosley TQ66K where it has been long known, and on a chalky bank at Detling TQ75Z. **2** (3).

Glechoma hederacea L.   Ground-ivy

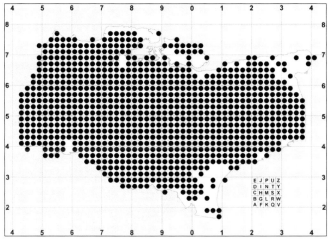

Native. In woods, grassland, hedgerows and waste ground. **900** (920).

Melissa officinalis L.   Balm

Introduced (neophyte). A herb of cultivation, increasingly found growing wild on old walls, roadside banks and verges, and on waste ground, usually near human habitation. **79** (24).

Prunella vulgaris L.   Selfheal

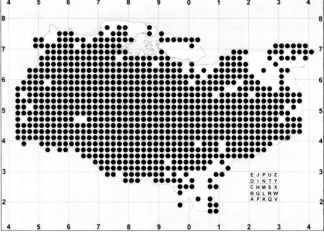

Native. In grassland in woods, meadows, roadside verges, lawns and waste areas. **842** (827).

Prunella vulgaris x *laciniata*
= *P.* x *intermedia* Link

With both parents on a chalky bank at Detling TQ75Z. **1** (2).

Ziziphora capitata L.

Introduced. One casual plant recorded from West Kent in 1980 (Palmer, 1981). **0** (0).

Clinopodium ascendens   Common Calamint
(Jord.) Samp.

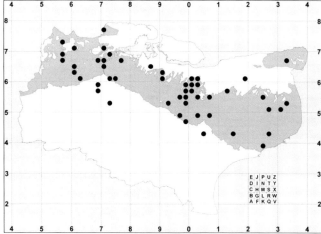

Native. On dry banks and roadside verges, and in scrubby grassland, usually on the chalk. **50** (78).

Clinopodium calamintha (L.) Stace   Lesser Calamint

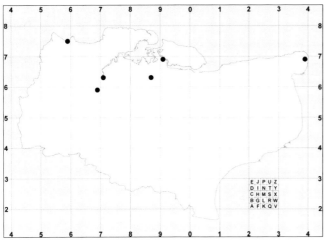

Native. On dry banks and roadside verges. Rather local and scarce, and appears to have gone from some of its former sites. Noted in the Red List Category, 'Vulnerable'. **6** (11).

Clinopodium vulgare L.   Wild Basil

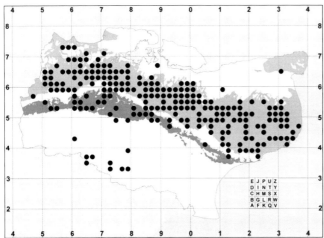

Native. Roadside banks, woodland edges and scrubby grassland on dry, usually calcareous, soils. **229** (332).

Clinopodium acinos (L.) Kuntze   Basil Thyme

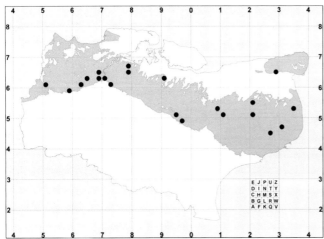

Native. At the edges of arable fields, and in disturbed open grassland, usually on calcareous soils. Has declined in recent years through more efficient weed control on agricultural land, reinforcing its national listing as 'Vulnerable'. **21** (87).

Origanum vulgare L.   Wild Marjoram

Native. Roadside verges, dry banks, rough grassland, cliffs and quarries, usually on the chalk or other calcareous soils. **321** (396).

Thymus vulgaris L.   Garden Thyme

Introduced (neophyte). Still persists at a site in the old Darenth hospital grounds TQ57R where it was originally planted. **1** (1).

Thymus pulegioides L.   Large Thyme

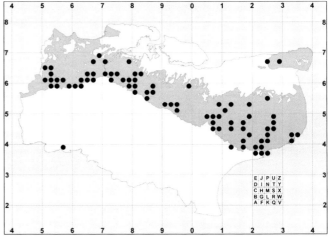

Native. On dry grassland and banks on the chalk, and just occasionally on dry banks on sandy soils. **80** (114).

Thymus polytrichus A. Kern. ex Borbás **Wild Thyme**

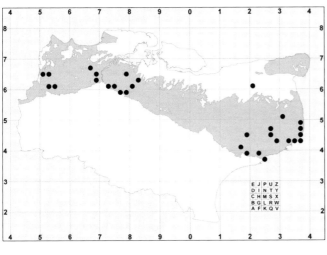

Native. On dry grassland and banks, usually on the chalk. Appears to have been lost from some of its former sites. **30** (100).

Mentha arvensis x aquatica **Whorled Mint**
= **M. x verticillata** L.

At the edge of ponds and in marshy places, not always with both parents present. **9** (8).

Lycopus europaeus L. **Gipsywort**

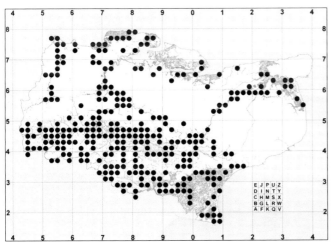

Native. On the banks of rivers, streams, lakes and ditches, and in marshy places. **307** (387).

Mentha arvensis x aquatica x spicata **Tall Mint**
= **M. x smithiana** R.A. Graham

Has been recorded in the past, but was not noted during the present mapping. **0** (1).

Mentha arvensis x spicata **Bushy Mint**
= **M. x gracilis** Sole

Has been noted from a few sites in West Kent in the past, but was not seen during the present mapping. **0** (1).

Mentha arvensis L. **Corn Mint**

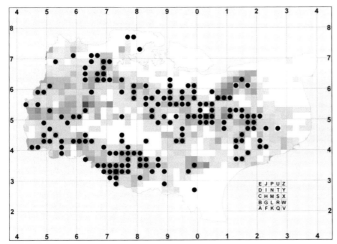

Native. In woodland rides and open wet areas within woods. Also as a weed of arable fields where it has become less frequent in recent years. **170** (286).

Mentha aquatica L. **Water Mint**

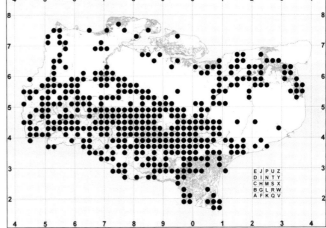

Native. In permanently wet habitats such as by ditches, streams, rivers, ponds, lakes and in marshes. **428** (519).

Mentha aquatica x spicata = **M. x piperita** L.   Peppermint

Introduced (neophyte). By a marsh dyke near Kingsnorth TQ87C, a roadside verge at Sutton TR34J, and in rough vegetation on a cliff-top at Foreness Point TR37V. **3** (6).

Mentha spicata L.   Spear Mint

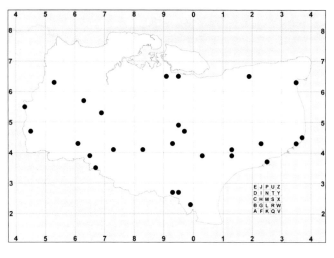

Introduced (archaeophyte). A common pot-herb of gardens and widely naturalised by roadsides and waste ground. **46** (115).

Mentha spicata x suaveolens = **M. x villosa** Huds.   Apple-mint

Introduced (neophyte). Another mint commonly grown in gardens and found naturalised on roadsides and waste places in a few scattered localities. **27** (35).

Mentha spicata x longifolia = **M. x villosonervata** Opiz   Sharp-toothed Mint

Introduced (neophyte). On waste ground by a car park at Aylesford TQ75J and on waste ground at Kingsdown TR34T. **2** (9).

Mentha suaveolens Ehrh.   Round-leaved Mint

Introduced (neophyte). On a chalky bank by Park Wood TR05L. **1** (0).

Mentha pulegium L.   Pennyroyal

Native, although the only recent record in the survey period was probably introduced. By the River Darent on the Dartford Marshes TQ57H. It is listed as 'Endangered' in the Red List.. **1** (0).

Mentha requienii Benth.   Corsican Mint

Introduced (neophyte). Casual records from the grounds of Penshurst Place and Scotney Castle in the past, and although probably still present at these localities, it was not noted during the present mapping. **0** (1).

Lavendula angustifolia x latifolia = **L. x intermedia** Loisel.   Hybrid Lavender

Introduced (neophyte). A relic of cultivation or garden outcast noted at Edenbridge TQ44N, Borough Green TQ65D, Bearsted TQ75X and Canterbury TR15P. **4** (1).

Rosmarinus officinalis L.   Rosemary

Introduced (neophyte). A relic, escape or throw-out of cultivation noted at Seal TQ55N, Borough Green TQ65D, Bearsted TQ75X, Littlestone-on-Sea TR02X, Rhode Common TR05T and Canterbury TR15P. **6** (2).

Salvia sclarea L.   Clary

Introduced. Casual plants in the past, but not seen during the present survey. **0** (2).

Salvia glutinosa L.   Sticky Clary

Introduced (neophyte). Well established in Sharsted Woods TQ95P. **1** (1).

Salvia pratensis L.   Meadow Clary

Native. Still present in the Cobham-Cuxton area TQ66Z & TQ76D where it has been known since at least 1699, and at Queendown Warren TQ86G where records go back to 1839. It could not be found at the few other former sites. On the Dover cliffs site new plants have been planted out (in the name of 'conservation'), so we will never know if the old population ever survived. In the Red List Category, 'Near Threatened'. **3** (5).

Salvia verbenaca L.   Wild Clary

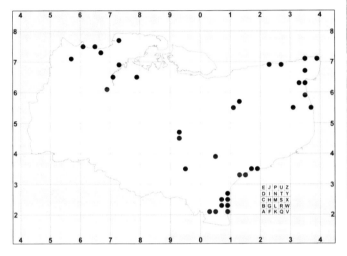

Meadow Clary *Salvia pratensis* © J. Shorter

Native. On open grassland on dry sunny banks and roadside verges, and also found on shingle and sand-dunes. It is also occasionally found in churchyards. **37** (54).

Salvia officinalis L.   Sage

Introduced. Casual plants on waste land near Eythorne TR24U. **1** (0).

Salvia viridis L.   Annual Clary

Introduced. Casual plants in the past, but not seen during the present survey. **0** (2).

HIPPURIDACEAE

Salvia verticillata L.   Whorled Clary

Introduced. Casual plants noted on waste ground near Hacklinge TR35M. **1** (0).

Hippuris vulgaris L.   Mare's-tail

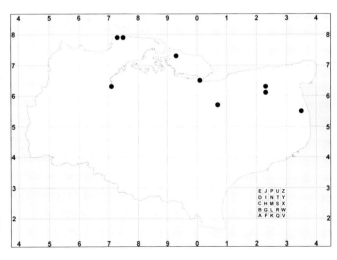

Salvia reflexa Hornem.   Mintweed

Introduced. A casual from bird seed waste, noted from a few rubbish-tips during the 1971-80 mapping, but not seen during the present survey. **0** (3).

Native. In marsh dykes and flooded gravel pits. Very local and appears to have gone from some sites. **9** (21).

CALLITRICHACEAE

Callitriche spp.   Water-starworts

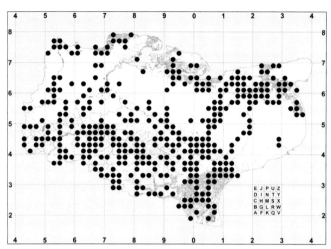

Native. The individual species of Callitriche are difficult to name for various reasons. There has been some confusion over the names of the various species in the past, and this still does not appear to be completely resolved. The plants are very variable in growth and leaf-shape depending on the depth and speed of the water, or if no water at all. They are very shy-fruiting and it appears that the size and shape of mature fruits is the only reliable character than can be used. So the above map shows records of all named and un-named plants of Water-starwort recorded during the present mapping. The records of named species that follows have all been checked with mature fruits. **377** (339).

Callitriche truncata Guss.   Short-leaved Water-starwort

Native. Only recorded from flooded gravel-pits and marsh dykes in the Dungeness-Lydd area TR01N, 01P, 01U & TR02Q. **4** (2).

Callitriche stagnalis Scop.   Common Water-starwort

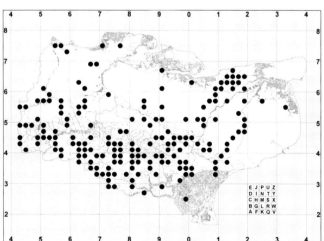

Native. In rivers, streams and ponds, and frequent along damp rutted woodland tracks. **181** (261).

Callitriche platycarpa   Various-leaved Water-starwort
Kütz.

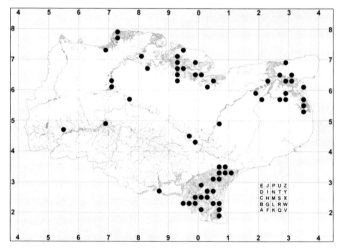

Native. In rivers and ditches, and occasionally on mud on partly drying-up marshes or ponds. A very shy-fruiting plant and so almost certainly under-recorded. **11** (101).

Callitriche obtusangula   Blunt-fruited Water-starwort
Le Gall

Native. In rivers and dykes, particularly in coastal areas. **62** (135).

Callitriche brutia   Intermediate Water-starwort
Petagna

Native. Var. brutia recorded from a pond at Sevenoaks TQ55L, a dyke at Yalding TQ64Z, a flooded gravel-pit at Snodland TQ76A, and at the edge of a river at Kennington TR04H. **4** (-).
Var. hamulata (Kutz. ex W.D.J. Koch) Lansdown was recorded from a pond near Stansted TQ56W, and in a marsh dyke near Snodland TQ76A. During the mapping these two varieties were accorded species status which could only be identified by ripe fruit, and so many records are missing from this account. **5** (67).

208

Plantago coronopus L.   Buck's-horn Plantain

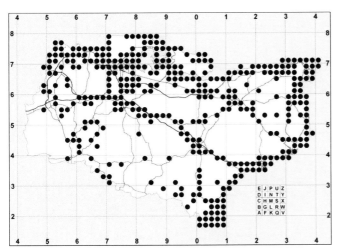

Native. On sea-walls, sand-dunes, gravel beaches, cliffs, and between paving slabs or cracks in buildings in coastal areas. It also occurs naturally on sandy heathland inland. In recent years it has increasingly been found on the salt-splashed verges of motorways and other main roads, and is now beginning to be found in similar situations on minor roads. **384** (202).

Plantago major L.   Greater Plantain

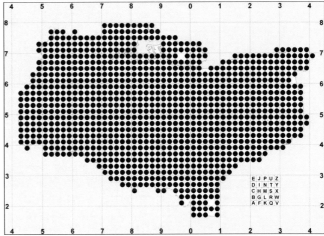

Native. On open habitats such as trampled paths and tracks, disturbed field edges, roadside verges, and in gardens. All records shown refer to ssp. *major*. **1022** (1031).
Ssp. *intermedia* (Gilib.) Lange has been found in damp grassy areas on the coast at Elmley TQ96T and Dungeness TR01U. **2** (1).

Hoary Plantain *Plantago media* © K. Kersey

Plantago maritima L.   Sea Plantain

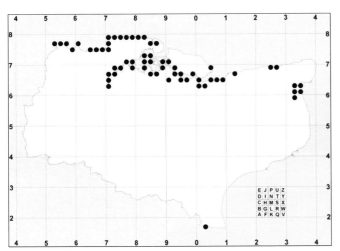

Native. Muddy shores, salt-marshes and cliffs on the coast. **61** (98).

Plantago media L.   Hoary Plantain

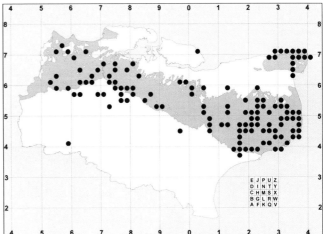

Native. On dry grassy areas on the chalk, for example on downland, pastures, roadside verges, and mown grassy areas such as are found in churchyards. **129** (222).

Plantago lanceolata L.   Ribwort Plantain

Native. Meadows, lawns, roadside verges, cultivated and waste land. Common throughout the county. **1031** (1031).

Plantago arenaria Waldst. & Kit.   Branched Plantain

Introduced. A specimen in **MNE** from Brabourne Lees in 1957 was the first record in the county since 1891. There have been no further sightings. **0** (0).

Plantago sempervirens Crantz   Shrubby Plantain

Introduced (neophyte). Recorded from the Meopham area from 1902 until 1920, but there are no subsequent records. **0** (0).

Plantago afra L.   Glandular Plantain

Introduced. Casual plants on a rubbish-tip at Northfleet from 1971 until 1973, but with no subsequent records. **0** (1).

Littorella uniflora (L.) Asch.   Shoreweed

Native, although perhaps only casual in Kent. Recorded at Brabourne Lees in 1829 and in the Dungeness area in the 1890s. It was re-found at Dungeness in 1947 but there are no subsequent records. **0** (0).

Buddleja alternifolia   Alternate-leaved Butterfly-bush
Maxim.

Introduced (neophyte). Persists in scrub at Darenth Wood TQ57R in an area that was originally the gardens of the former Darenth hospital. **1** (0).

Buddleja davidii Franch.   Butterfly-bush

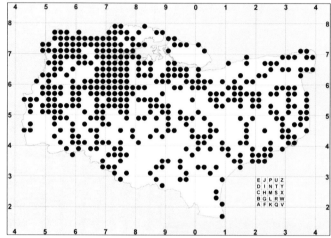

Introduced (neophyte). Introduced into gardens in this country in the 1890s, this bush has escaped and is now well established on waste ground, by railways, in quarries, on roadsides, and frequently on old buildings and walls. It is common in urban areas and is spreading its range as more development takes place within the county. **453** (263).

OLEACEAE

Forsythia suspensa x viridissima   Forsythia
= F. x intermedia hort. ex Zabel

Introduced (neophyte). Relics from cultivation noted at Sutton-at-Hone TQ56P and Shorne TQ67W. **2** (1).

Jasminum officinale L.   Summer Jasmine

Introduced. A casual garden relic recorded from Gravesend in 1980, but with no subsequent sightings. **0** (1).

Jasminum nudiflorum Lindl.   Winter Jasmine

Introduced. Casual records in the past, but not noted during the present mapping. **0** (2).

Fraxinus excelsior L.   Ash   *Ligustrum vulgare* L.   Wild Privet

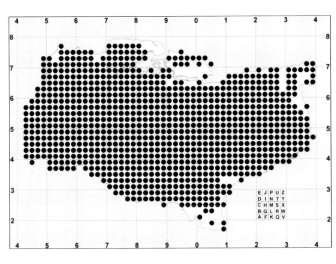 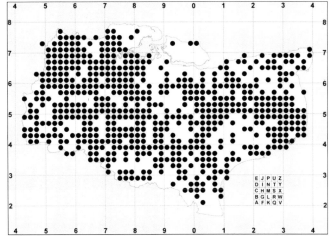

Native. In woods and hedgerows, and readily seeding in scrub, gardens and waste ground. Mature trees to seedlings of the variety *diversifolia* (Single-leaved Ash) are to be found in the Stone area TQ57S where it has long been established. **930** (930).

Native. In woods, hedgerows and scrub, particularly on the chalk. **626** (720).

Fraxinus ornus L.   Manna Ash   *Ligustrum ovalifolium* Hassk.   Garden Privet

Introduced (neophyte). Several wild growing trees at St. Margaret's TR34R, but almost certainly originally planted. **1** (0).

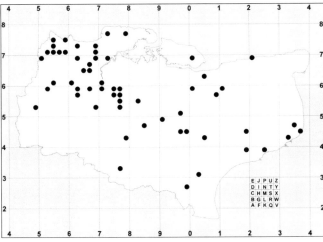

Syringa vulgaris L.   Lilac

Introduced (neophyte). Commonly used as a hedging plant and now widely naturalised in hedgerows and derelict ground, and occasionally bird-sown in various habitats. **150** (75).

Introduced (neophyte). Well naturalised in hedgerows, roadsides, railway banks and waste ground as a relic of cultivation. **58** (101).

Ligustrum lucidum W.T. Aiton   Tree Privet

Introduced (neophyte). Self-sown seedlings were recorded from West Kent in 1980, but there are no subsequent records. **0** (1).

211

SCROPHULARIACEAE

Verbascum blattaria L.   Moth Mullein

Introduced (neophyte). Casual plants on disturbed roadsides or waste ground at Bewl Water TQ63W, Yalding TQ64Z, Offham TQ65N, Teston TQ75B and Ferry Marshes TQ96E, but with a few but regular plants at Putt Wood TQ96Q, and a persistent population on the shingle at Dungeness TR01Y. **7** (2).

Verbascum virgatum Stokes   Twiggy Mullein

Introduced. Casual plants on field borders and disturbed waste ground at Oldbury Hill TQ55T, Snodland TQ76A and Teynham TQ96L. **3** (3).

Verbascum pyramidatum M. Bieb.   Caucasian Mullein

Introduced. A casual plant at Snodland TQ76A. **1** (0).

Verbascum bombyciferum Boiss.   Broussa Mullein

Introduced. Casual plants recorded in the 1970s, but with no subsequent records. **0** (2).

Verbascum phlomoides L.   Orange Mullein

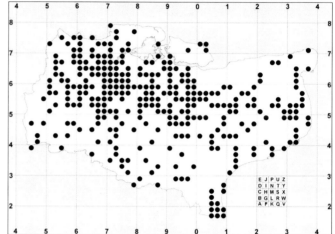

Introduced (neophyte). On roadside verges and open rough ground. In spite of its name, the flowers are usually a fine bright yellow. **13** (13).

Verbascum phlomoides x *thapsus*
= *V.* x *kerneri* Fritsch

Introduced. Casual records in the past, but not noted during the present mapping. **0** (4).

Verbascum densiflorum Bertol.   Dense-flowered Mullein

Introduced (neophyte). Casual plants on roadsides and waste ground at Tonbridge TQ54Y, South Darenth TQ56P, Yalding TQ64Z and Higham TQ77B. **4** (0).

Verbascum thapsus L.   Great Mullein

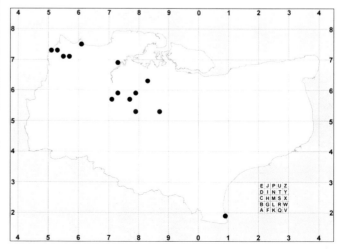

Native. Roadside verges, railway banks, quarries, scrub and disturbed rough ground. **328** (399).

Verbascum thapsus x *nigrum*
= *V.* x *semialbum* Chaub.

With both parents on Queendown Warren L.N.R. TQ86G. **1** (1).

Verbascum thapsus x *lychnitis* = *V.* x *thapsi* L.

Growing together with both parents at Shoreham TQ56G, Darenth TQ57Q, Higham TQ67W, Hollingbourne TQ85H and Westwell TQ94U & 94Z. **6** (4).

Verbascum nigrum L.   Dark Mullein

Native. On grassy banks, roadside verges and open rough ground. **14** (16).

Verbascum nigrum x lychnitis
= V. x incanum Gaudin

Native. Found growing together with both parents at Darenth TQ57Q. **1** (0).

Verbascum speciosum Schrad.   Hungarian Mullein

Introduced (neophyte). A garden escape noted at Sutton TR34J is the only record. **1** (2).

Verbascum lychnitis L.   White Mullein

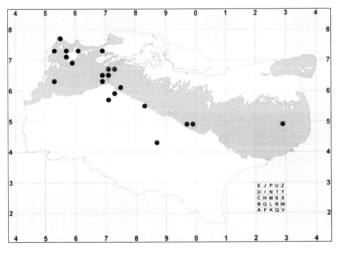

Native. On railway banks, old quarries and rough grassy banks, particularly on the chalk. **21** (31).

Scrophularia nodosa L.   Common Figwort

Native. In damp woods, woodland rides and shaded hedgerows. **507** (598).

Scrophularia auriculata L.   Water Figwort

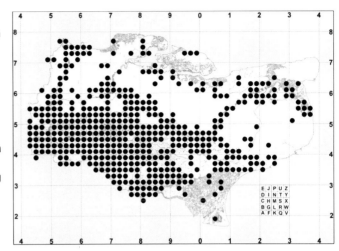

Native. At the margins of lakes, rivers, pond and ditches, at times in damp woodland rides, and very occasionally as a street weed. **482** (510).

Scrophularia scorodonia L.   Balm-leaved Figwort

Introduced. Casual plants found on disturbed soil at Westbere TR16V in 1995 were new to Kent. **1** (0).

Scrophularia vernalis L.   Yellow Figwort

Introduced (neophyte). Well naturalised, but in small numbers, on old walls and waste ground at Canterbury TR15N where it has been known for over a hundred years. **1** (1).

Scrophularia peregrina L.   Nettle-leaved Figwort

Introduced (neophyte). Discovered by M. Brown growing around buildings in streets and car parks in Dartford TQ57H in 1995, where it still persists. **1** (0).

Phygelius capensis   Cape Figwort
E. Mey. ex Benth.

Introduced (neophyte). A garden relic recorded in the past, but not seen during the present mapping. **0** (0).

Paulownia tomentosa   Foxglove-tree
(Thunb.) Steudel

Introduced (neophyte). Noted as a relic of cultivation in the past, but only seen as a tended tree in parks and cemeteries during the present survey. **0** (1).

Mimulus moschatus Douglas ex Lindl.   Musk

Introduced (neophyte). A garden escape recorded from sites in West Kent in the past, but not seen during the present mapping. **0** (7).

Mimulus guttatus DC.   Monkeyflower

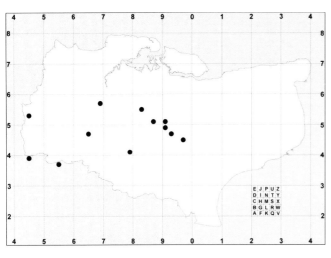

Introduced (neophyte). In wet places by rivers, streams and ponds, and on marshy ground. **12** (31).

Mimulus guttatus x *luteus*
= *M.* x *robertsii* Silverside

Was recorded from near Hawkhurst in 1975, but has not been re-found. **0** (1).

Calceolaria chelidonioides Kunth   Slipperwort

Introduced (neophyte). Persistent in garden grounds near Sandling for about ten years around 1900 (Lousley, 1964), but with no subsequent records. **0** (0).

Antirrhinum majus L.   Snapdragon

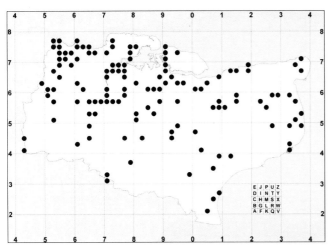

Introduced (neophyte). Widely naturalised on old walls, chalk cliffs, pavement cracks and disturbed waste ground. **130** (149).

Chaenorhinum origanifolium   Malling Toadflax
(L.) Kostel.

Introduced (neophyte). Known for over a century on old walls at West Malling TQ65Y, and still present there. A few plants also found on an old wall at Littlebourne TR25D. **2** (1).

Chaenorhinum minus (L.) Lange   Small Toadflax

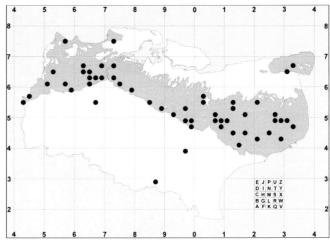

Introduced (archaeophyte). Once a common, and looking native, weed of arable fields, particularly on the chalk, this plant has declined quite markedly in recent years. **54** (150).

Misopates orontium (L.) Raf.   Weasel's-snout

Introduced (archaeophyte). Formerly a widespread, although never common, plant of cultivated and disturbed soils. During the present mapping only recorded from freshly disturbed roadside soil at Maidstone TQ75T, and on disturbed soil from the construction of the new railway line at Hothfield TQ94T. It is treated as "Vulnerable' under the Red List. **2** (7).

Asarina procumbens Mill.   Trailing Snapdragon

Introduced (neophyte). Well naturalised on an old wall at Otterden TQ95M. **1** (2).

Cymbalaria muralis   Ivy-leaved Toadflax
P. Gaertn., B. Mey. & Scherb.

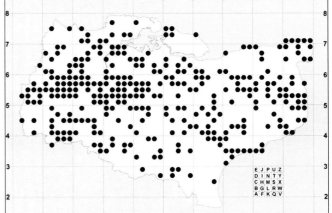

Introduced (neophyte). First recorded in Kent in 1762, but now well naturalised on old walls and bridges, and at times on shingle beaches and other bare stony places. **327** (382).

Cymbalaria hepaticifolia (Poir.) Wettst.
Corsican Toadflax

Introduced (neophyte). Well established about a nursery at Seal Chart TQ55S. **1** (0).

Kickxia elatine (L.) Dumort.
Sharp-leaved Fluellen

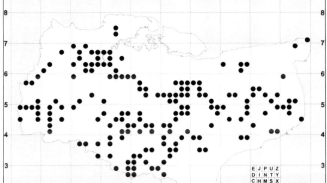

Introduced (archaeophyte). Long established as a weed on arable land, particularly cornfields, on well-drained soils. **177** (234).

Kickxia spuria (L.) Dumort.
Round-leaved Fluellen

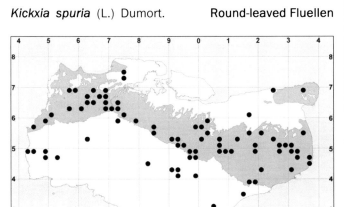

Introduced (archaeophyte). On arable land and open waste ground, particularly on the chalk. **81** (177).

Linaria vulgaris Mill.
Common Toadflax

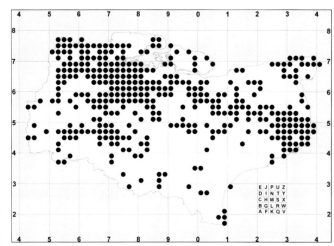

Native. Roadside verges, railway banks, hedgerows and field edges, and on stony waste ground, particularly on the chalk. **386** (535).

Linaria vulgaris x repens
= L. x sepium G.J. Allman

Has been recorded in the distant past, but there are no modern records. **0** (0).

Linaria purpurea (L.) Mill.
Purple Toadflax

Introduced (neophyte). A garden escape or outcast, now well established and spreading on waste ground, roadsides verges, railway banks, quarries, old walls and often as a pavement weed. **265** (168).

Linaria repens (L.) Mill.
Pale Toadflax

Introduced (archaeophyte). Never a common plant in the county and the only recent record is of casual plants on disturbed waste ground at Queenborough TQ97A. **1** (5).

Linaria maroccana Hook. f.   Annual Toadflax

Introduced (neophyte). Recorded once from a rubbish-tip in West Kent during the 1970s, but with no subsequent sightings. **0** (1).

Digitalis purpurea L.   Foxglove

Native. Heaths, open woodland, hedge banks and shingle beaches, particularly on acidic soils. **435** (491).

Foxglove *Digitalis purpurea* © H. Silk

Digitalis lutea L.   Straw Foxglove

Introduced (neophyte). Recorded from Monkton Chalk Pit N.R. TR26X, and in good quantity on chalky banks of the M2 near Canterbury TR15M. **2** (0).

Digitalis lanata Ehrh.   Grecian Foxglove

Introduced. Casual plants in field borders near Dartford 1947-1952 were relics from former cultivation. There are no recent records. **0** (0).

Erinus alpinus L.   Fairy Foxglove

Introduced (neophyte). Long known on old walls at Scotney Castle TQ63X and still present there. **1** (4).

Veronica serpyllifolia L.   Thyme-leaved Speedwell

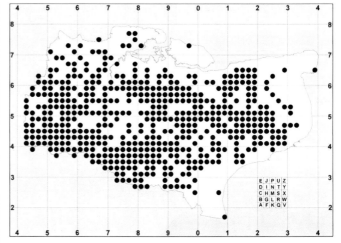

Native. Woodland rides, damp grassy areas, garden lawns, cultivated land and waste ground. **527** (414).

Veronica austriaca L.   Large Speedwell

Introduced (neophyte). Casual plants in the past, the last was on the cliffs at St. Margaret's Bay in 1966. It is a frequent plant on the other side of the Channel, in the Pas de Calais area. **0** (0).

Veronica officinalis L.   Heath Speedwell

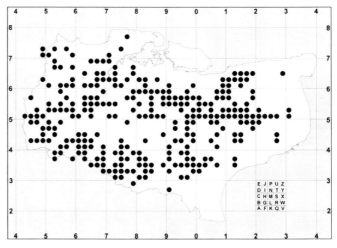

Native. In open woods and woodland rides, and on heathland, usually on sandy soils. **290** (308).

Veronica chamaedrys L.   Germander Speedwell

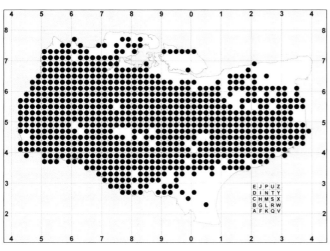

Native. In woodland, hedgerows, rough grassland, railway banks and roadside verges. **769** (854).

Veronica montana L.   Wood Speedwell

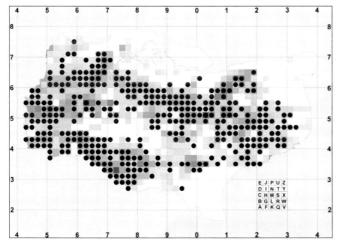

Native. In damp, long-established woodland and hedgerows. **351** (443).

Veronica scutellata L.   Marsh Speedwell

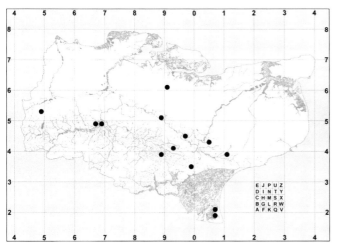

Native. At the edge of streams and ponds, in ditches, and on swampy ground. It has always been a rather local and scarce species in Kent. **13** (9).

Veronica beccabunga L.   Brooklime

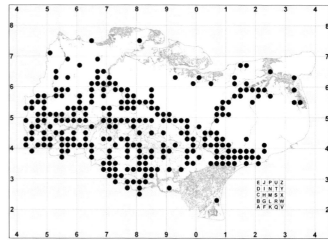

Native. In shallow water at the edge of ponds, streams and ditches, and in wet woodland rides and by spring trickles. **269** (331).

Veronica anagallis-aquatica L.   Blue Water-speedwell

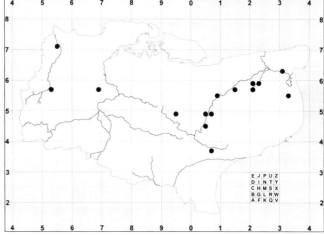

Native. In shallow water at the edges of rivers, ponds, streams and ditches. Perhaps over-recorded in the past for *V. catenata*. **15** (60).

Veronica anagallis-aquatica x *catenata*
= *V.* x *lackschewitzii* J.B. Keller

Native. In quantity at the edge of a marsh dyke near Conyer TQ96M, and a few plants by a large pond near Smeeth TR03U. **2** (0).

Veronica catenata Pennell   **Pink Water-speedwell**

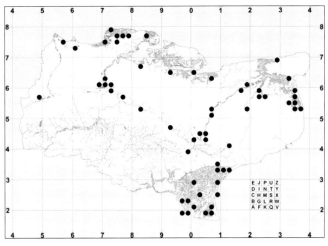

Native. On the muddy edges, or in shallow water, at the edges of rivers, ponds, streams and ditches. **60** (93).

Veronica arvensis L.   **Wall Speedwell**

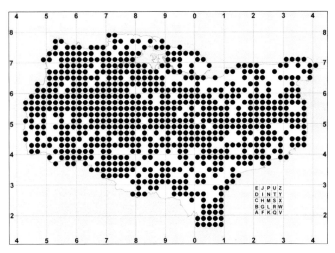

Native. On old walls, coastal sand-dunes, open grassland, and on cultivated and waste land. **761** (748).

Veronica peregrina L.   **American Speedwell**

Introduced (neophyte). A casual weed in gardens and other cultivated ground at Penshurst TQ54G, Tonbridge TQ54Y and Scotney Castle TQ63X. **3** (2).

Veronica agrestis L.   **Green Field-speedwell**

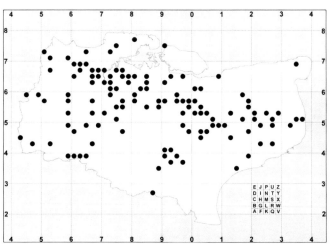

Introduced (archaeophyte). A long established plant of cultivated ground in arable fields, gardens and allotments. **67** (123).

Veronica polita Fr.   **Grey Field-speedwell**

Introduced (neophyte). In arable fields, gardens, allotments, and other cultivated or disturbed ground. **124** (176).

Veronica persica Poir.   **Common Field Speedwell**

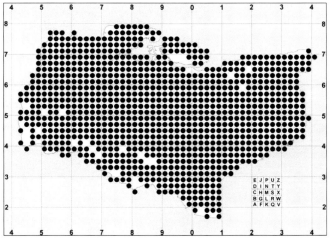

Introduced (neophyte). First recorded in Kent in 1837, and now, after some 170 years, this annual plant is still regarded as an alien! On cultivated and disturbed ground throughout the county. **964** (947).

Veronica filiformis Sm.　　　　Slender Speedwell

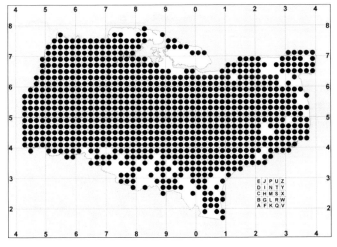

Introduced (neophyte). A garden plant first recorded naturalised in the county in 1950. Since then it has spread rapidly over the county in lawns, churchyards and mown roadside verges. It rarely sets seed and this spread has been mainly through the dispersal of fragments. **375** (394).

Veronica hederifolia L.　　　　Ivy-leaved Speedwell

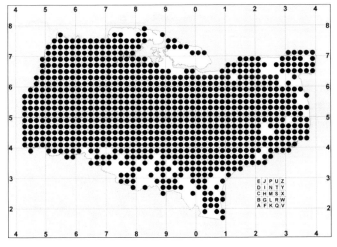

Introduced (archaeophyte). Cultivated and waste ground, and in woodland edges. The two subspecies *hederifolia* and *lucorum* were mapped separately where possible, but many plants were intermediate or showed characters of both subspecies, so the species as a whole is shown on the map. Of the plants that could be identified clearly to subspecies, *hederifolia* was found throughout the range whilst *lucorum* was rarely found in coastal areas. **874** (641).

Veronica longifolia L.　　　　Garden Speedwell

Introduced (neophyte). A garden plant found naturalised on waste ground near Dunton Green TQ56A. **1** (4).

Hebe salicifolia (G. Forst.) Pennell　　　　Koromiko

Introduced (neophyte). Seedlings noted from West Kent in the 1970s, but not seen during the present mapping. **0** (1).

Hebe elliptica x speciosa　　　　Hedge Veronica
= H. x franciscana (Eastw.) Souster

Introduced (neophyte). Much planted and recorded in the past, but not seen growing wild during the present mapping. **0** (2).

Note. Many species and cultivars of *Hebe* are now in cultivation and regularly set seed in gardens, and some will probably escape to the wild in the future.

Sibthorpia europaea L.　　　　Cornish Moneywort

Introduced (neophyte). Found growing on a lawn in Tunbridge Wells in the late 1960s, but with no subsequent records. **0** (0).

Melampyrum arvense L.　　　　Field Cow-wheat

Introduced (neophyte) but now extinct. Was recorded from near Dover in the 1890s, but with no subsequent records. **0** (0).

Melampyrum pratense L.　　　　Common Cow-wheat

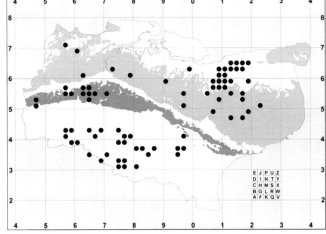

Native. In woods, copses, heaths and scrub. Ssp. *pratense* occurs on the more neutral and acid soils, ssp. *commutatum* is found on chalky soils, but they have not been mapped separately. **79** (153).

Euphrasia anglica Pugsley   English Eyebright

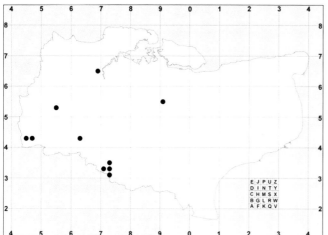

Native. In grassy areas on sandy or acid soils. Listed as 'Endangered' in the Red List. **10** (19).

Euphrasia anglica x *nemorosa*

Native. Recorded from Luddesdown TQ66S, Mount Ephraim TQ66W, Thurnham TQ85E and Queendown Warren TQ86G. **4** (0).

Euphrasia tetraquetra (Bréb.) Arrond.   Compact Eyebright

Native. Has been recorded from coastal chalk cliffs in the past but there are no recent records. **0** (1).

Euphrasia nemorosa (Pers.) Wallr.   Common Eyebright

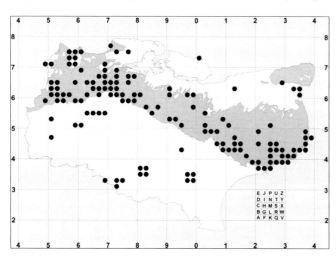

Native. In grassland on chalk downs, heaths and woodland rides. Frequent on the chalk, but more local elsewhere. **139** (184).

Euphrasia nemorosa x *pseudokerneri*

Native. With both parents near Otford TQ56A is the only record, but would be expected to be found elsewhere. **1** (0).

Euphrasia pseudokerneri Pugsley   **Large-flowered Eyebright**

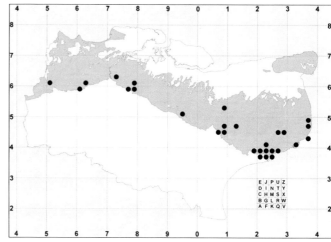

Native. In short grassland along the chalk downs and regarded as 'Endangered' under the Red List. **28** (42).

Euphrasia confusa Pugsley   Confused Eyebright

Native. In heathy grassland in the Sandling Park area TR13I & 13N. Although looked for, it was not re-found on Dartford Heath. **2** (2).

Odontites vernus (Bellardi) Dumort.   Red Bartsia

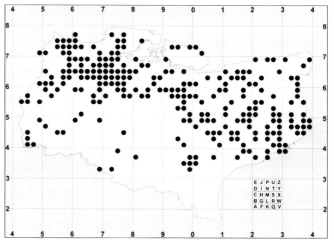

Native. In rough grassland at the edge of arable fields, railway banks, roadside verges, neglected meadows and waste ground. All plants checked have proved to be subsp. *serotinus* (Syme) Corb. **258** (325).

Parentucellia viscosa (L.) Caruel   Yellow Bartsia

Native. Long known, and still present, from hollows in the dunes at Sandwich Bay TR35N. Elsewhere it has been found on sandy heathland at Lenham TQ85V and near Ashford TR04C. It was also found on part of a landscaped former quarry at Ditton TQ75D where it had almost certainly been introduced. **4** (2).

Rhinanthus minor L.   Yellow Rattle

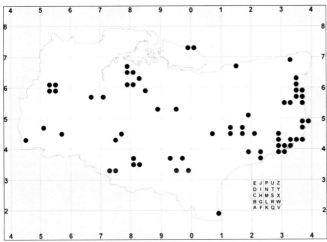

Native. On fixed sand-dunes, chalk downland and grazing meadows. This plant is very susceptible to herbicides, land drainage and other modern farming practices. Its presence is usually indicative of a herb-rich area. Subsp. *minor* is the common plant, subsp *calcareus* (Wilmott) E.F. Warb. occurs on the chalk, and subsp. *stenophyllus* O. Schwarz has been recorded from damp areas on a few occasions, but they have not been mapped separately. **66** (80).

Pedicularis palustris L.   Marsh Lousewort

Native, extinct. A plant of wet heaths, valley bogs and wet meadows, last recorded in the county from Worth Minnis in 1954. **0** (0).

Pedicularis sylvatica L.   Lousewort

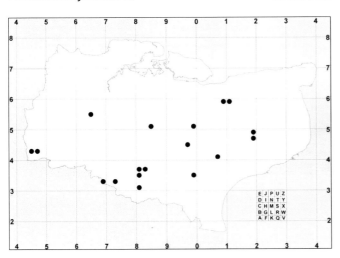

Native. On damp heaths, bogs, marshes and wet woodland rides. Never a common plant in the county, Lousewort appears to have become less frequent in recent years. **18** (43).

OROBANCHACEAE

Lathraea squamaria L.   Toothwort

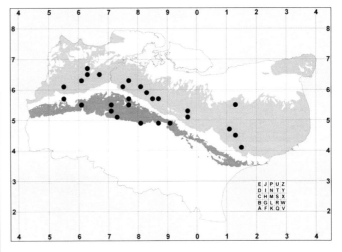

Native. Parasitic on the roots of a range of woody plants, in particular on *Corylus*. In deciduous woodland, hedgerows and roadside banks. **27** (65).

Lathraea clandestina L.   Purple Toothwort

Introduced (neophyte). Persists in a garden at Mereworth TQ65L, and with a large, long established colony under *Populus x canadensis* at Smeeth TR03Z. **2** (1).

Orobanche ramosa L.   Hemp Broomrape

Introduced (neophyte), now long extinct. Casual records in the 18th century only. 0(0).

Orobanche purpurea Jacq.   Yarrow Broomrape

Native. Parasitic on *Achillea millefolium*. Twenty one flowering spikes present at Bishopsbourne TR15W in 1991 and with a few in 1992, but not seen there since. It has been erratically recorded at this site since 1830. In the Red List Category, 'Vulnerable'. **1** (0).

Orobanche rapum-genistae Thuill.   Greater Broomrape

Native. Parasitic on *Cytisus* and *Ulex*. A few plants most years on a sandy bank at Eyhorne Street TQ85H. In the Red List Category, 'Near Threatened'. **1** (2).

Bedstraw Broomrape *Orobanche caryophyllacea* © D. Mills

Orobanche minor Sm.   Common Broomrape

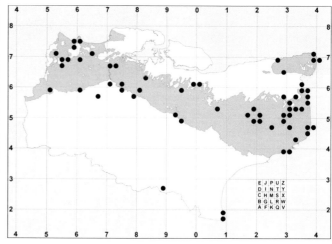

Native. Parasitic on a wide range of plants, particularly on the Fabaceae and Asteraceae. A very variable plant and includes here taxa formerly known as *O. amethystea* and *O. maritima*. The varieties *compositarum, flava, maritima* and *minor* are currently recognised and all of these have been found in the county. However, there are some plants that do not fit clearly into any of these named varieties and the map just shows the species. It has failed to show at several former known sites and the Common Broomrape appears to be in decline. **61** (120).

Orobanche caryophyllacea Sm.   Bedstraw Broomrape

Native. Parasitic on *Galium mollugo* and *G. verum*. Recorded from Folkestone TR23I, and from the Sandwich Bay area TR35P, 35T & 35U where it is relatively common. This plant is not known in the British Isles outside East Kent and is listed nationally as 'Near Threatened'. **4** (6).

Orobanche elatior Sutton   Knapweed Broomrape

Native. Parasitic on *Centaurea scabiosa*, usually on the chalk. Recorded from Westwell TQ94Z and Dover TR34G. **2** (8).

Orobanche hederae Duby   Ivy Broomrape

Native. Parasitic on *Hedera*. Recorded from a roadside bank at Stone TQ57X, and from a laneside at Stockbury TQ86F. **2** (2).

Orobanche picridis F.W. Schultz   Oxtongue Broomrape

Native. Parasitic on *Picris hieracioides*. At Dover TR34F & 34G where numbers of flowering spikes can vary between 1 to 50, and on the cliffs at Oldstairs Bay TR34Y with up to ten flowering spikes most years. Nationally a rare plant and listed as 'Endangered'. **3** (1).

ACANTHACEAE

Acanthus mollis L.   Bear's-breech

Introduced (neophyte). A garden plant recorded growing on waste ground at East Farleigh TQ75G, Snodland TQ76A and Woodnesborough TR35D. **3** (2).

Acanthus spinosus L.   Spiny Bear's-breech

Introduced. Casual records from West Kent in the past, but not seen during the present mapping. **0** (1).

LENTIBULARIACEAE

Utricularia vulgaris L.   Greater Bladderwort

Native. In marsh dykes. A difficult plant to identify as it can only be distinguished from *U. australis* by obscure characters in the flower, which it is rather shy to produce. The only positive records are from the Hacklinge-Worth Minnis area TR35M & 35N. **2** (17).

Utricularia australis R. Br.   Bladderwort

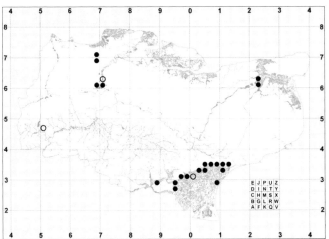

Native. In lakes, ponds and ditches. The solid circles show where the plant has been positively identified, the open circles are for plants without flowers, but probably this species. **20** (2).

Utricularia minor L.   Lesser Bladderwort

Native, extinct. Two doubtful 19th century records only. A 1966 record has proved to be in error. **0** (0).

BIGNONIACEAE

Eccremocarpus scaber   Chilean Glory-flower
(D. Don) Ruíz & Pav.

Introduced (neophyte). Recorded as a pavement weed at Cranbrook in 1979 (Clement, 1980), but with no subsequent records. **0** (0).

Catalpa bignonioides Walter   Indian-bean-tree

Introduced (neophyte). Widely planted in parks and large gardens. Casual seedlings noted on waste ground at Maidstone TQ75T. **1** (0).

CAMPANULACEAE

Campanula patula L.   Spreading Bellflower

Native, extinct. Recorded from Dartford Heath (1821) and Cobham (1890s), but with no subsequent records. In the Red List Category, 'Endangered'. **0** (0).

Campanula rapunculus L.   Rampion Bellflower

Introduced (archaeophyte). Casual records in the past, the last in 1961. **0** (0).

Campanula lactiflora M. Bieb.   Milky Bellflower

Introduced. A casual escape from cultivation was noted in the early 1970s, but has not been seen growing wild since. **0** (1).

Campanula persicifolia L.   Peach-leaved Bellflower

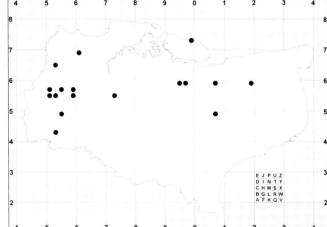

Introduced (neophyte). A fine garden plant which is found, as an escape, on roadside banks and verges, and occasionally on other rough or waste land. **17** (15).

Campanula medium L.   Canterbury-bells

Introduced (neophyte). On railway cutting at Eynsford TQ56H, Swanscombe TQ67C, Maidstone TQ75N, and on chalky banks at Snodland TQ66W & TQ76B, and at the edge of a chalk pit near Bekesbourne TR25C. **6** (18).

Campanula alliariifolia Willd.   Cornish Bellflower

Introduced. A casual garden escape recorded in 1961, but with no subsequent records. **0** (0).

Campanula glomerata L.   Clustered Bellflower

Native. On dry chalky banks in the Cuxton-Halling area in TQ66W & X and TQ76D. Also found in a quarry at Ditton (TQ76D) where it had almost certainly been introduced. **4** (9).

Campanula pyramidalis L.   Chimney Bellflower

Introduced (neophyte). Occasional plants on an old wall at East Malling TQ65Y where it has been known for about fifty years. **1** (1).

Campanula portenschlagiana Schult. Adria Bellflower

Introduced (neophyte).   Established on old walls at Tunbridge Wells TQ54V, Plaxtol TQ65B, Hoo St. Werburgh TQ77W, Bearsted TQ85C, Appledore TQ92P, Teynham TQ96L, Faversham TR06F and Ringwould TR34P. **8** (10).

Campanula rapunculoides L. Creeping Bellflower

Introduced (neophyte). A frequently grown plant in gardens, and well established on a roadside bank at Dartford TQ57L. Also noted on an old wall at Maidstone TQ75N where it has been known for at least fifty years. **2** (15).

Campanula poscharskyana Degen Trailing Bellflower

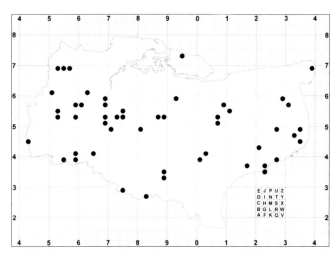

Campanula rotundifolia L. Harebell

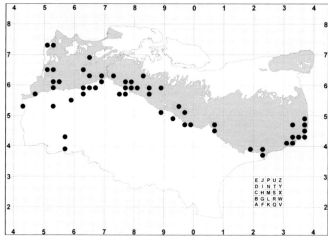

Introduced (neophyte). Widely grown in gardens and now well established on old walls, in pavement cracks and sparsely vegetated roadside banks. **50** (2).

Native. On open chalk downland and on sandy heathland. Many former sites appear to have been lost through building development or the ploughing up of grassland. **54** (127).

Campanula latifolia L. Giant Bellflower

Introduced.   Casual garden escapes in the past, the last in 1949. **0** (0).

Campanula trachelium L. Nettle-leaved Bellflower

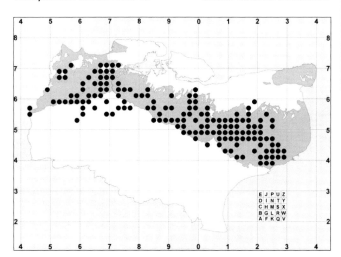

Native. In woodland rides and edges, shaded hedgerows and roadside banks, usually on the chalk. **160** (186).

Legousia hybrida (L.) Delarbre Venus's-looking-glass

Introduced (archaeophyte).   At the edge of arable fields on the chalk, particularly in cornfields. In keeping with most other 'cornfield weeds' it has declined significantly in recent years. **32** (71).

Legousia speculum-veneris Large Venus's-looking-glass
(L.) Chaix

Introduced (neophyte). Found at Upper Halling in 1905, but with no other records. **0** (0).

Wahlenbergia hederacea   Ivy-leaved Bellflower
(L.) Rchb.

Native. Only found in a woodland ride at Roundshill Park Wood
TQ83E in spite of a careful search of all previous known sites.
Whilst it is nationally listed as 'Near Threatened', it is at the edge
of its range in the county, where it has never been a common
plant; its Kentish decline is probably due to natural causes.
1 (2).

Phyteuma orbiculare L.   Round-headed Rampion

Native, extinct. A few past records from the chalk, the last in the
1890s. **0** (0).

Jasione montana L.   Sheep's-bit

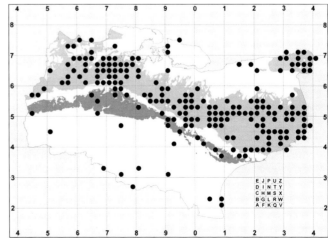

Native. On the shingle beach in the Lydd-Dungeness area, and
still present at one site on the ragstone at Sevenoaks. **9** (16).

Lobelia urens L.   Heath Lobelia

Native. Claimed to have been found in a wood near Ashford in
about 1860, but never re-found there or anywhere else in the
county. It still occurs at a site near Flimwell in East Sussex in an
area where there is some dispute as to where the vice-county
boundary was actually drawn. **0** (0).

Lobelia erinus L.   Garden Lobelia

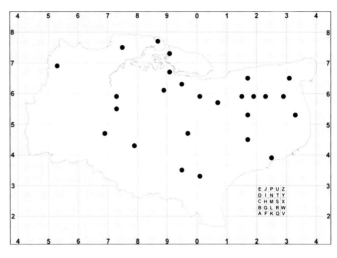

Introduced (neophyte). A casual escape from cultivation found
growing in roadsides, pavement cracks and waste ground.
26 (5).

Pratia angulata (G. Forst.) Hook. f.   Lawn Lobelia

Introduced (neophyte). Recorded from a mown lawn at Hever
Castle TQ44X in 1960 and still present there in small quantity.
1 (1).

RUBIACEAE

Sherardia arvensis L.   Field Madder

Native. Arable fields, sand-dunes, roadside verges and disturbed
waste ground. **206** (243).

Phuopsis stylosa
(Trin.) Benth. & Hook. f. Ex
B.D. Jacks.

Caucasian Crosswort

Introduced. Casual plants on roadside verges in the past, but not seen during the present mapping. **0** (1).

Galium uliginosum L.

Fen Bedstraw

Native. In base-rich marshes and fens. It has always been a scarce plant in Kent and from 1991-2005 was only recorded from Snodland TQ76B, Charing TQ94P, Graveney Marshes TR06R, Ham Fen TR35H and Northbourne Fen TR35L. **5** (15).

Asperula cynanchica L.

Squinancywort

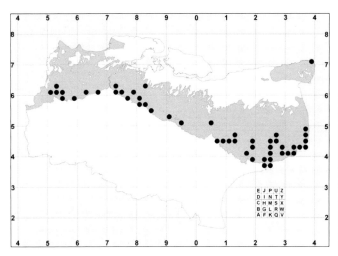

Native. On cliffs, grassland and roadside banks on the chalk. Has been lost from some sites because they have either been ploughed up, or have been invaded by scrub. **50** (83).

Galium palustre L.
ssp. *palustre*

Common Marsh-bedstraw

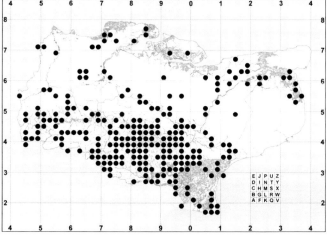

Native. At the sides of ponds and ditches, and in marshes and damp woodland rides. **252** (302).

Asperula arvensis L.

Blue Woodruff

Introduced. Casual plants on waste ground at Gravesend in 1979, but with no subsequent records. **0** (1).

Galium odoratum (L.) Scop.

Woodruff

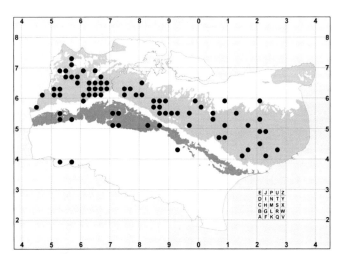

Native. In open deciduous woodland, scrub and shaded hedge banks, particularly on calcareous soils. **78** (131).

Galium palustre L.
ssp. *elongatum* (C. Presl) Arcang.

Great Marsh-bedstraw

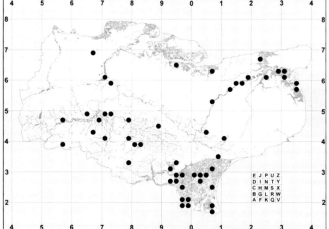

Native. In ponds and wet ditches, practically always in standing water. **53** (121).

Galium verum L.   Lady's Bedstraw

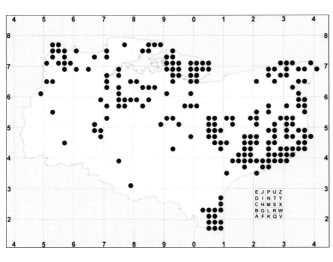

Native. In well-drained grassland or sand-dunes, on neutral or calcareous soils. **211** (281).

Galium saxatile L.   Heath Bedstraw

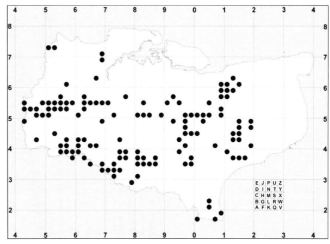

Native. On heaths and in open woods on sandy, usually acidic, soils. **132** (181).

Galium verum x mollugo
 = G. x pomeranicum Retz.

Native. On the sand-dunes in the Sandwich Bay area TR35P & 35U where it has been known for at least 150 years. **2** (4).

Galium mollugo L.   Hedge Bedstraw

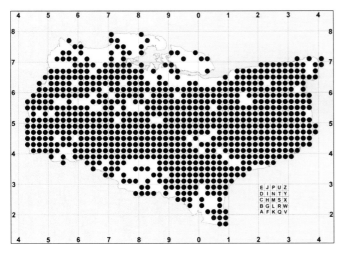

Native. Woodland edges, hedgerows, scrub and roadside banks. Plants conforming to subsp. *erectum* have been found in many areas on the chalk and typical subsp. *mollugo* elsewhere. However, there is an overlap of characters and most plants could not be positively assigned and so the subspecies were not mapped separately. **802** (899).

Galium aparine L.   Cleavers

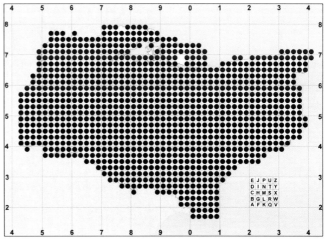

Native. In hedgerows, roadside banks, cultivated ground including gardens, and disturbed waste ground. **1027** (1031).

Galium spurium L.   False Cleavers

Introduced. Casual records in the past, but not seen during the present mapping. **0** (1).

Galium pumilum Murray   Slender Bedstraw

Native. All the previous recorded localities for this species have been specifically searched and the plant has not been found. It was a tale of being ploughed up, scrubbed up, or grazed off, but an area or two of chalk grassland within the county might just still hold this species. Nationally the plant is listed as 'Endangered'. **0** (1).

Galium tricornutum Dandy   Corn Cleavers

Introduced (archaeophyte). Formerly a widespread weed in cereal fields and disturbed ground, mainly on the chalk. Has been in steady decline since about 1930 and is now probably extinct in the county. The last record was of casual plants near Gravesend in 1980. **0** (1).

Galium parisiense L.   Wall Bedstraw

Native. On old walls at Lullingstone TQ56H, Farningham TQ56N and Northfleet Green TQ67F. In the Red List Category, 'Vulnerable'. **3** (3).

Galium murale (L.) All.   Small Goosegrass

Introduced. A wool shoddy casual recorded from Wateringbury in 1979, but not seen since. **0** (1).

Galium verrucosum Huds.

Introduced. A few casual plants recorded from Gravesend in 1979, but with no subsequent sightings. **0** (1).

Cruciata laevipes Opiz   Crosswort

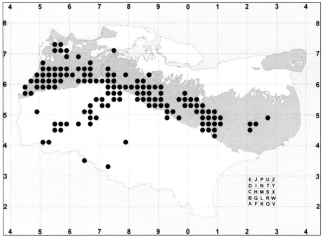

Native. Woodland edges, open scrub, rough grassland and roadside banks on the chalk, and in similar habitats, plus river banks along the Medway Valley. Occasional records elsewhere. **137** (201).

Rubia peregrina L.   Wild Madder

Native. On the chalk cliffs from Folkestone to Deal TR23U, 23Z, TR33E & TR34L from where it was first recorded in 1805. **4** (4).

Sambucus racemosa L.   Red-berried Elder

Introduced (neophyte). Well naturalised in the woods above Shoreham TQ65A & 56B. **2** (1).

Sambucus nigra L.   Elder

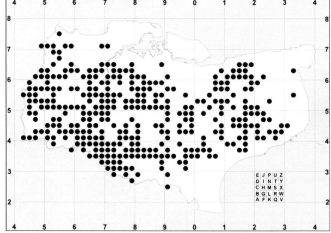

Native. In woodland, hedgerows, roadside banks, scrub and waste land, particularly near old buildings. **1015** (1013).

Sambucus ebulus L.   Dwarf Elder

Introduced (archaeophyte). On roadside banks and waste land at Sevenoaks TQ55I, Cooling TQ77M, Ashford TR04B, Molash TR05G, Boughton Street TR05P, and Brooksend TR26Y. **6** (7).

Viburnum opulus L.   Guelder-rose

Native, although perhaps planted at some roadside sites. In hedgerows, scrub, damp woodland and banks of rivers and streams. **351** (443).

Viburnum lantana L.   Wayfaring-tree

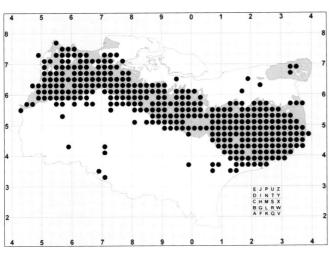

Native. Woodland edges, scrub, hedgerows and roadside banks on calcareous soils. Some trees away from the chalk have probably been introduced. **353** (375).

Viburnum lantana x rhytidophyllum
= V. x rhytidophylloides J.V. Suringar

Established plants, apparently self-sown, at Eynsford TQ56H and Darenth TQ57Q. **2** (0).

Viburnum tinus L.   Laurustinus

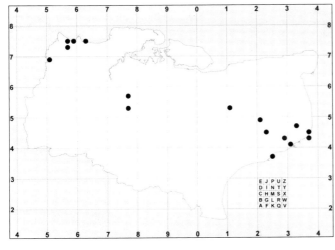

Introduced (neophyte). Well naturalised in woods, rough grassland and coastal cliffs and banks, either as garden escapes, bird-sown or relics from planting. **16** (11).

Viburnum rhytidophyllum Hemsl.   Wrinkled Viburnum

Introduced (neophyte). Often planted in parks, shrubberies and large gardens and noted as an escape on waste land at New Ash Green TQ66C. **1** (2).

Symphoricarpos albus (L.) S.F. Blake   Snowberry

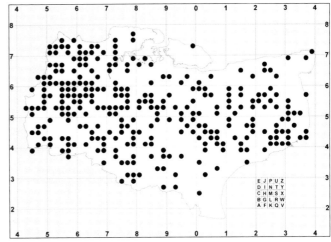

Introduced (neophyte). Formerly widely planted in large gardens or as cover for game in woodland. Now found widely naturalised in woods, hedgerows and scrub throughout the county. **297** (335).

Linnaea borealis L. ssp. americana (Forbes) Hultén

Introduced (neophyte). Found by D. McClintock naturalised in woodland by Crown Point Nurseries, Seal in 1965 where it persisted for a number of years, but could not be found during the present survey. **0** (0).

Leycesteria formosa Wall.   Himalayan Honeysuckle

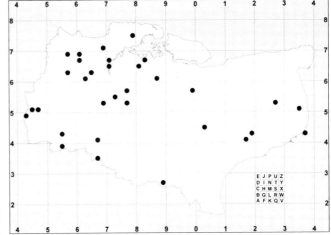

Introduced (neophyte). A garden plant often bird-sown and now established in hedgerows, roadside banks and scrub. Also formerly planted as pheasant cover in woodland where now it is often well naturalised and spreading. **32** (7).

Lonicera pileata Oliv.   Box-leaved Honeysuckle

Introduced (neophyte). Reported as becoming naturalised at New Ash Green in 1988 (Palmer, 1989) but with no subsequent records in the present survey. **0** (0).

Lonicera nitida E.H. Wilson   Wilson's Honeysuckle   *Lonicera periclymenum* L.   Honeysuckle

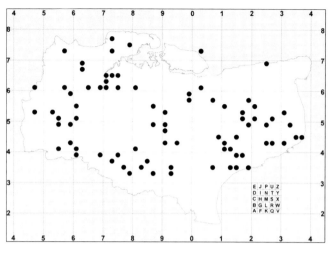

Introduced (neophyte). Much planted as a hedgerow plant and now widely naturalised on woodland edges and roadsides. **80** (16).

Native. In woodland, hedgerows and scrub. **722** (778).

Lonicera caprifolium L.   Perfoliate Honeysuckle

Introduced (neophyte). An occasional garden escape and only noted at Darenth TQ57K during the present mapping. **1** (5).

Lonicera involucrata   Californian Honeysuckle
(Richardson) Banks ex Spreng.

Introduced (neophyte). A plant at New Romney TR02S, where it has persisted for many years, is the only record. **1** (0).

Lonicera caprifolium x *etrusca*   Garden Honeysuckle
= *L.* x *italica* Schmidt ex Tausch

Introduced. In a hedgerow at Chipstead TQ55D. **1** (0).

Lonicera xylosteum L.   Fly Honeysuckle   *Kolkwitzia amabilis* Graebn.   Beauty-bush

Introduced (neophyte). Established on waste ground at Maidstone TQ75T. **1** (1).

Introduced. A garden plant recorded once in the past, but has little claim for inclusion in the Kentish flora. **0** (1).

ADOXACEAE

Lonicera japonica Thunb.   Japanese Honeysuckle   *Adoxa moschatellina* L.   Moschatel

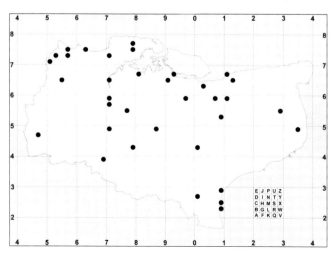 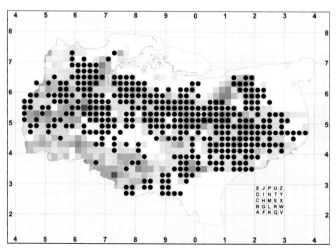

Introduced (neophyte). Well naturalised, and increasing, on roadside banks, hedgerows and in scrub. **35** (6).

Native. Woodland edges and by shaded river and hedge banks. **387** (356).

Honeysuckle *Lonicera periclymenum* © L. Manning

VALERIANACEAE

Valerianella locusta (L.) Laterr.   Common Cornsalad

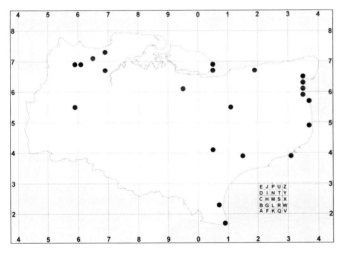

Native. Sand-dunes, coastal shingle and sandy, sparsely vegetated areas inland. **22** (72).

Valerianella carinata Loisel.   Keeled-fruited Cornsalad

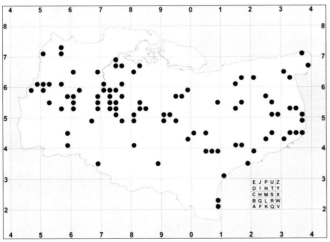

Introduced (archaeophyte). In gardens, on old walls, roadside verges and waste places. **94** (36).

Valerianella rimosa Bastard   Broad-fruited Cornsalad

Introduced (archaeophyte), now extinct. A cornfield weed that has always been scarce in Kent and was last recorded in 1963. In the Red List Category, 'Endangered'. **0** (0).

Valerianella dentata (L.) Pollich   Narrow-fruited Cornsalad

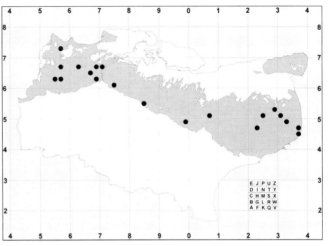

Introduced (archaeophyte). At the edge of cornfields, and occasionally other arable fields on chalky soils. Has declined in recent years and is now listed as 'Endangered'. **20** (43).

Valerianella eriocarpa Desv.   Hairy-fruited Cornsalad

Introduced (neophyte). A casual plant of disturbed soils, last recorded in the county in 1946. **0** (0).

Valeriana officinalis L.   Common Valerian

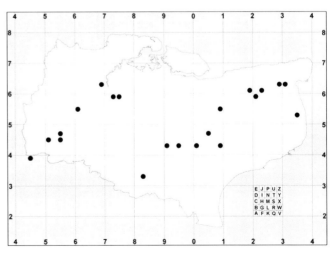

Native. The frequent form is the subsp. *sambucifolia* which is found in damp grassland, river banks, marshes and ditches, whilst the much rarer subsp. *collina* is occasionally found in dry chalk grassland or scrub. This plant appears to have declined in recent years. **21** (55).

Valeriana dioica L.   Marsh Valerian

Native. The decline of this species noted in the previous Atlas continues, and during the present mapping it was only recorded from Cowden TQ44K, Brenchley Wood TQ64K, Cinderhill Wood TQ64L, West Peckham TQ65G and Gibbin's Brook TR13E. **5** (12).

Centranthus ruber (L.) DC.   Red Valerian

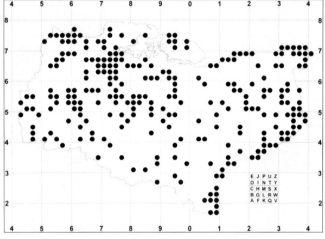

Introduced (neophyte). Completely naturalised on old buildings, walls, chalk cliffs, quarries and railway banks. **262** (220).

DIPSACACEAE

Dipsacus fullonum L.   Wild Teasel

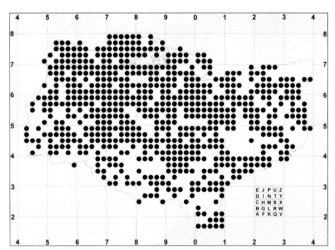

Native. Rough grassland, wood margins, scrub, hedgerows, roadside banks and waste land. **679** (652).

Dipsacus sativus (L.) Honck.   Fuller's Teasel

Introduced. Casual plants on rubbish-tips or waste land reported in the past, but not seen since the 1970s. **0** (5).

Dipsacus pilosus L.   Small Teasel

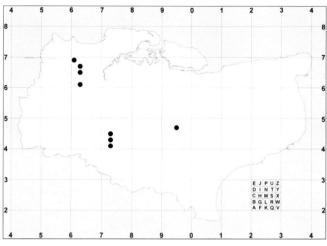

Native. In woodland edges and rides, by stream-banks and wet marshy areas. Always a very local species in Kent, and it remains so. **8** (9).

Cephalaria gigantea   Giant Scabious
(Ledeb.) Bobrov

Introduced (neophyte). A garden plant reported from a railway bank at Tunbridge Wells in 1980, but not noted since. **0** (1).

Wild Teasel   Dipsacus fullonum © L. Manning

Knautia arvensis (L.) Coult.   Field Scabious

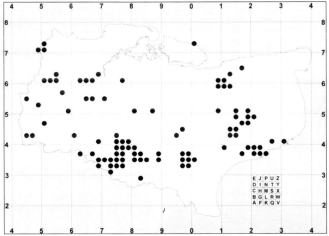

Native. In rough pastures, hedgerows, wood borders and roadside verges, particularly on the chalk. **243** (382).

Succisa pratensis Moench   Devil's-bit Scabious

Native. In woodland rides, rough grassland and occasionally in marshes, on both mildly acid and chalky soils. **95** (166).

Scabiosa columbaria L.   Small Scabious

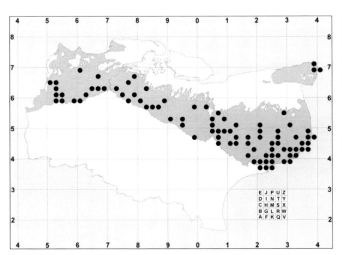

Native. Grassy areas and banks on the chalk. Appears to have declined in recent years through loss of habitat which has either been ploughed up or invaded by scrub and coarse grasses. **89** (148).

Scabiosa atropurpurea L.   Sweet Scabious

Introduced (neophyte). On the chalk cliffs at Ramsgate TR36S. However, although searched for on several occasions, it could not be re-found at Folkestone, where it has been known from 1862 until at least 1980. **1** (3).

ASTERACEAE

Echinops sphaerocephalus L.   Glandular Globe-thistle

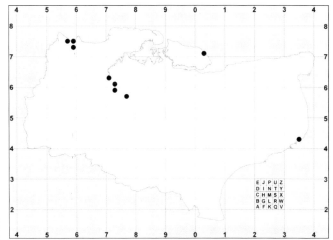

Introduced (neophyte). A garden plant now well established on roadside banks, disused quarries and waste ground particularly in the Greenhithe, Maidstone and Dover areas. **9** (13).

Echinops bannaticus   Blue Globe-thistle
Rochel ex Schrad.

Introduced (neophyte). A garden plant found naturalised on waste ground at Swanley TQ56E and near Wingham TR25P. **2** (2).

Carlina vulgaris L.   Carline Thistle

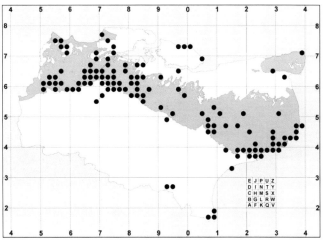

Native. On the chalk on dry, rather infertile grassland, cliffs and quarries, and occasionally on sand-dunes and other calcareous soils. **123** (154).

Arctium lappa L.   Greater Burdock

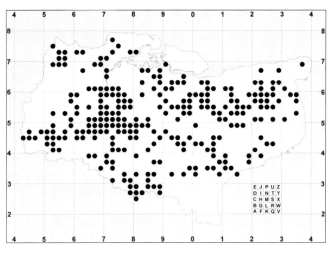

Native. On roadside verges, river banks, field margins and waste places. **274** (354).

Arctium minus (Hill.) Bernh.
ssp. *pubens* (Bab.) Arènes   Hairy Burdock

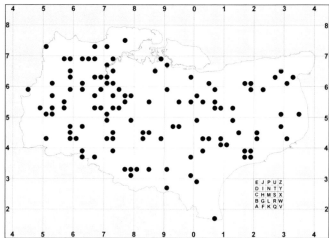

Native. On roadside verges, woodland borders, scrub and rough grassland. **118** (165).

Arctium minus (Hill) Bernh. **ssp. *minus***   Lesser Burdock

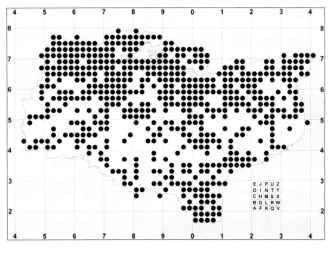

Native. Roadside verges, woodland margins, sea walls and waste places, being particularly frequent in coastal areas. **579** (633).

Carduus tenuiflorus Curtis   Slender Thistle

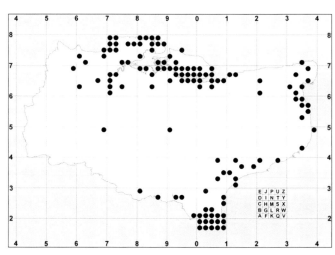

Native. On sea-walls, upper edges of beaches and coastal rough grassland, and occasionally on roadside verges and field margins inland. **125** (101).

Arctium minus (Hill.) Bernh.
ssp. *nemorosum* (Lej.) Syme   Wood Burdock

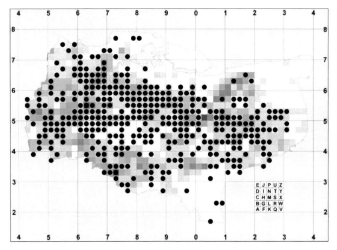

Native. In woodland rides, clearings and margins, and occasionally in hedgerows as a relic of former woodland. **381** (495).

Musk Thistle *Carduus nutans* © S. Poyser

Carduus pycnocephalus L. Plymouth Thistle

Introduced. Casual plants in the past from wool shoddy or bird seed, last recorded in 1974. **0** (3).

Cirsium eriophorum (L.) Scop. Woolly Thistle

Native. On roadside verges and other grassy areas on the chalk. Only found at Sellindge TR03Y, Beachborough TR13U, Arpinge TR13Z and Folkestone TR23E. **4** (6).

Carduus crispus L. Welted Thistle

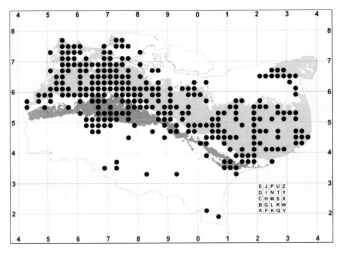

Native. On roadside verges, woodland margins and stream banks. Appears to have become much less frequent in recent years. **291** (406).

Cirsium vulgare (Savi) Ten. Spear Thistle

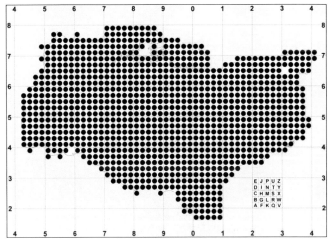

Native. A common plant of over-grazed meadows, arable fields, open scrub, rough grassland and waste places. **1027** (1027).

Carduus crispus x nutans
= *C.* x *stangii* H. Buek ex Nyman

Native. One plant at Queendown Warren TQ86G growing with both parents. **1** (1).

Cirsium dissectum (L.) Hill Meadow Thistle

Native. Appears to have gone from all its former sites through drying out or development and is now probably extinct in the county. **0** (2).

Carduus nutans L. Musk Thistle

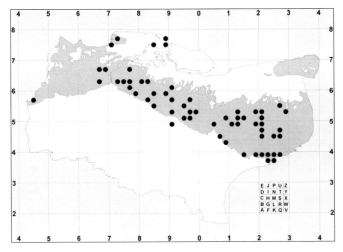

Native. Over-grazed pastures, roadside verges and disturbed places on the chalk. Although specifically looked for, this thistle also appears to have declined in numbers and range in recent years. **60** (115).

Cirsium acaule (L.) Scop. Dwarf Thistle

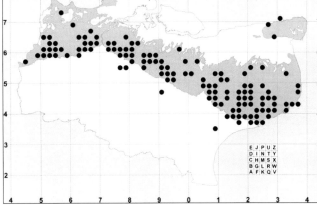

Native. On dry calcareous grassland where the overall vegetation is kept quite short. It is particularly frequent on chalk banks that, from a distance, appear ideal to picnic upon. **129** (209).

Cirsium palustre (L.) Scop.   Marsh Thistle

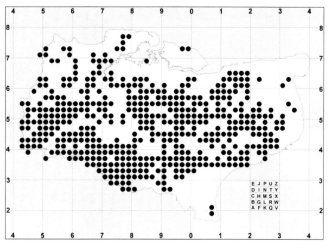

Native. In marshes, damp grassland and wet woodland. **482** (587).

Onopordum acanthium L.   Cotton Thistle

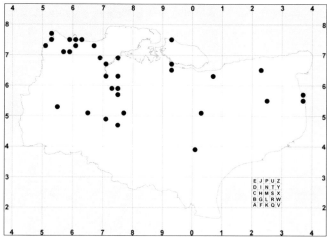

Introduced (archaeophyte). Roadside banks, rough grassland and waste ground. **33** (50).

Cirsium palustre x arvense
C. x **celakovskianum** Knaf

Native. Was once recorded in the county (over a hundred years ago), but with no subsequent sightings. **0** (0).

Cynara cardunculus L.   Globe Artichoke

Introduced (neophyte). A garden plant recorded in the past, but not noted growing wild during the present survey. **0** (1).

Cirsium arvense (L.) Scop.   Creeping Thistle

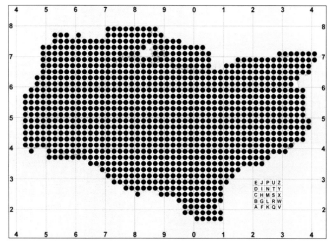

Native. A common weed of over-grazed meadows, cultivated fields, gardens, roadside verges, scrub and waste land. **1038** (1039).

Silybum marianum (L.) Gaertn.   Milk Thistle

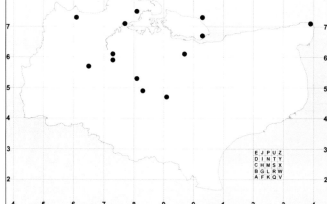

Introduced (archaeophyte). Old meadows, rough grassland and waste ground. **13** (28).

Serratula tinctoria L.   Saw-wort

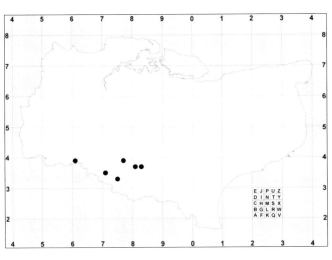

Native. A scarce plant of woodland edges and roadside banks. **6** (7).

Centaurea scabiosa L.   Greater Knapweed

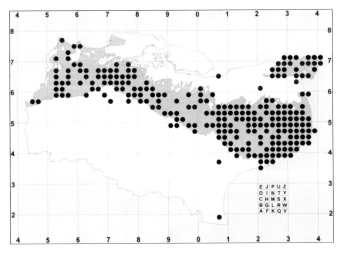

Native. On roadside verges, rough grassland, quarries and woodland edges, usually on the chalk. **239** (324).

Centaurea montana L.   Perennial Cornflower

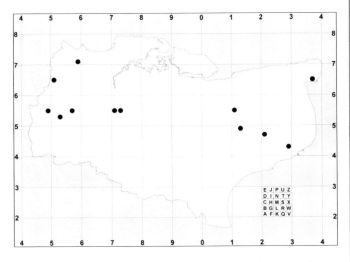

Introduced (neophyte). On roadside verges and waste places, often as a relic from cultivation. **12** (21).

Centaurea cyanus L.   Cornflower

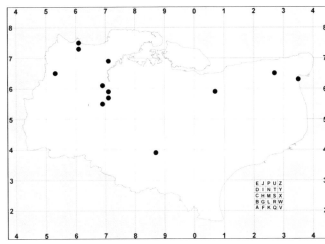

Introduced (archaeophyte). Formerly a frequent weed of cornfields but now a plant of disturbed waste ground and only occasionally on deeply ploughed cornfields. **12** (11).

Centaurea calcitrapa L.   Red Star-thistle

Introduced (archaeophyte). Still present in The Lines at Chatham TQ76T where it has been known since at least 1839, but with very limited distribution outside the county and so regarded nationally as 'Critically Endangered'. **1** (2).

Greater Knapweed *Centaurea scabiosa* © L. Rooney

Centaurea solstitialis L.   Yellow Star-thistle

Introduced (neophyte). A casual plant of arable fields in the past, but not recorded during the present mapping. **0** (2).

Carthamus tinctorius L.   Safflower

Introduced (neophyte). On waste ground at Swanscombe TQ67C is the only record. **1** (9).

Centaurea diluta Aiton   Lesser Star-thistle

Introduced. Casual records in the past from wool shoddy or bird seed, but not seen during the present mapping. **0** (7).

Carthamus lanatus L.   Downy Safflower

Introduced (neophyte). A wool shoddy casual, last recorded in 1960. **0** (0).

Centaurea jacea L.   Brown Knapweed

Introduced (neophyte). Has been recorded in the past from Kent, but there are no recent records. **0** (1).

Cichorium intybus L.   Chicory

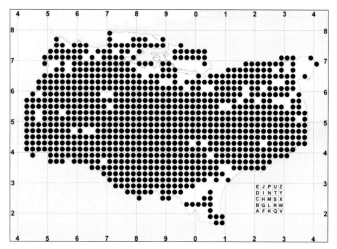

Introduced (archaeophyte) but with some justification to be called native. On roadside verges, field margins and rough grassland. **70** (143).

Centaurea nigra L.   Common Knapweed

Native. A very variable plant that is split by some authorities into *C. nigra* which is found on heavier soils, and *C. debeauxii* which occurs on lighter soils, both of which have named subspecies and varieties. However, in practice it has been found that there is a whole range of intermediates between the named forms and, in keeping with the majority of taxonomic opinion, just one species is recognised here. On roadside verges, woodland margins, meadows, pastures, cliffs and field borders. **870** (904).

Lapsana communis L.   Nipplewort

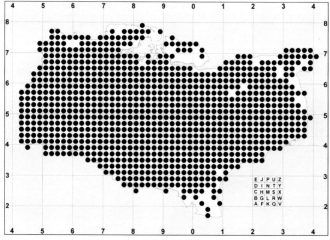

Native. Open woodland, roadside verges, cultivated ground including gardens, scrub, and occasionally on old walls. **931** (947).

Centaurea eriophora L.   Woolly Star-thistle

Introduced. A bird seed casual recorded at Birchington in 1962 but with no further sightings. **0** (0).

Hypochaeris radicata L.   Cat's-ear

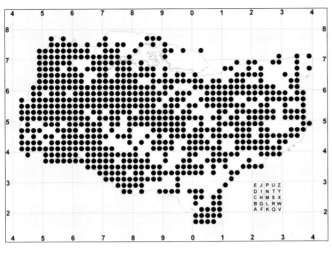

Native. Meadows, lawns, sand-dunes, roadside verges and grassy banks. **716** (873).

Hypochaeris glabra L.   Smooth Cat's-ear

Native. On dune-grassland and sandy heaths. A rare plant recorded in the National Red List as 'Vulnerable'. On a sandy grassland verge at Lydd TR02K, and on fixed sand-dunes at St. Mary's Bay TR02X & 02Y. **3** (0).

Leontodon autumnalis L.   Autumn Hawkbit

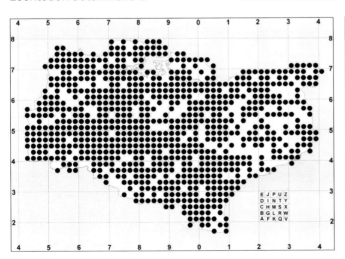

Native. Meadows, heaths, open scrub and roadside verges. **801** (881).

Leontodon hispidus L.   Rough Hawkbit

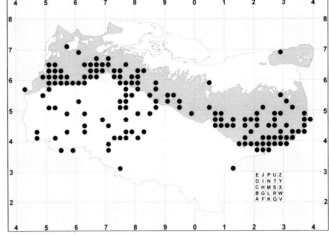

Native. On dry grassland in meadows, roadside verges and neglected ground, particularly on the chalk. **152** (290).

Leontodon saxatilis Lam.   Lesser Hawkbit

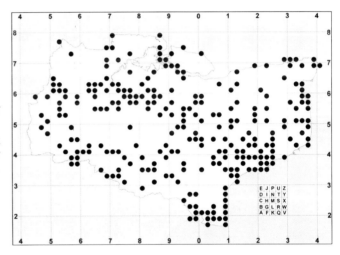

Native. Grassy banks, roadside verges and open grassy areas on well-drained soils. **264** (399).

Picris echioides L.   Bristly Oxtongue

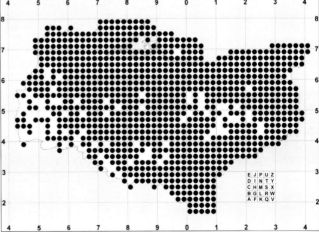

Introduced (archaeophyte). First recorded in Kent in 1629 and has steadily spread, perhaps more quickly in recent years. It is now a widespread and common plant on roadside banks, rough grassland, sea-walls, field margins and on disturbed waste ground. **926** (733).

Picris hieracioides L. Hawkweed Oxtongue

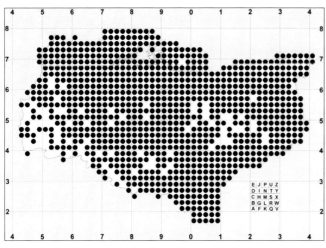

Native. On roadside verges, open scrub, lightly grazed rough meadows, and waste places, particularly on the chalk. **455** (309).

Tragopogon pratensis L. ssp. *minor* (Mill.) Wahlenb. Goat's-beard

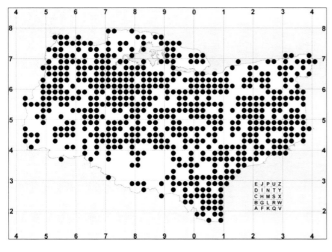

Native. In meadows, pastures, field margins, roadside verges and rough grassland. **635** (805).

Tragopogon pratensis L. ssp. *pratensis*

Introduced (neophyte). Great care has been taken over the identification of this plant which has only been found on roadside verges and waste ground by railway lines. Recorded from near Penshurst TQ54I, Wrotham Heath TQ65J; West Malling TQ65Y; Stansted TQ66B; Luddesdown TQ66S; Barming TQ66I; Stockbury TQ86F and Throwley TQ95X. **8** (9).

Tragopogon pratensis x *porrifolius* = *T.* x *mirabilis* Rouy

Native. The only sighting during the present survey was on Dartford Heath TQ57B. **1** (1).

Tragopogon porrifolius L. Salsify

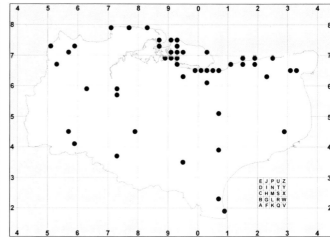

Introduced (neophyte), but now well naturalised along some parts of the North Kent coast. On sea-walls and rough grassland on the coast, and on roadside verges and disturbed ground inland. **49** (39).

Sonchus palustris L. Marsh Sow-thistle

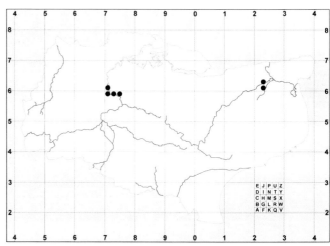

Native. In reed beds and other vegetation at the edge of rivers. **6** (10).

Sonchus arvensis L. Perennial Sow-thistle

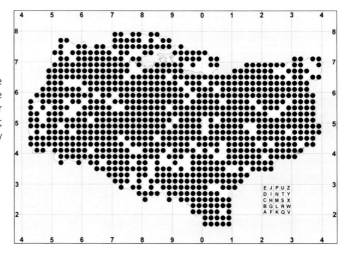

Native. On roadside verges, sea-walls, upper parts of beaches, river banks, cultivated and waste land. **870** (941).

Sonchus oleraceus L.   Smooth Sow-thistle

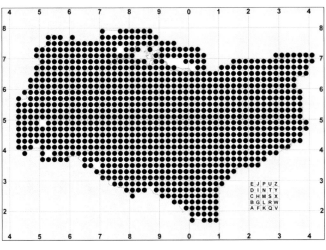

Native. On roadside verges, disturbed grassland, arable fields, gardens and waste land. **1011** (998).

Sonchus asper (L.) Hill   Prickly Sow-thistle

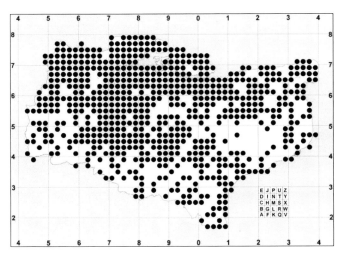

Native. Roadside verges, disturbed waste ground, at the edges of arable fields and in gardens. **978** (1005).

Lactuca serriola L.   Prickly Lettuce

Introduced (archaeophyte), but now well established and behaving as a native. On roadside verges, sea-walls, sand and gravel pits, and on disturbed waste land. **695** (360).

Lactuca virosa L.   Great Lettuce

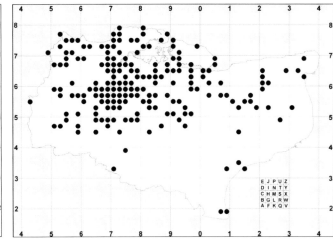

Native. On sea-walls, roadside verges, rough grassland and disturbed waste land. Appears to have increased in range in recent years. **192** (94).

Lactuca saligna L.   Least Lettuce

Native. A rare plant, now in the Red List Category, 'Endangered'. All the previous known Kent localities have been searched and the plant not found except for one site on the sea-wall near Allhallows TQ87P. Even at this one locality there was a suspicion that it had been planted there. **1** (6).

Lactuca sativa L.   Garden Lettuce

Introduced (neophyte). Casual records from rubbish-tips in the past, but not seen growing wild during the present survey.

Cicerbita macrophylla (Willd.) Wallr.   Common Blue-sow-thistle

Introduced (neophyte). A garden plant that is naturalised in a few roadside banks and hedgerows. Only recorded during the present survey from near Edenbridge TQ44P, Brasted TQ45R and Godden Green TQ55M. **3** (15).

Mycelis muralis (L.) Dumort.   Wall Lettuce

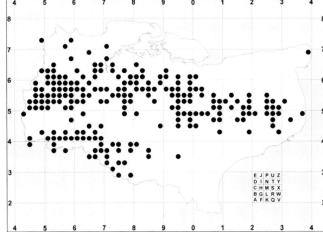

Native. On old walls, and in shaded woodland, roadsides and hedge banks. **221** (239).

Taraxacum agg.   Dandelion

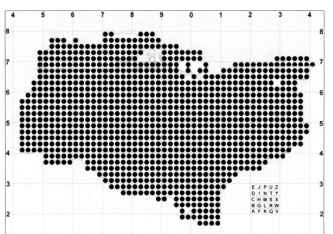

Native. The microspecies of this interesting genus have not been studied in detail during the present survey and are here mapped as the aggregate. Some of these microspecies are restricted to sand-dunes, chalk grassland, fens and marshes, whilst others are only found on disturbed soils such as roadside verges, lawns and waste places. The dandelions would warrant an in depth study and without doubt some interesting patterns of distribution would be found. The following microspecies have been recorded from the county and more are still likely to be found.   1015 (-).

Taraxacum arenastrum A.J. Richards
Taraxacum argutum Dahlst.
Taraxacum brachyglossum (Dahlst.) Raunk.
Taraxacum commixtum G.E. Haglund
Taraxacum dunense Soest
Taraxacum fulviforme Dahlst.
Taraxacum fulvum Raunk.
Taraxacum glauciniforme Dahlst.
Taraxacum lacistophyllum (Dahlst.) Raunk.
Taraxacum oxoniense Dahlst.
Taraxacum proximiforme Soest
Taraxacum proximum (Dahlst.) Raunk.
Taraxacum retzii Soest
Taraxacum rubicundum (Dahlst.) Dahlst.
Taraxacum wallonicum Soest
Taraxacum euryphyllum (Dahlst.) Hjelt
Taraxacum bracteatum Dahlst.
Taraxacum duplidentifrons Dahlst.
Taraxacum gelertii Raunk.
Taraxacum hygrophilum Soest (in Britain is restricted to a few wet meadows near Stodmarsh).
Taraxacum nordstedtii Dahlst.
Taraxacum ostenfeldii Raunk.
Taraxacum subbracteatum A.J. Richards
Taraxacum atactum Sahlin & Soest
Taraxacum boekmanni Borgv.
Taraxacum fusciflorum H. Øllg.
Taraxacum hamatiforme Dahlst.
Taraxacum hamatum Raunk.
Taraxacum hamiferum Dahlst.
Taraxacum kernianum Hagend., Soest & Zevenb.
Taraxacum lamprophyllum M.P. Christ.
Taraxacum pseudohamatum Dahlst.
Taraxacum quadrans H. Øllg.
Taraxacum acroglossum Dahlst.
Taraxacum aequilobum Dahlst.
Taraxacum aequisectum M.P. Christ.

Taraxacum alatum H. Lindb.
Taraxacum ancistrolobum Dahlst.
Taraxacum aurosulum H. Lindb.
Taraxacum cophocentrum Dahlst.
Taraxacum cordatum Palmgr.
Taraxacum croceiflorum Dahlst.
Taraxacum cyanolepis Dahlst.
Taraxacum dahlstedtii H. Lindb.
Taraxacum ekmanii Dahlst.
Taraxacum exacutum Markl.
Taraxacum expallidiforme Dahlst.
Taraxacum exsertum Hagend., Soest & Zevenb.
Taraxacum fagerstroemii Såltin
Taraxacum fasciatum Dahlst.
Taraxacum adiantifrons E. Ekman ex Dahlst.
Taraxacum insigne E. Ekman ex M.P. Christ. & Wiinst.
Taraxacum interveniens G.E. Haglund
Taraxacum laciniosifrons Wiinst.
Taraxacum laeticolor Dahlst.
Taraxacum laticordatum Markl.
Taraxacum lingulatum Markl.
Taraxacum longisquameum H. Lindb.
Taraxacum macrolobum Dahlst.
Taraxacum mimulum Dahlst. ex H. Lindb.
Taraxacum obliquilobum Dahlst.
Taraxacum oblongatum Dahlst.
Taraxacum obtusilobum Dahlst. ex G.E. Haglund
Taraxacum pachymerum G.E. Haglund
Taraxacum pannucium Dahlst.
Taraxacum pannulatum Dahlst.
Taraxacum pectinatiforme H. Lindb.
Taraxacum piceatum Dahlst.
Taraxacum polyodon Dahlst.
Taraxacum pulchrifolium Markl.
Taraxacum sagittipotens Dahlst. & R.Ohlsen ex G.E.Haglund
Taraxacum scotiniforme Dahlst. ex G.E. Haglund
Taraxacum sellandii Dahlst.
Taraxacum stenacrum Dahlst.
Taraxacum subcyanolepis M.P. Christ
Taraxacum subexpallidum Dahlst.
Taraxacum subundulatum Dahlst.
Taraxacum undulatiflorum M.P. Christ.
Taraxacum xanthostigma H. Lindb.

Crepis biennis L.   Rough Hawk's-beard

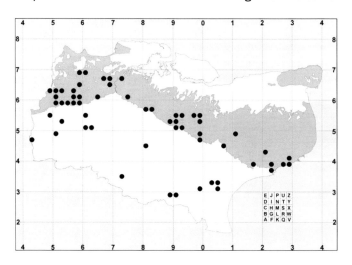

Native. On roadside verges, wood-margins and rough grassland, particularly on the chalk. 58 (85).

Crepis nicaeensis Balb.　　　　French Hawk's-beard

Introduced.　Casual records in the past, the last in 1832. 0 (0).

Crepis capillaris (L.) Wallr.　　Smooth Hawk's-beard

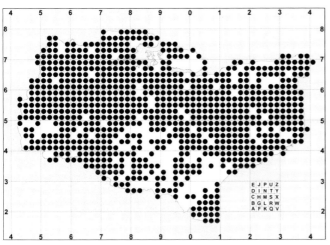

Native.　In open grassland, lawns, roadside verges, fixed sand-dunes, gardens and other open ground. **821** (908).

Crepis vesicaria L.　　　　Beaked Hawk's-beard

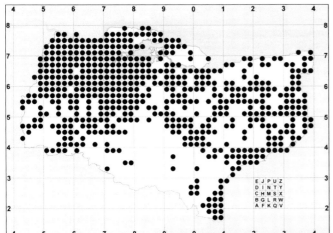

Introduced (neophyte).　On roadside verges, lawns, lightly grazed grassland, railway banks, and disturbed waste ground.　Our plant is subspecies *taraxacifolia* (Thuill.) Thell. ex Schinz & R. Keller. **581** (715).

Crepis setosa Haller f.　　　Bristly Hawk's-beard

Introduced.　Casual plants noted on roadside banks at Eynsford TQ56H and Staplehurst TQ74X. **2** (1).

Crepis foetida L.　　　　Stinking Hawk's-beard

Introduced (archaeophyte).　Formerly well established on a few chalky and gravelly places.　It finally became extinct at its last site in Britain, at Dungeness, in 1981.　It was re-introduced at Dungeness TR01U in 1992 but had become extinct there again by 2002.　In 2002 it was introduced, under licence, to sites on private land in TQ76B, TR04U and TR25X, and these sites continue to be monitored.　**0** wild, **4** planted / tended, (2).

Pilosella aurantiaca 　　　　Fox-and-cubs
(L.) F.W. Schultz & Sch. Bip.

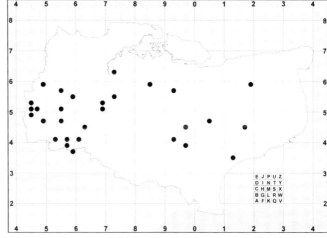

Introduced (neophyte).　A garden plant that has become well naturalised on roadside verges, railway banks, churchyards and other grassy and waste places.　All the specimens checked have proved to be subspecies *carpathicola* (Nägeli & Peter) Soják. **29** (5).

Pilosella officinarum 　　　Mouse-ear-hawkweed
F.W. Schultz & Sch. Bip

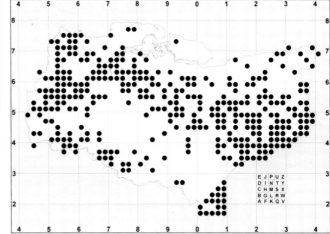

Native. In dry short grassland on heaths, downland and roadside verges, in chalk and ragstone quarries, on cliffs, fixed sand-dunes, and on old walls. Subspecies *micradenia*, *officinarum*, *tricholepia* and *melanops* all occur in the county but have not been mapped separately. **370** (373).

Pilosella peleteriana (Merat) F.W. Schultz & Sch.　　　Shaggy Mouse-ear-hawkweed

Native. Has been recorded from the Folkestone-Dover area in the past, but was not found during the present mapping. **0** (0).

Unlike the Dandelions, the Hawkweeds have been carefully studied during the survey for this Flora. Voucher specimens for most records are housed in Maidstone Museum (**MNE**) and identification was based on Pugsley (1948), greatly helped by the key in Sell & West (1965). As the mapping finished, the long-awaited new work on Hawkweeds was published, Sell & Murrell (2006), and so the classification and names in that work are followed here.

Hieracium vagum Jord.　　　Glabrous-headed Hawkweed

Native, but probably only as a casual introduction in Kent. The only confirmed record is from Sittingbourne in 1978, but not found during the present survey. **0** (1).

Hieracium rigens Jord.　　　Rigid Hawkweed

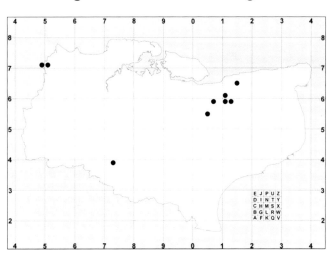

Native. On heaths, open woodland and roadside banks on sandy soils. **9** (4).

Hieracium salticola (Sudre) P.D. Sell & C. West　　　Bluish-leaved Hawkweed

Native. Woodland rides in Joyden's Wood TQ47V (where it was first recorded from Kent in 1978) & TQ57A; in scrub heathland on Dartford Heath TQ57G; and in a garden, probably introduced, at Borough Green TQ65D. **4** (1).

Hieracium virgultorum Jord.　　　Long-leaved Hawkweed

Native. Recorded from Tunbridge Wells, Mereworth Woods and Sturry in the past. The only record during the present mapping was of plants well naturalised in a garden at Borough Green TQ65D where it had originally probably been introduced. The records from Perry Wood in Philp (1982) were in error for *H. rigens*. **1** (1).

Hieracium sabaudum L.　　　Autumn Hawkweed

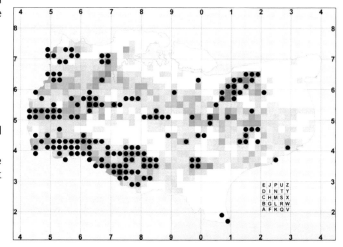

Native. On sandy, usually acid, soils on heaths, open woodland, and roadside verges where they pass through woodland. Occasional plants on open areas such as on the shingle at Dungeness. Both forma *sabaudum* and forma *bladonii* (Pugsley) P.D. Sell occur but have not been mapped separately. **165** (187).

Hieracium umbellatum L.　　　Umbellate Hawkweed

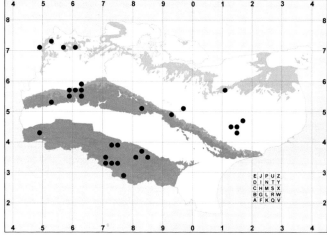

Native. On roadside banks, heaths and woodland rides, usually on sandy soils. All the plants checked have proved to be subspecies *umbellatum*. It has been lost from some former sites through housing development. **30** (39).

Hieracium eboracense Pugsley   Northern Hawkweed

Native, endemic. In Joyden's Wood TQ57A and Beacon Wood Country Park TQ57V are the only records during the present survey. Not found at the few previous recorded sites on the Hastings and Folkestone Sands. **2** (0).

Hieracium cantianum F. Hanb.   Kent Hawkweed

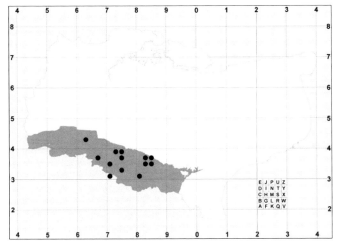

Native, endemic. First discovered near Cranbrook in 1889, this plant has a limited range within Hampshire, Sussex, Surrey and Kent. It occurs along woodland rides and woodland edges, often where a road passes through woodland. **13** (6).

Hieracium trichocaulon (Dahlst.) Johanss.   Hairy-stemmed Hawkweed

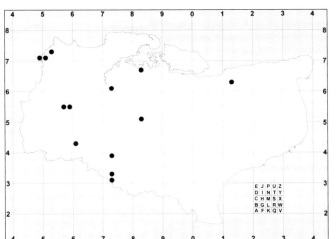

Native. On sandy heaths, open woodland and shady roadside banks. If not under-recorded, there appears to have been a serious decline in the distribution of this plant. **13** (38).

Hieracium calcaricola (F. Hanb.) Roffey   Toothed Hawkweed

Native, although perhaps introduced at its former sites at Maidstone (1971) and Sissinghurst (1974). It was not found during the present survey. **0** (2).

Hieracium cambricogothicum Pugsley   Llanfairfechan Hawkweed

Native, endemic. In Britain known at present from two localities, Llanfairfechan in Wales where it was discovered in 1903, and from Riverhead TQ55D in Kent, where it has been known since 1951. It was still present at this Riverhead locality in 1992 on and at the base of ragstone walls, where it has been suggested that it might have been introduced. The number of plants has greatly reduced in recent years (only nine plants counted in 2004, T. Rich *in litt.*), and there are now fears that it could eventually be lost to the county. There is a specimen in **MNE**, collected by Dr. West from Kingswood, Langley in 1950, but it has not been re-found there among a number of other hawkweeds that are present. **1** (1).

Hieracium lanatum Vill.   Woolly Hawkweed

Introduced (neophyte). A garden plant recorded growing on old walls at Canterbury in the 1950s, but not seen during the present survey. **0** (0).

Hieracium pilosum Schleich. ex Froel.   Fimbriate-pitted Hawkweed

Introduced (neophyte). Found established on the beach at Greatstone in 1966 and recorded there again in 1969, but with no subsequent records. **0** (0).

Hieracium pollichiae Sch. Bip.   Roffey's Hawkweed

Native. On a roadside verge at Detling TQ75Z, and scattered plants on roadside banks over a wide area at Kingswood TQ85F. **2** (1).

Hieracium lepidulum (Stenstr.) Omang   Irregular-toothed Hawkweed

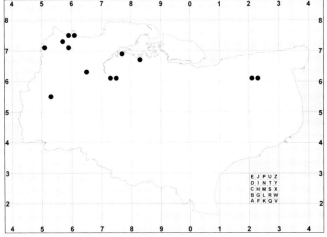

Introduced (neophyte). On roadside banks and disturbed waste ground. **13** (9).

Hieracium subviolascens Violet-leaved Hawkweed
P.D. Sell

Introduced. Has been recorded from a railway embankment at Swanley in the past, but was not found during the present survey. **0** (0).

Hieracium surrejanum F. Hanb. Surrey Hawkweed

Native, endemic. On a roadside verge at Goodley Stock TQ45G. **1** (0).

Hieracium spilophaeum Spotted Hawkweed
Jord. ex Boreau

Introduced (neophyte). On old walls at Hothfield TQ94S is the only record during the present survey. **1** (2).

Hieracium mammidens Breast-toothed Hawkweed
P.D. Sell

Probably native. Past records from Pembury in 1956-7; Maidstone in 1972, and Swanscombe in 1983, but not found during the present survey. **0** (0).

Hieracium diaphanum Fr. Dark-leaved Hawkweed

Probably introduced (neophyte). Has been recorded from Kent in the past, probably always in error, and was not found during the present survey. **0** (0).

Hieracium megapodium Fine-bracted Hawkweed
Dahlst.

Introduced. At Langton in 1943 and in a newly sown grass field at the same locality in 1952, but not since. Mentioned as *H. diaphanoides* in the 1982 Atlas, although its reference to a 1968 record was in error. There are no recent records. **0** (0).

Hieracium acuminatum Tall Hawkweed
Jord. sensu Kent (1992)

Possibly introduced (neophyte). On sandy roadside banks at Goodley Stock TQ45G, Toy's Hill TQ45Q, near Brasted TQ45T, Joyden's Wood TQ57A, Oaken Wood TQ75C, Cuxton TQ76D, Mintching Wood TQ95E, and Stodmarsh TR26A. These plants were identified using the key in Sell & West (1965).

However, since the completion of the mapping for this Atlas, Sell & Murrell (2006) have recognised three taxa which had previously been treated as this species. On re-checking the specimen from Brasted it was considered to be *H. consociatum* Jord. ex Boreau, and those from Cuxton, Minching Wood and Stodmarsh were considered to be *H. argillaceum* Jord. The true *H. acuminatum* sensu Sell & Murrell has not been recorded from Kent. **8** (15, recorded as *H. strumosum* in 1982 Atlas).

Hieracium chlorophyllum Green-leaved Hawkweed
Jord. ex Boreau

Possibly native. The only British record given by Sell & Murrell (2006) is at Stowting in Kent. No specimens from this locality could be found in **MNE** that exactly matched the description of this plant. Specimens nearest to this plant can be found in the *H. lepidulum* folder. Not found during the present survey. **0** (0).

Hieracium festinum Hairy-leaved Hawkweed
Jord. ex Boreau

Probably introduced. Reported from Pembury and Bitchet Common (Sell & Murrell, 2006), but not found during the present survey. **0** (0).

Hieracium cheriense Jord. ex Boreau Cher Hawkweed

Probably introduced (neophyte). On old walls and roadside banks. **12** (30).

Hieracium scotostictum Hyl. Dappled Hawkweed

Introduced (neophyte). A garden plant that at times escapes and becomes established on railway banks and roadsides. The only record during the present survey was from a roadside at The Moor, Hawkhurst TQ72P. **1** (5).

Hieracium liljeholmii Dahlst. Liljeholm's Hawkweed

Introduced (neophyte). Was once found in Joyden's Wood but has not been re-found there in spite of repeated searches. **0** (0).

Hieracium grandidens Grand-toothed Hawkweed
Dahlst.

Introduced. On roadside banks and old walls at Otford TQ55J, Burham TQ76G and Larkeyvalley Wood TR15H. **3** (0).

Hieracium kentii P.D. Sell   Kent's Hawkweed

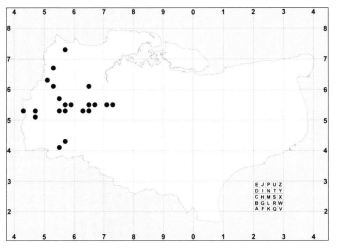

Native. On roadside banks and woodland edges. In the 1982 Atlas this taxon was recorded within *H. exotericum* agg. **21** (11, recorded as the 'Kentish exotericum').

All specimens recorded here have stellate hairs on the underside of the cauline leaves, but on the involucral bracts the stellate hairs were very variable in number and more often just confined to the base.

Hieracium sublepistoides   Grey-bracted Hawkweed
(Zahn) Druce

Introduced (neophyte). A few plants, growing with *H. kentii*, on a roadside bank at Borough Green TQ65D constitute the only record during the present mapping. **1** (11).

Hieracium cardiophyllum   Heart-leaved Hawkweed
(Jord. ex Sudre) Juxip

Introduced (neophyte). Known on railway banks near Dunton Green 1961-1978, but not found there since. **0** (1).

Hieracium severiceps Wiinst.   Strict-headed Hawkweed

Introduced (neophyte). On a roadside bank near Kipping's Cross in 1965 is the only Kent record; it has not been found there since. **0** (0).

Hieracium integratum   Toothless Hawkweed
(Dahlst. ex Stenstr.) Dahlst.

Introduced (neophyte). On a south-facing chalky bank at Detling in 1985 was the first record for Kent, but has not been re-found there. **0** (0).

Hieracium exotericum   Jordan's Hawkweed
Jord. ex Boreau

Introduced (neophyte). Well established on some old walls at Maidstone TQ75M & 75R. The record from Borough Green in the 1982 Atlas has proved to be *H. kentii*. **2** (2).

Hieracium gentile Jord. ex Boreau   Foreign Hawkweed

Introduced (neophyte). Reported from Ashurst Park in 1951 by Sell & Murrell (2006), but was not found during the present mapping. **0** (0).

Specimens from this locality in **MNE** match this species in that they lack stellate hairs on the involucral bracts, but they also have stellate hairs on the undersides of the cauline leaf, a character usually associated with *H. kentii*.

Arctotis breviscapa Thunb.

Introduced. Reported growing on a rubbish-tip at Dartford in 1976, but with no further sightings. **0** (1).

Filago vulgaris Lam.   Common Cudweed

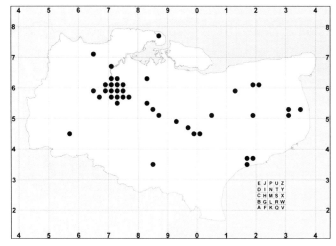

Native. On roadside banks, in quarries and on dry waste land, particularly on sandy soils. Nationally a scarce plant, listed as 'Near Threatened'. **41** (23).

Filago lutescens Jord.   Red-tipped Cudweed

Native. A rare plant of sandy fields now listed as 'Endangered'. Was recorded from near Farningham Wood in 1945 and 1960, and from Hothfield in 1963. There have been no further records. **0** (0).

Filago pyramidata L.   Broad-leaved Cudweed

Introduced (archaeophyte). Another rare cudweed, again listed as 'Endangered'. It is still to be found in arable fields in the Cobham-Cuxton area TQ66Y, 66Z and TQ76D. **3** (2).

Filago minima (Sm.) Pers.   Small Cudweed

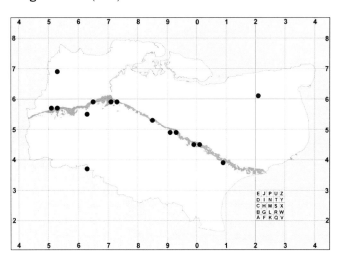

Native. On sandy heaths, quarries, roadside verges and other dry sandy areas. **15** (12).

Filago gallica L.   Narrow-leaved Cudweed

Introduced (archaeophyte), now extinct. First recorded from near Dartford in 1739, and with further casual records from that area until 1813. **0** (0).

Stuartina hamata Philipson   Hooked Cudweed

Introduced. A wool shoddy plant found at Barming in 1976 is the only record. **0** (1).

Antennaria dioica (L.) Gaertn.   Mountain Everlasting

Introduced. A casual garden outcast, last recorded growing wild in the county in 1900. **0** (0).

Anaphalis margaritacea (L.) Benth.   Pearly Everlasting

Introduced. A casual garden escape. The only record during the present mapping was from the banks of the Canterbury by-pass TR15M. **1** (1).

Gnaphalium sylvaticum L.   Heath Cudweed

Native. On heaths and dry, open woodland, usually on sandy soils. Its 'Endangered' listing reflects decline across the British Isles, and the survey results are consistent with this for the county. **24** (52).

Gnaphalium uliginosum L.   Marsh Cudweed

Native. In damp woodland rides, compacted arable and cultivated land, and wet areas trampled by cattle. **336** (434).

Gnaphalium luteoalbum L.   Jersey Cudweed

Introduced (neophyte). Discovered on the RSPB reserve at Dungeness TR01U in 1996 and since then the colony has increased to several thousand plants. **1** (0).

Gnaphalium undulatum L.   Cape Cudweed

Introduced. Established in and around a garden at South Darenth for a year or so in the late 1970s, but with no subsequent records. **0** (1).

Helichrysum bracteatum   Strawflower
(Vent.) Andrews

Introduced. Casual garden escapes noted in the past, but not seen growing wild during the present mapping. **0** (5).

Helichrysum italicum (Thunb.) Less.   Curry-plant

Introduced. A casual escape from cultivation, noted on the shingle beach at Dungeness TR01Y, and waste sandy ground at Sandwich Bay TR35T. **2** (0).

Inula crithmoides L.   Golden-samphire

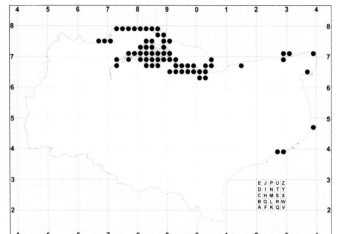

Native. In saltmarshes, sea-walls and amongst drift-litter on beaches and occasionally on sea-cliffs. **67** (63).

Inula helenium L.   Elecampane

Introduced (archaeophyte). On roadsides and in hedgerows, often near old farm buildings, and long established. Recorded from Benover TQ74E, Potman's Heath TQ82U, Kingsnorth TR03E, near Aldington Frith TR03I, Naccolt TR04M. **5** (5).

Dittrichia viscosa (L.) Greuter   Woody Fleabane

Introduced. Casual plants recorded from Northfleet TQ67G and Stonelees TR36G. **2** (0).

Inula orientalis Lam.   Eastern Fleabane

Introduced. A casual garden escape noted from the Tunbridge Wells area in the 1970s, but with no subsequent records. **0** (1).

Dittrichia graveolens (L.) Greuter.   Stinking Fleabane

Introduced (neophyte). Recorded as a wool shoddy alien in the past, but not since 1960. **0** (0).

Inula conyzae   Ploughman's-spikenard
(Griess.) Meikle

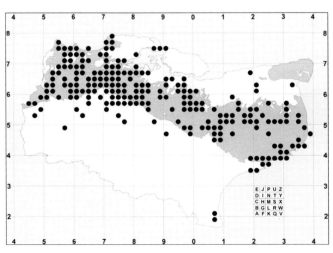

Native. Occurs in dry sites on roadside banks, woodland margins, quarries and scrub, particularly on calcareous soils. **220** (239).

Pulicaria dysenterica (L.) Bernh.   Common Fleabane

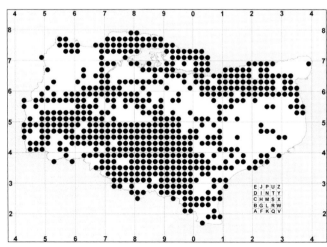

Native. In damp or wet open habitats by rivers, streams, ponds, ditches, wet woods and damp meadows. **604** (648).

Pulicaria vulgaris Gaertn.   Small Fleabane

Native, extinct.   A rare plant of damp meadows last recorded in the county in the late 19th century.   **0** (0).

Telekia speciosa (Schreb.) Baumg.   Yellow Oxeye

Introduced.   A casual garden escape, recorded in the 1970s, but not seen during the present mapping.   **0** (2).

Calotis cuneifolia R. Br.   Purple Bur-daisy

Introduced.   A casual wool shoddy alien last recorded in the county in 1960.   **0** (0).

Calotis hispidula (F. Muell.) F. Muell.   Hairy Bur-daisy

Introduced.   A wool shoddy plant with a few casual records from 1948 until 1960, but not since.   **0** (0).

Calotis lappulacea Benth.   Yellow Bur-daisy

Introduced. Casual plants from wool shoddy in 1960 constitute the only record for the county.   **0** (0).

Bellium bellidioides L.

Introduced. A garden plant reported seen on the coast at Broadstairs in 1980, but with no further records.   **0** (1).

Solidago virgaurea L.   Goldenrod

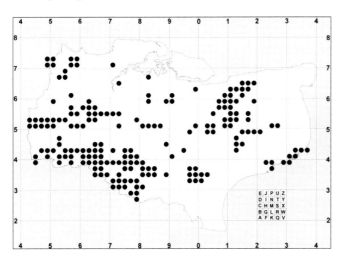

Native.   In woods and heaths usually on acidic soils, but occasionally on chalk banks and cliffs.   **195** (272).

Solidago virgaurea x canadensis
= S. x niederederi Khek

Native. Discovered on a railway bank at Swanley in 1979, but not seen during the present mapping.   **0** (1).

Solidago rugosa Mill.   Rough-stemmed Goldenrod

Introduced.   Casual garden escapes reported in the past, but there are no recent records.   **0** (0).

Solidago canadensis L.   Canadian Goldenrod

Introduced (neophyte).   A garden plant now well naturalised and persistent on roadsides, railway banks and waste ground.   **86** (150).

Solidago gigantea Aiton   Early Goldenrod

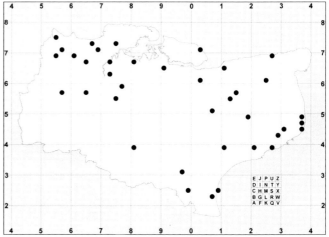

Introduced (neophyte). A garden plant well naturalised on roadsides and waste places in scattered localities throughout the county.   **38** (52).

There has been much confusion over the naming of the various Michaelmas-daisies in the past and so great care has been taken in naming these plants in accordance to the latest nomenclature. As this can only be done when the plants are in full flower, this has resulted in some under-recording of this group. However, the results do reflect the present distribution and relative abundance of these plants.

Aster novi-belgii L.   Confused Michaelmas-daisy

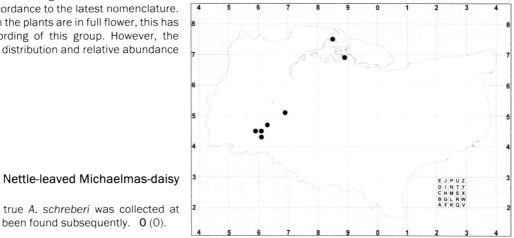

Introduced (neophyte). On roadside banks and waste places. Only found along the Medway Valley from the estuary back to Tonbridge, and almost certainly over-recorded in the past. **7** (116).

Aster schreberi Nees   Nettle-leaved Michaelmas-daisy

Introduced (neophyte). The true *A. schreberi* was collected at Swanley in 1946 but has not been found subsequently. **0** (0).

Aster novae-angliae L.   Hairy Michaelmas-daisy

Introduced (neophyte). On a roadside bank by Darenth Wood TQ57R and on waste ground at Rochester TQ76P. **2** (5).

Aster novi-belgii x lanceolatus   Common
= A. x salignus Willd.   Michaelmas-daisy

Aster laevis L.   Glaucous Michaelmas-daisy

Introduced. Casual plants recorded in the past, but with no recent sightings. **0** (2).

Aster laevis x novi-belgii   Late Michaelmas-daisy
= A. x versicolor Willd.

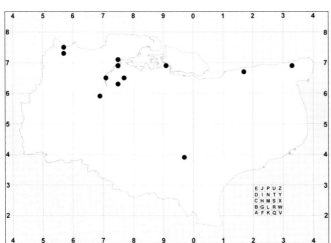

Introduced (neophyte). A common garden plant now widely naturalised on roadsides, railway banks and waste places. **36** (2).

Introduced (neophyte). On roadsides, railway banks and waste places. **12** (3).

Aster lanceolatus   Narrow-leaved Michaelmas-daisy
Willd.

Introduced (neophyte). A few records in the past but not noted during the present mapping. **0** (6).

Aster tripolium L.   Sea Aster

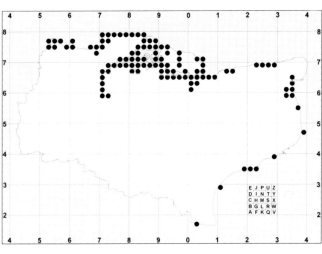

Native.   In salt-marshes and on the banks of sea-walls and tidal creeks.   **107** (129).

Plants referable to *Aster dumosus* x *novi-belgii* were recorded from a few rubbish-tips in the 1970s but with no subsequent records.   **0** (4).

Chrysocoma tenuifolia   Fine-leaved Goldilocks
P.J. Bergius

Introduced.   Casual records from wool shoddy, last recorded in 1960.   **0** (0).

Erigeron glaucus Ker Gawl.   Seaside Daisy

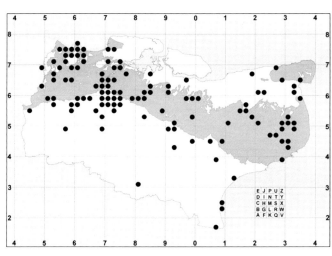

Introduced (neophyte).   A garden plant now established on shingle, cliffs, walls and waste places, particularly on the coast. **11** (0).

Erigeron karvinskianus DC.   Mexican Fleabane

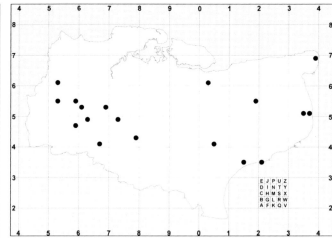

Introduced (neophyte). Although only rarely in cultivation, this plant is now well established on old walls, in pavement cracks and on waste stony ground in scattered localities over the county. **18** (4).

Erigeron acer L.   Blue Fleabane

Native.   On dry roadside and railway banks, old quarries, sand-dunes, spoil heaps and old walls.   **119** (170).

Erigeron speciosus (Lindl.) DC.   Garden Fleabane

Introduced (neophyte).   Established on an old wall at Knole Park TQ55H where it has been known since at least 1978.   **1** (1).

Erigeron acer x Conyza canadensis
= x Conyzigeron huelsenii (Vatke) Rauschert

Native.   Recorded from the edge of Farningham Wood in 1945, Burham in 1945, 1946 and 1956, and from Leybourne in 1957, but with no subsequent records up to the end of the survey period. **0** (0).

Conyza canadensis (L.) Cronquist   Canadian Fleabane

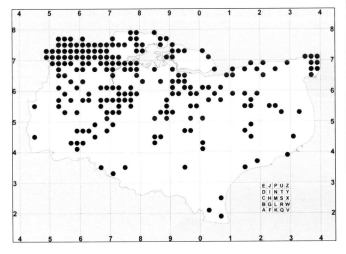

Introduced (neophyte). In gardens and other cultivated ground, on old walls and in pavement cracks, and on waste ground. First recorded in Kent in 1836. **400** (355).

Conyza sumatrensis
(Retz.) E. Walker   Guernsey Fleabane

Introduced (neophyte). The first Kent record was from Swanscombe in 1985 (G.D. Kitchener, pers. comm.). Since then it has spread rapidly on open well-drained and disturbed ground, on old walls and in pavement cracks, particularly in built-up areas. **218** (0).

Conyza bilbaoana J. Rémy   Bilbao's Fleabane

Introduced (neophyte). Discovered, new to Kent, at the edge of a car park at Dry Hill near Sevenoaks TQ45X in 2001. Further records would be expected in the future. **1** (0).

Conyza bonariensis (L.) Cronquist   Argentine Fleabane

Introduced. Casual plants with wool shoddy and industrial waste in the past, the last in 1978. **0** (1).

Callistephus chinensis (L.) Nees   China Aster

Introduced. A garden outcast recorded in the past, mainly from rubbish-tips, but not seen growing wild during the present mapping. **0** (10).

Olearia macrodonta Baker   New Zealand Holly

Introduced (neophyte). Reported from waste ground near Chevening in the 1970s, but with no subsequent records. **0** (1).

Olearia avicenniifolia x moschata
= **O. x haastii** Hook. f.   Daisy-bush

Introduced. Reported from Darenth Wood in 1980 in an area that was formerly hospital gardens. There are no subsequent records. **0** (1).

Bellis perennis L.   Daisy

Native. In lawns, roadside verges and other mown, or heavily grazed grassland. Widespread and common throughout the county. **1016** (1029).

Tanacetum parthenium (L.) Sch. Bip.   Feverfew

Introduced (archaeophyte). A common plant in cultivation and now widely naturalised in gardens, roadside verges, on old walls and waste land. **419** (380).

Tanacetum macrophyllum Rayed Tansy
(Waldst. & Kit.) Sch. Bip.

Introduced. A garden outcast recorded from Wrotham in 1954, but with no subsequent sightings. **0** (0).

Tanacetum vulgare L. Tansy

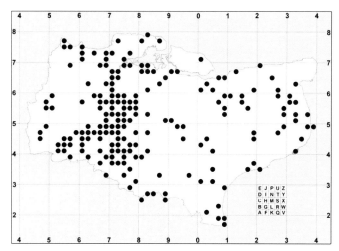

Native. In grassy places on the banks and edges of rivers and streams. Also on roadside verges and waste places where, in some places, it could be an escape from cultivation. **195** (245).

Tanacetum leucophyllum Regel

Introduced. A casual plant on rubbish-tip at Dartford in the 1970s is the only record. **0** (1).

Seriphidium maritimum (L.) Poljakow Sea Wormwood

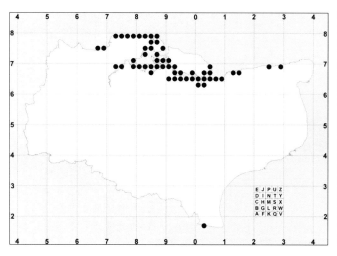

Native. On the drier parts of salt-marshes and at the edges of sea-walls. **55** (75).

Artemisia vulgaris L. Mugwort

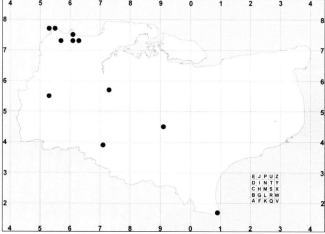

Introduced (archaeophyte), although behaving much as a native plant. On roadside verges, rough ground and waste places. **922** (910).

Artemisia vulgaris x verlotiorum
= **A.** x **wurzellii** C.M. James & Stace

Native. On rubbish-tip at Swanscombe TQ67C in 1994 (G. D. Kitchener & M. Keene). **1** (0).

Artemisia verlotiorum Lamotte Chinese Mugwort

Introduced (neophyte). First recorded from Kent in 1949 and now sparingly found on roadside verges and waste places. **11** (25).

Artemisia absinthium L.   Wormwood

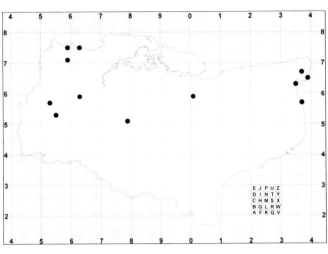

Introduced (archaeophyte). On roadside verges, quarries and disturbed waste land. Searched for and appears to have gone from several former localities. **12** (18).

Artemisia abrotanum L.   Southernwood

Introduced. Casual escapes from cultivation noted in the 1970s, but there are no recent records. **0** (3).

Artemisia biennis Willd.   Slender Mugwort

Introduced. Casual plants on waste ground at South Darenth in the 1970s, but with no subsequent records. **0** (1).

Santolina chamaecyparissus L.   Lavender-cotton

Introduced. A garden plant, once recorded as a casual in the 1970s. **0** (1).

Otanthus maritimus   Cottonweed
(L.) Hoffmanns. & Link

Perhaps originally native but long extinct. Recorded from Sheppey at some date before 1778. **0** (0).

Achillea ptarmica L.   Sneezewort

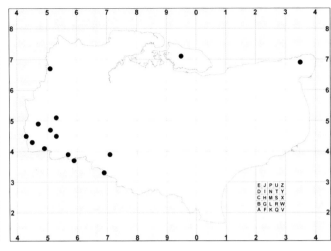

Native. In damp meadows and waste ground near rivers. Never common in the county, this plant appears to have become much scarcer in recent years, in many cases, due to loss or destruction of habitat. **14** (38).

Achillea millefolium L.   Yarrow

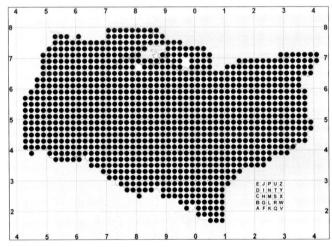

Native. In meadows, lawns, roadside verges and other grassland habitats, and also on stabilised sand and shingle areas. **1024** (1032).

Achillea tomentosa L.   Yellow Milfoil

Introduced. Noted in a gravel pit near Gravesend in 1910, but with no subsequent records. **0** (0).

Achillea filipendulina Lam.   Fern-leaf Yarrow

Introduced. A casual garden escape once recorded from West Kent. **0** (0).

255

Chamaemelum nobile (L.) All.   Chamomile

Native. A rare plant now listed as 'Vulnerable'. It still persists on Southborough Common TQ54R where it has been known for many years. The only other records are of casual plants on a roadside verge at Barham TR25A. **2** (4).

Anthemis punctata Vahl.   Sicilian Chamomile

Introduced (neophyte). An escape from cultivation well naturalised on shingle waste ground at Lade TR02V. **1** (0).

Anthemis arvensis L.   Corn Chamomile

Introduced (archaeophyte). Formerly a frequent plant of arable field, but now rare and listed nationally as 'Endangered'. Not found during the present mapping and perhaps now extinct in the county. **0** (5).

Anthemis cotula L.   Stinking Chamomile

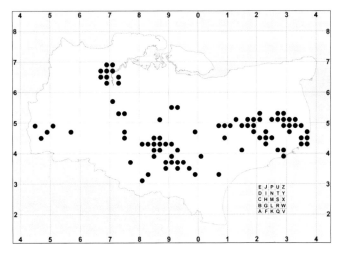

Introduced (archaeophyte). A plant of arable fields on both the chalk and clayey soils. Recorded as common by Hanbury & Marshall in 1899, this plant has been in decline since the last war and is fast becoming a scarce plant, being listed in the category 'Vulnerable'. **89** (177).

Anthemis tinctoria L.   Yellow Chamomile

Introduced (neophyte). Casual plants noted at the edge of an arable field at Longfield TQ65E, and on disturbed waste ground at Leybourne TQ65Z where it had probably been introduced with 'wild-flower' seed. **2** (6).

Anthemis austriaca Jacq.   Austrian Chamomile

Introduced. On the verges of a car park at Tenterden TQ83W and in a clearing in a wood near Bethersden TQ93E, in both cases probably introduced with a wild-flower seed mix said to contain *A. arvensis*. **2** (0).

Chrysanthemum segetum L.   Corn Marigold

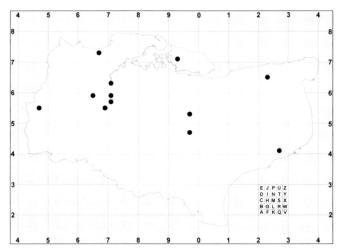

Introduced (archaeophyte). Formerly a common plant of arable fields, particularly on sandy soils. Now a scarce plant and listed nationally as 'Vulnerable'. **12** (28).

Chrysanthemum x *morifolium* Ramat.   Florist's Chrysanthemum

Introduced. A few casual records of this garden plant in the 1970s on rubbish-tips and waste ground, but with no recent sightings. **0** (5).

Chrysanthemum x *rubellum* Sealy   Korean Chrysanthemum

Introduced. Casual plants on rubbish-tips at Dartford in 1978 are the only records. **0** (2).

Ismelia carinata (Schousb.) Sch. Bip.   Tricolour Chrysanthemum

Introduced. A garden outcast reported from a rubbish-tip at Longfield in 1956. **0** (0).

Leucanthemum vulgare Lam.   Oxeye Daisy

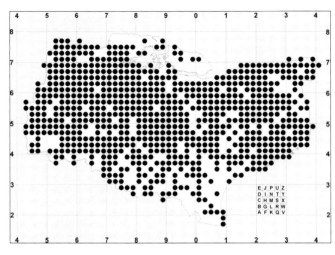

Native. In meadows and pastures that are not too heavily grazed, and on roadside verges and rough grassy areas. The common native plant is subsp. *vulgare*, but subsp. *ircutianum* (DC.) P.D. Sell is now regularly found along motorway and other main road verges where it has been introduced with 'wild-flower mix' seed **769** (842).

Leucanthemum x *superbum*   Shasta Daisy
(Bergmans ex J.W. Ingram) D.H. Kent

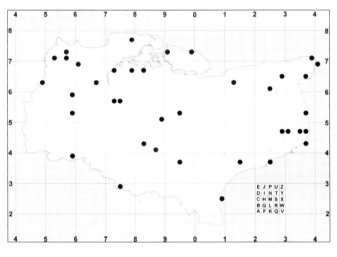

Introduced (neophyte). A common plant of cultivation now widely established on roadside verges and disturbed rough or waste ground. **38** (59).

Matricaria recutita L.   Scented Mayweed

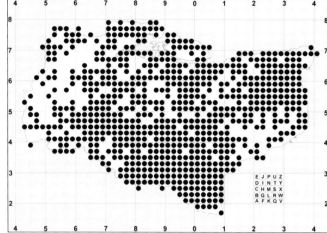

Introduced (archaeophyte). A long established plant, first recorded in the county in 1777, and now widespread in arable fields and waste places. **743** (800).

Matricaria discoidea DC.   Pineappleweed

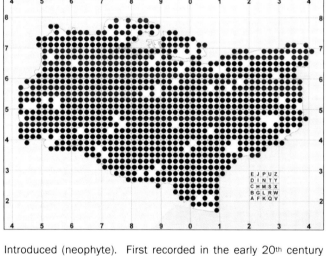

Introduced (neophyte). First recorded in the early 20th century and now widely established on roadside verges, tracks, field gateways and other trampled areas, and also in arable fields. **923** (1010).

Oxeye Daisiy *Leucanthemum vulgare* © L. Manning

257

Tripleurospermum maritimum
(L.) W.D.J. Koch
Sea Mayweed

Senecio cineraria DC.
Silver Ragwort

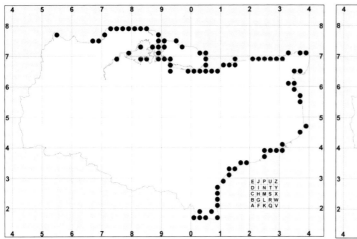

Native. On sea-walls, upper parts of shores, edges of salt-marshes and waste areas on sand and shingle in coastal areas. **84** (29).

Introduced (neophyte). A common ornamental plant of gardens. Well established in some coastal areas in county, but inland records tend to be of casual garden escapes. **20** (13).

Tripleurospermum inodorum
(L.) Sch. Bip.
Scentless Mayweed

Senecio cineraria x **jacobaea**
= **S.** x **albescens** Burb. & Colgan

Plants referable to this hybrid found growing on roadside verges and waste ground at Shoreham TQ56A, Bewl Water TQ63W, Longfield TQ66E, Cranbrook TQ73S, Hythe TR13M and Sandwich Bay TR35T. **6** (3).

Senecio cineraria x **erucifolius**
= **S.** x **thuretii** Briq. & Cavill.

Several plants still to be found on the beach at Walmer TR34U where it was first discovered in 1978. **1** (1).

Introduced (archaeophyte). Arable fields, roadside verges and disturbed waste ground. **902** (1000).

Senecio inaequidens DC.
Narrow-leaved Ragwort

Cotula coronopifolia L.
Buttonweed

Introduced (neophyte). An aggressive escape from cultivation and recorded from marsh dykes near Gravesend TQ67R & 67S, in a marshy area at Motney Hill TQ86J, a pond at Minster TQ97L, and a marsh dyke near Greatstone-on-Sea TR02R. **5** (0).

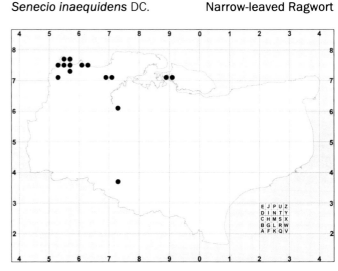

Cotula australis
(Sieber ex Spreng.) Hook. f.
Annual Buttonweed

Introduced. A casual wool shoddy plant, last recorded in 1960. **0** (0).

Introduced (neophyte). On roadside verges, pavement cracks and waste land. Now frequent in the north-west of the county and spreading. **15** (1).

Senecio fluviatilis Wallr.　　　　Broad-leaved Ragwort

Introduced (neophyte). A garden escape reported growing wild from Tunbridge Wells, Plaxtol and Maidstone in the past, but not seen during the present mapping. **0** (1).

Senecio jacobaea L.　　　　Common Ragwort

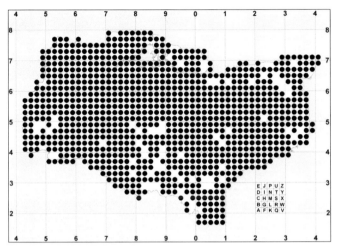

Native. In neglected, rabbit-grazed or overgrazed meadows, and on sand-dunes, scrub, roadside verges, open woodland and waste land. **950** (888).

Senecio squalidus L.　　　　Oxford Ragwort

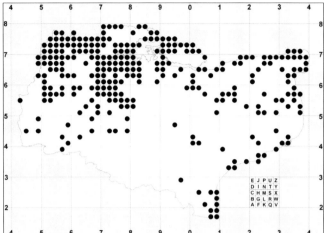

Introduced (neophyte). Hanbury & Marshall (1899) recorded this plant only from Canterbury where it had been known since at least 1875, plants having originally been introduced from Oxford. The next record from our area appears to be from Greenhithe in 1930, plants having spread from the London area. From then on the Oxford Ragwort spread quite quickly, particularly along the railways. It now appears to have reached its peak and has become less frequent in recent years. **288** (507).

Senecio aquaticus Hill　　　　Marsh Ragwort

Native. In marshes and wet meadows, and by ponds and ditches. Has become very scarce in recent years and is now only recorded from near Cowden TQ44V, Sevenoaks TQ55D & 55I, and Westbere TR16V. **4** (35).

Senecio squalidus x *viscosus*
= *S.* x *subnebrodensis* Simonk.

Native. Scattered records in the past, but not found during the present survey. **0** (4).

Senecio erucifolius L.　　　　Hoary Ragwort

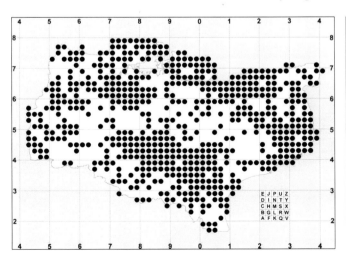

Native. Hay meadows, field borders, roadside verges, fixed sand-dunes, shingle banks and disturbed waste places, usually on well-drained soils. **630** (745).

Senecio vulgaris L.　　　　Groundsel

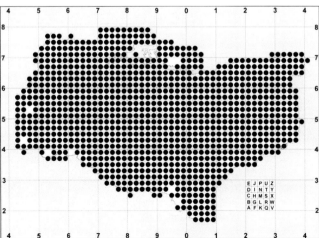

Native. A common plant of cultivated and waste ground, fixed sand-dunes, and occasionally on old walls and buildings. **1013** (1021).

Senecio sylvaticus L.   Heath Groundsel

Native. In open habitats on heaths, coppiced woodland, fixed sand-dunes and shingle beaches, usually growing on sandy, non-calcareous soils. **132** (180).

Senecio sylvaticus x viscosus
= *S.* x *viscidulus* Scheele

Native. A plant at Sevenoaks in 1963 is the only record for the county. **0** (0).

Senecio viscosus L.   Sticky Groundsel

Introduced (neophyte). Railway banks, gravel pits, sand and shingle beaches, and on waste sandy ground. **106** (196).

Tephroseris integrifolia (L.) Holub   Field Fleawort

Native. Known from chalk downland on Scarborough Spur near Burham since 1839 and last recorded there in the mid-1970s. Repeated searches to re-find this plant over the last fifteen years have been fruitless, the whole area is now scrubbed up and the Field Fleawort must now be considered extinct in the county. Nationally it is listed as 'Endangered'. **0** (1).

Sinacalia tangutica (Maxim.) B. Nord.   Chinese Ragwort

Introduced (neophyte). A garden plant recorded growing wild at Tunbridge Wells in 1957. There are no subsequent records. **0** (0).

Doronicum pardalianches L.   Leopard's-bane

Introduced (neophyte). An escape from cultivation noted well established near Matfield TQ64K. **1** (8).

Doronicum pardalianches x *plantagineum*   Willdenow's
= *D.* x *willdenowii* (Rouy) A.W. Hill   Leopard's-bane

Introduced. Naturalised in a wood at Hildenborough TQ54U (G.D. Kitchener). **1** (0).

Doronicum x excelsum   Harpur-Crewe's Leopard's-bane
(N.E. Br.) Stace

Introduced. Naturalised in a wood at Hildenborough TQ54U (G.D. Kitchener). **1** (0).

Tussilago farfara L.   Colt's-foot

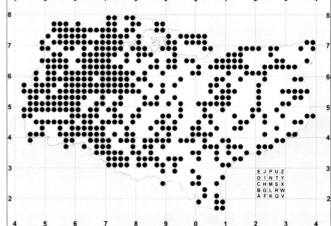

Native. On sand-dunes, shingle beaches, slumping cliffs, disused quarries, clayey field borders, river banks and roadside verges. Colt's-foot appears to have become less frequent in recent years. **522** (881).

Petasites hybridus   Butterbur
(L.) P. Gaertn., B. Mey. & Scherb.

Native. In marshes, wet meadows and river banks. **18** (59).

Petasites japonicus   Giant Butterbur
(Siebold & Zucc.) Maxim.

Introduced (neophyte). On the banks of a stream at Groombridge TQ53I where it was first recorded in 1944; and also well established by a small stream at Hocker Edge TQ73U. **2** (3).

Petasites albus (L.) Gaertn.   White Butterbur

Introduced (neophyte). Persistent on a roadside verge at Plaxtol TQ55W where it has been known for at least fifty years now. **1** (1).

Petasites fragrans (Vill.) C. Presl   Winter Heliotrope

Introduced (neophyte). A plant of cultivation first recorded growing wild in the county in 1867. It is now found widely throughout the county on roadside verges and on the banks of rivers and streams. **342** (398).

Petasites palmatus   Palmate-leaved Butterbur
(Aiton) A. Gray

Introduced. A good patch in a copse at Tunbridge Wells between 1955-60 had probably originally been planted there. The site was later destroyed and there are no subsequent records. **0** (0).

Calendula officinalis L.   Pot Marigold

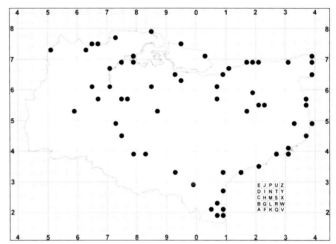

Introduced (neophyte). A common garden plant now well established along sea-walls and waste ground around the coast, and also as casual plants on roadside verges and rough waste ground inland. **60** (69).

Calendula arvensis L.   Field Marigold

Introduced. Casual plants at South Darenth in the 1970s are the only record. **0** (1).

Ambrosia artemisiifolia L.   Ragweed

Introduced (neophyte). Records from Aylesford TQ75J, Bearsted TQ75X, Borstal TQ76I and Harrietsham TQ85R were probably the result of contaminants from wild bird seed. **4** (3).

Ambrosia trifida L.   Giant Ragweed

Introduced. Casual records from the Dartford-Greenhithe area during the 1970s, as a contaminant from the oil-seed industry. There are no recent sightings. **0** (6).

Iva xanthiifolia Nutt.   Marsh-elder

Introduced. A few casual plants on the beach at Greenhithe in the 1970s are the only record. **0** (1).

Xanthium strumarium L.   Rough Cocklebur

Introduced (neophyte). Formerly as an oil-seed adventive, but the only recent record is from waste ground at Aylesford TQ75J. **1** (14).

Xanthium spinosum L.   Spiny Cocklebur

Introduced (neophyte). In fields and waste places where wool shoddy had been used, but not seen since 1985. **0** (7).

Xanthium ambrosioides   Argentine Cocklebur
Hook. & Arn.

Introduced. A few casual records in the past from West Kent of this wool shoddy alien. **0** (0).

Guizotia abyssinica (L. f.) Cass.   Niger

Introduced. A bird seed casual noted on waste ground at Swanscombe TQ67C and Barming TQ75H. **2** (14).

Sigesbeckia orientalis L.   Eastern St Paul's-wort

Introduced. Casual records of this wool shoddy adventive in the past, the last in 1959. **0** (0).

Sigesbeckia serrata DC   Western St Paul's-wort

Introduced. On cultivated ground at a nursery at Fairseat in 1960 is the only record for the county. **0** (0).

Rudbeckia hirta L.   Black-eyed-Susan

Introduced. A garden plant reported growing wild at Dartford and Ramsgate in the 1970s, but with no recent records. **0** (2).

Rudbeckia laciniata L.   Coneflower

Introduced. A garden plant reported as growing wild at Sutton-at-Hone, Dartford and Longfield in the 1970s, but with no recent records. **0** (3).

Helianthus annuus L.   Sunflower

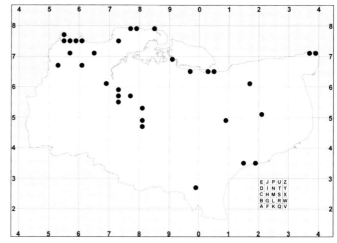

Introduced (neophyte). An escape from cultivation and also a contaminant from food put out for birds and small mammals. On roadside verges, wood borders, waste ground and occasionally on sea-shores. **33** (45).

Helianthus annuus x decapetalus   Thin-leaved Sunflower
= **H. x multiflorus** L.

Introduced. A garden plant recorded growing wild near Kemsing in the 1970s, but with no further records. **0** (1, as *H. decapetalus*).

Helianthus tuberosus x pauciflorus   Perennial Sunflower
= **H. x laetiflorus** Pers.

Introduced (neophyte). A common garden plant found established on waste ground at Borough Green TQ66D, Swanscombe TQ67B, Maidstone TQ75T, Otham TQ85B, and Larkeyvalley Wood TR15H. **5** (3).

Helianthus tuberosus L.   Jerusalem Artichoke

Introduced (neophyte). An escape from cultivation, well naturalised at Kemsing TQ55P and in small quantity at Longfield TQ66E. **2** (10).

Helianthus petiolaris Nutt.   Lesser Sunflower

Introduced. Casual plants recorded from rubbish-tips in the Dartford area in the 1970s, but with no subsequent records. **0** (2).

Heliopsis helianthoides (L.) Sweet   Rough Oxeye

Introduced. A garden plant reported established on waste ground at Swanscombe in the 1970s, but with no subsequent records. **0** (1).

Bidens cernua L.   Nodding Bur-marigold

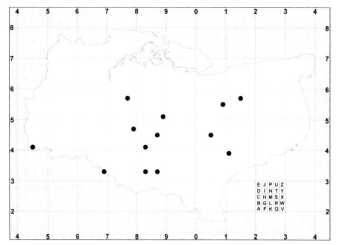

Native. At the margins of dykes, ponds, streams and slow-flowing rivers. This species is in decline through loss of habitats with land drainage and other developments. **13** (27).

Galinsoga parviflora Cav.   Gallant-soldier

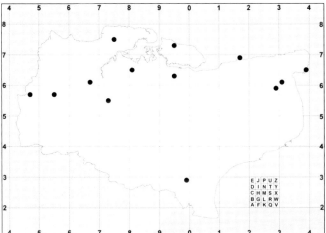

Introduced (neophyte). Casual records from arable fields, gardens and other disturbed soils. Both species of *Galinsoga* appear to have become less frequent in recent years. **13** (56).

Bidens tripartita L.   Trifid Bur-marigold

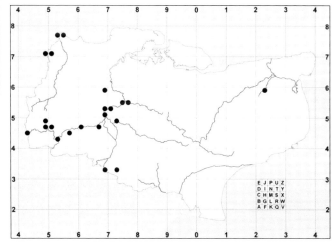

Native. In nutrient-rich mud or gravel at the margins of slow-flowing rivers, streams, ditches and ponds. Appears to have gone from some former sites through land drainage or other development, but has appeared, often in abundance around new reservoirs and flooded quarries. **22** (56).

Bidens frondosa L.   Beggarticks

Introduced. Casual records in the past, but not seen growing wild during the present survey. **0** (2).

Bidens pilosa L.   Black-jack

Introduced. Casual records from wool shoddy in the past, but not since 1959. **0** (0).

Galinsoga quadriradiata Ruiz & Pav.   Shaggy-soldier

Introduced (neophyte). Arable fields, gardens and disturbed waste ground. The Shaggy-soldier is now the commoner of the two species of *Galinsoga*. **26** (38).

Bidens bipinnata L.   Spanish-needles

Introduced. Another casual wool shoddy plant, last recorded in 1959. **0** (0).

Coreopsis grandiflora   Large-flowered Tickseed
Hogg ex Sweet

Introduced (neophyte). A garden escape recorded from Swanley in the 1970s, but with no further records. **0** (1, as *C. coronaria*).

Coreopsis tinctoria Nutt.   Garden Tickseed

Introduced. A garden outcast on a rubbish-tip at Stone in the 1970s is the only record. **0** (1).

Cosmos bipinnatus Cav.   Mexican Aster

Introduced. Casual records from wool shoddy or as a garden escape from 1960 until 1980, but no recent records. **0** (7).

Dahlia x *hortensis* Guillaumot   Garden Dahlia

Introduced. Garden outcasts recorded during the 1970, mainly from rubbish-tips, but with no subsequent sightings. **0** (8).

Tagetes minuta L.   Southern Marigold

Introduced. A casual wool shoddy plant recorded from 1960 until 1975, but with no further records. **0** (2).

Tagetes patula L.   French Marigold

Introduced. Casual records of this garden plant from waste ground and roadside verges at Dartford TQ57M, New Hythe TQ75E, Bekesbourne TR25C and Chislet TR26H. **4** (2).

Schkuhria pinnata (Lam.) Kuntze   Dwarf Marigold

Introduced. Recorded from East Kent in 1959 as a wool shoddy alien. **0** (0).

Gaillardia aristata x *pulchella*   Blanketflower
= *G.* x *grandiflora* hort. ex Van Houtte

Introduced (neophyte). Well naturalised, and in vast quantity, on the sand-dunes at Greatstone-on-Sea TR02W and at St. Mary's Bay TR02Y. **2** (1, as *G. aristata*).

Eupatorium cannabinum L.   Hemp-agrimony

Native. In marshes, and in damp vegetation at the edge of rivers, ponds, streams and ditches. It also is found in open scrub and rough grassland on well-drained soils on the chalk. **291** (340).

Ageratum houstonianum Mill.   Flossflower

Introduced. A casual garden escape reported from waste ground near Richborough in 1975, but with no further sightings. **0** (1).

Pond at Hamstreet Woods © S. Poyser

264

BUTOMACEAE

Butomus umbellatus L.   Flowering-rush

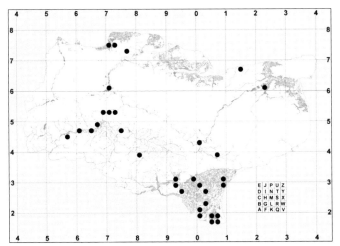

Native. At the edges of rivers, lakes and ponds, and in wet ditches. **32** (81).

ALISMATACEAE

Sagittaria sagittifolia L.   Arrowhead

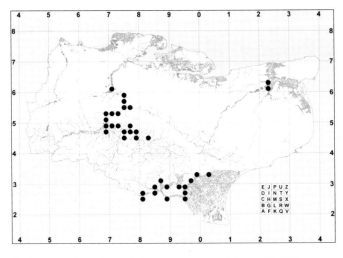

Native. At the edges of rivers, canals and lakes. **36** (40).

Sagittaria latifolia Willd.   Duck-potato

Introduced (neophyte). Established in ponds near Haysden TQ54S and near Rochester TQ76E. Also seen elsewhere freshly planted in the name of 'conservation' in mistake (ignorance) for the native Arrowhead. **2** (0).

Baldellia ranunculoides (L.) Parl.   Lesser Water-plantain

Native. At the edges of ponds, lakes and ditches at Dungeness TR01Y & 01Z, and in the Ham Fen/Hacklinge Marshes area TR35H & 35M. Nationally this is a declining species and is now listed as 'Near Threatened'. **4** (5).

Alisma plantago-aquatica L.   Water-plantain

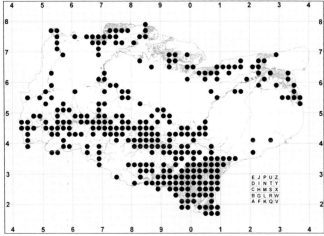

Native. At the edge of ponds, ditches and slow-flowing rivers. **315** (434).

Alisma lanceolatum With.   Narrow-leaved Water-plantain

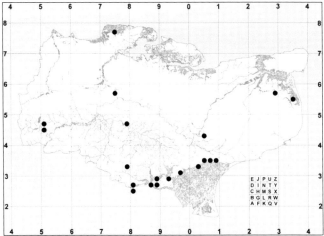

Native. At the edge of ponds, ditches, canals and slow-flowing rivers. Rather local and scarce in the county. **20** (26).

Damasonium alisma Mill.   Starfruit

Native, extinct. In marshes and at the edge of ponds. Formerly recorded from a few localities in East Kent, the last in the early 19th century. Nationally listed as 'Critically Endangered'. **0** (0).

HYDROCHARITACEAE

Hydrocharis morsus-ranae L. — Frogbit

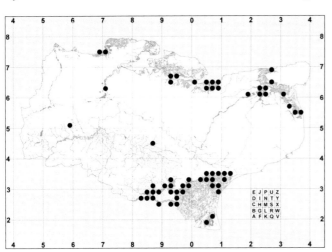

Native. In ponds and marsh dykes. Appears to be lost from some former sites where adjoining grazing fields have been turned to arable; nationally, this species is listed as 'Vulnerable'. **60** (89).

Stratiotes aloides L. — Water-soldier

Introduced (neophyte). Long established and beginning to spread in dykes on the Higham Marshes TQ67W & TQ77B; and now well established on the Royal Military Canal near Hythe TR13C & 13H. Also recorded from a pond at Maidstone TQ75T and in a marsh dyke at Ash TR25Z. **6** (2).

Elodea canadensis Michx. — Canadian Waterweed

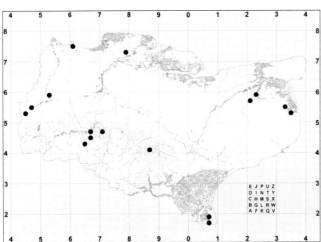

Introduced (neophyte). First recorded in the county in 1855 and soon became a common plant in rivers, streams and ponds. In the 1982 Atlas it was recorded from 201 sites in the county, but since then there has been a rapid decrease in this plant and is being replaced by *E. nuttallii*. The map shows where the Canadian Waterweed has been recorded during the present survey, but at the present rate of decrease it will probably be extinct in the county within the next ten years. **16** (201).

Elodea nuttallii (Planch.) H. St. John — Nuttall's Waterweed

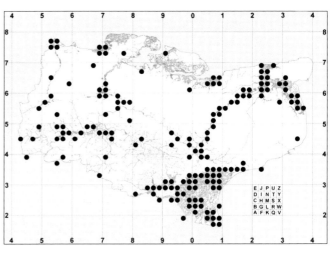

Introduced (neophyte). First recorded in the county in 1974, this plant is now found in rivers, canals, ponds and streams throughout most of the county. Once into any stretch of water it appears to take over from *E. canadensis*, and it is predicted that Nuttall's Waterweed will be present in every un-polluted waterway in the county within the next few years. **165** (48).

Lagarosiphon major (Ridl.) Moss ex V.A. Wager — Curly Waterweed

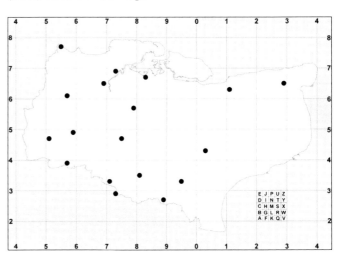

Introduced (neophyte). An aquatic plant sold for aquariums and garden ponds but sometimes accidentally, or deliberately, introduced, and now well established in some flooded gravel pits, ponds and other still or very slow-flowing waters. **18** (16).

APONOGETONACEAE

Aponogeton distachyos L. f. — Cape-pondweed

Introduced. Casual plants on a pond at East Malling TQ65Y constitute the only record during this survey. **1** (1).

JUNCAGINACEAE

Triglochin palustre L.   Marsh Arrowgrass

Native. At the edges of marsh dykes and in marshes and wet grazing meadows. Appears to have gone from several former localities through drainage, agricultural intensification or development. Only noted at Burham TQ76A, Fairfield TQ92T, Ham Fen TR35H and Worth Minnis TR35M. It may yet still exist in a few other coastal marshes. **4** (19).

Triglochin maritimum L.   Sea Arrowgrass

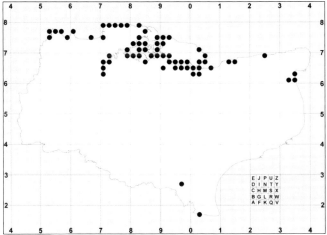

Native. In coastal and estuarine salt-marshes. **66** (97).

POTAMOGETONACEAE

Potamogeton natans L.   Broad-leaved Pondweed

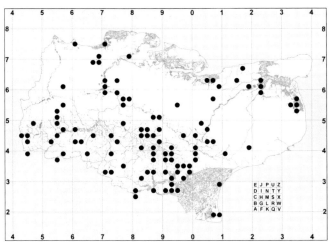

Native. In lakes, ponds, ditches and slow-flowing streams and rivers. **106** (176).

Potamogeton polygonifolius   Bog Pondweed
Pourr.

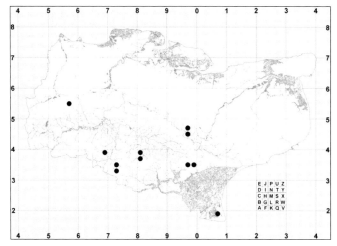

Native. In bogs and other shallow water in the more acid areas. **11** (8).

Potamogeton coloratus Hornem.   Fen Pondweed

Native. In calcium-rich marsh dykes in the Ham Fen/Worth Minnis area TR35H, 35M & 35N. **3** (2).

Potamogeton lucens L.   Shining Pondweed

Native. In relatively deep water in rivers, canals, marsh dykes and ponds. **38** (42).

Potamogeton lucens x perfoliatus Willow-leaved
= P. salicifolius Wolfg.   Pondweed

Native. In the River Great Stour at Godmersham TR05Q where it has been known for over forty years. **1** (1).

Potamogeton alpinus Balb.   Red Pondweed

Native. A plant formerly recorded from a few rivers and streams in the central Wealden area of the county, but repeated searches have failed to find it during the present survey. It is to be hoped that it might still be present in this general area. **0** (2).

Potamogeton pusillus L.   Lesser Pondweed

Native. All specimens have been sectioned and carefully examined under a microscope, and only the following records were confirmed. In a dyke on the Swanscombe marshes TQ57X, in a flooded gravel pit at Aylesford TQ75J, in a marsh dyke on The Dowels TQ93Q, in a flooded gravel pit at Dungeness TR01Y, and in a marsh dyke at Stodmarsh TR26G. **5** (37).

Potamogeton perfoliatus L.   Perfoliate Pondweed

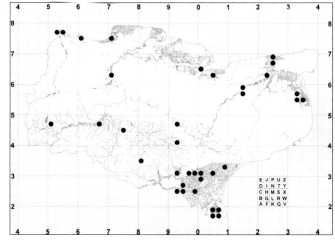

Native. In rivers, canals and other large water bodies. **17** (30).

Potamogeton obtusifolius   Blunt-leaved Pondweed
Mert. & W.D.J. Koch

Native. Formerly well scattered in ponds in the central Wealden area of the county, but not found during the present survey. The only explanation is that the correct habitats have not been looked at during the right time of year, as the plant must surely still exist in a few ponds in the county. **0** (13).

Potamogeton berchtoldii Fieber   Small Pondweed

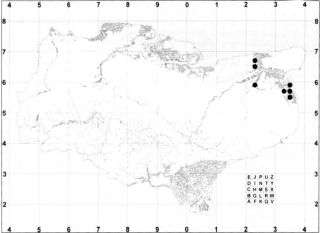

Native. In dykes, ponds and slow-flowing rivers, often growing with other fine-leaved pondweeds. **36** (33).

Potamogeton friesii Rupr.   Flat-stalked Pondweed

Native. In lakes, marsh dykes and slow-flowing rivers or streams. A scarce plant that appears to be restricted to a limited area in the north-east of the county, and nationally listed as 'Near Threatened'. **7** (4).

Potamogeton trichoides   Hairlike Pondweed
Cham. & Schltdl.

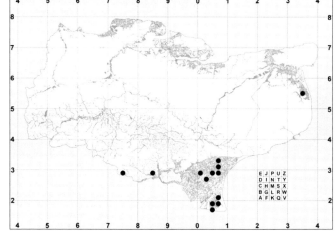

Native. Canals, ponds and marsh dykes. First recorded from Kent in 1946, and although now better understood, it appears to have a rather restricted distribution within the county. **13** (10).

Potamogeton friesii x crispus   Linton's Pondweed
= **P.** x **lintonii** Fryer

Native. Recorded from two localities in the past, but not seen in the county for more than fifty years now. **0** (0).

Potamogeton acutifolius Link   Sharp-leaved Pondweed

Native. Recorded from marsh dykes at Small Hythe TQ82Z, The Dowels TQ93Q and Stodmarsh TR26G. A rare plant, listed nationally as 'Critically Endangered'. **3** (2).

Groenlandia densa (L.) Fourr.   Opposite-leaved Pondweed

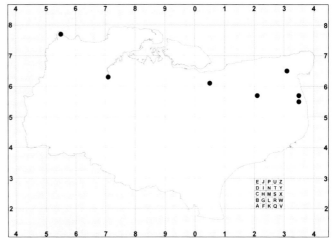

Native. In streams ponds, ditches and marsh dykes. There has been a decline in the abundance of this species, mainly through loss of habitat, reinforcing its national listing as 'Vulnerable'. **7** (25).

Potamogeton crispus L.   Curled Pondweed

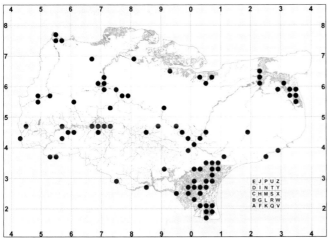

Native. In lakes, ponds, rivers, canals and dykes. **86** (155).

RUPPIACEAE

Ruppia maritima L.   Beaked Tasselweed

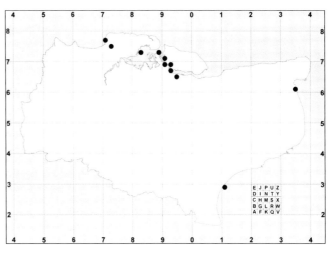

Native. In brackish dykes, lagoons and ponds near the coast. **11** (16)

Potamogeton pectinatus L.   Fennel Pondweed

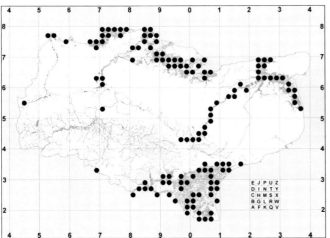

Native. In lakes, ponds, rivers, canals and dykes, and it will often be found in brackish waters. **130** (174).

Ruppia cirrhosa (Petagna) Grande   Spiral Tasselweed

Native. In brackish or saline ponds, lagoons and ditches. Only recorded from Allhallows TQ87P and Plumpudding Island TR26U. Nationally listed as 'Near Threatened'. **2** (6).

ZANNICHELLIACEAE

Zannichellia palustris L.   Horned Pondweed

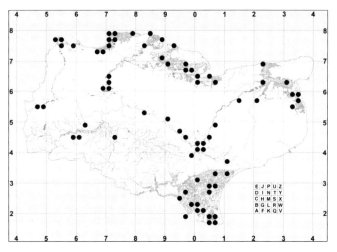

Native. In shallow waters in rivers, streams, lakes and ponds, and it is found in both fresh and brackish habitats. **73** (120).

ZOSTERACEAE

Zostera marina L. var. *marina*   Eelgrass

Native, now extinct. On coastal mud-flats from low-water springs to 4 metres below. Recorded in the county up to about 1933, but not since. **0** (0).

Zostera marina L.   Narrow-leaved Eelgrass
var. *stenophylla* Asch. & Graebn.

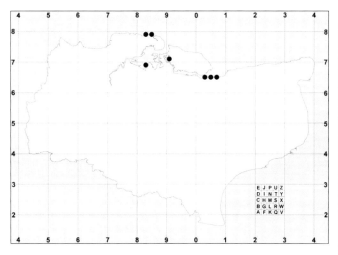

Native. Formerly known as *Z. angustifolia*, this plant occurs on coastal mud-flats from half-tide mark down to low-tide mark. Along the North Kent coast, but probably under-recorded in the Medway Estuary through difficulty of access. **7** (14).

Zostera noltei Hornem.   Dwarf Eelgrass

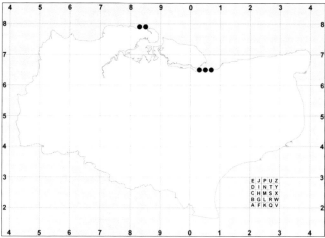

Native. Found growing with the previous species, but usually on slightly firmer, slightly raised mud-banks. Recorded from along the Thames near Allhallows TQ87J & 87P, and along the Swale from Graveney through to Seasalter TR06H, 06M & 06S. Nationally a scarce plant and listed as 'Vulnerable'. **5** (6).

ARECACEAE

Phoenix dactylifera L.   Date Palm

Introduced. Casual seedlings noted in the past growing on rubbish-tips, but not seen during the present survey due to modern practices on such sites. **0** (8).

ARACEAE

Acorus calamus L.   Sweet-flag

Introduced (neophyte). Well naturalised on the River Medway at Wateringbury TQ65W, and on lakes at Mote Park, Maidstone TQ75S, Vinter's Park, Maidstone TQ75T, and Leeds Castle TQ86G. **4** (7).

Lords-and-Ladies *Arum maculatum*   © L. Manning

Lysichiton americanus
Hultén & H. St. John

American Skunk-cabbage

Arum italicum Mill.
ssp. *italicum*

Italian Lords-and-Ladies

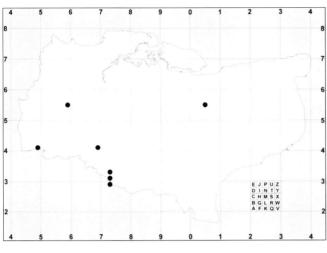

Introduced (neophyte). Often planted in parks and water-gardens where it can set seed and spread rapidly if not controlled. In all the recorded localities it had escaped and was growing wild, and is likely to further its range in the near future. **7** (2).

Introduced (neophyte). An escape from cultivation and now well naturalised in woodland edges, hedgerows and neglected ground. **30** (9).

Calla palustris L.

Bog Arum

Dracunculus vulgaris Schott

Dragon Arum

Introduced (neophyte). Found growing in a woodland bog at Pembury in 1956, but with no subsequent records. **0** (0).

Introduced. A casual plant in a hedgerow near Hildenborough TQ55Q. **1** (2).

Zantedeschia aethiopica (L.) Spreng.

Altar-lily

Colocasia esculenta (L.) Schott

Taro

Introduced. A casual plant recorded from Darenth Wood in 1978, but with no subsequent records. **0** (1).

Introduced. Occasional plants on rubbish-tips in the north-west of the county in the 1970s, but none since. **0** (2).

Arum maculatum L.

Lords-and-Ladies

Spirodela polyrhiza (L.) Schleid.

Greater Duckweed

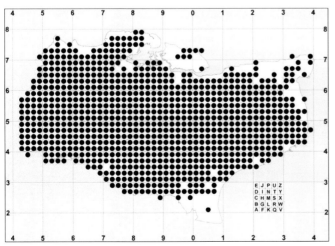

Native. In woods and shaded hedgerows. Common, except in a few coastal areas. **872** (887).

Native. In canals, ponds, dykes and other still waters, and also in slow-flowing rivers during the late summer. **74** (75).

271

Lemna gibba L.   Fat Duckweed

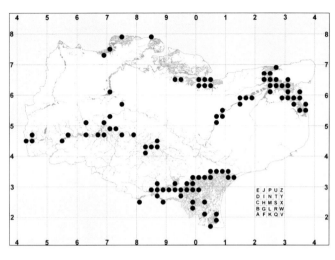

Native. In canals, marsh dykes and river backwaters from where it will spill into the main rivers late in the year. **98** (142).

Lemna minor L.   Common Duckweed

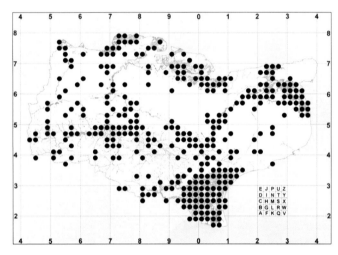

Native. On lakes and ponds and other still waters, and in slow-flowing dykes and streams. It has even been found in cattle water troughs, probably carried there by birds. **334** (562).

Lemna trisulca L.   Ivy-leaved Duckweed

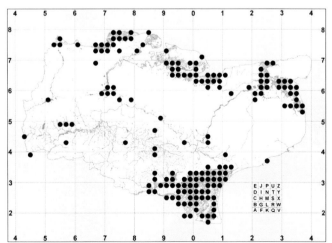

Native. In ponds, ditches and dykes, particularly in coastal areas. **166** (219).

Lemna minuta Kunth.   Least Duckweed

Introduced (neophyte). First recorded in the county in 1981 and since then it has spread rapidly to lakes, ponds, rivers and ditches throughout the county. It can be a troublesome weed at times because of its ability to cover completely a pond or small lake and exclude the light to (and so kill off) any other aquatic plants present. **330** (2).

Wolffia arrhiza   Rootless Duckweed
(L.) Horkel ex Wimm.

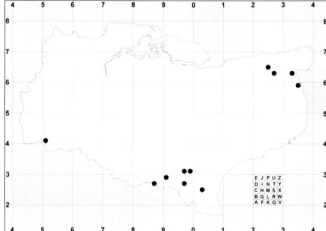

Native. In ponds and marsh dykes. A rare and declining species and noted in the Red List Category, 'Vulnerable'. **11** (25).

JUNCACEAE

Juncus squarrosus L.   Heath Rush

Native. A plant of wet peaty heaths and always a rare plant in Kent. Now only recorded from Hothfield Common TQ94S & 94T. **2** (4).

Juncus tenuis Willd.   Slender Rush

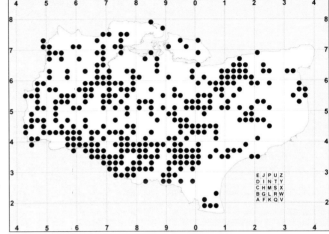

Introduced (neophyte). Almost restricted to woodland and forest rides, but occasionally on damp open ground near woods. **60** (38).

Juncus foliosus Desf.   Leafy Rush

Native. Last recorded in the county from near Canterbury in 1890. **0** (0).

Juncus bufonius L.   Toad Rush

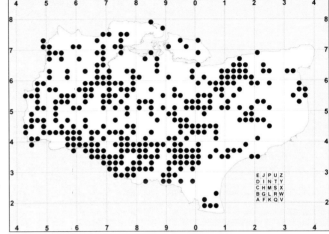

Native. In woodland rides, muddy areas by ponds, lakes and rivers, and also in damp arable fields and other damp, disturbed areas. **356** (414).

Juncus compressus Jacq.   Round-fruited Rush

Native. A scarce plant of marshes and wet meadows. Several former sites have now been destroyed through land drainage, and although searched for in likely localities, it has not been found during the present survey, and could now be extinct in the county. Nationally it is listed as 'Near Threatened'. **0** (6).

Juncus ambiguus Guss.   Frog Rush

Native. A coastal species, last recorded from Deal in 1862. **0** (0).

Juncus gerardii Loisel.   Saltmarsh Rush

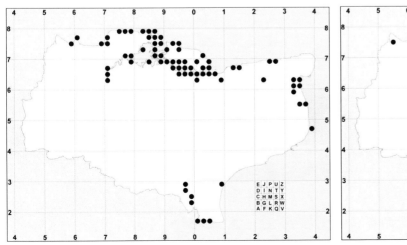

Native. In salt-marshes, grazing meadows and other grassy areas on the coast. **75** (119).

Juncus subnodulosus Schrank   Blunt-flowered Rush

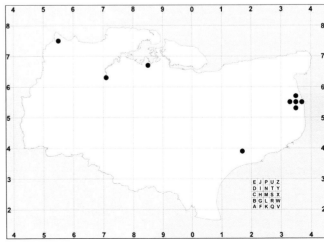

Native. In fens, marshes and dykes in base-rich conditions. **9** (21).

Juncus articulatus L.   Jointed Rush

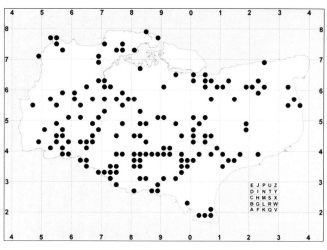

Native.   At the edge of ponds and lakes, in ditches, woodland rides and wet-flushes.   **158** (273).

Juncus acutiflorus
Ehrh. ex Hoffm.   Sharp-flowered Rush

Native.   On wet heaths, and by ponds, streams and marshy areas in more acid areas.   **65** (105).

Juncus bulbosus L.   Bulbous Rush

Native.   In ponds and damp woodland rides on neutral to acid soils.   **47** (55).

Juncus maritimus Lam.   Sea Rush

Native.   In salt-marshes and other brackish areas on the coast. **37** (63).

Juncus acutus L.   Sharp Rush

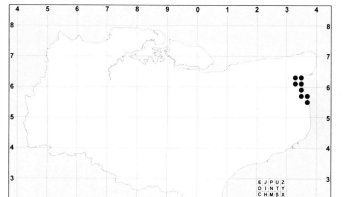

Native. On fixed sand-dunes, shingle-sand banks and the drier parts of salt-marsh. Only ever known in Kent from the Sandwich Bay/Pegwell Bay area where the population appears stable. **8** (8).

Juncus inflexus L.   Hard Rush

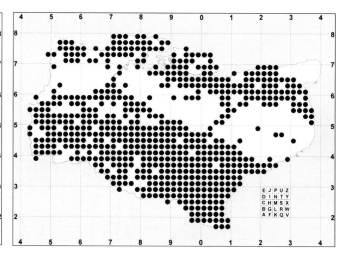

Native. By ponds, rivers and streams, damp meadows, poor pasture and roadside verges. Throughout the county, but usually avoiding the chalk. **631** (670).

Juncus inflexus x *effusus* = *J.* x *diffusus* Hoppe

Native. A rarely recorded hybrid in the county and only noted from Knockholt Pound TQ45Z. **1** (2)

Juncus pallidus R. Br.   **Great Soft-rush**

Introduced (neophyte). Several plants at Wrotham in 1960 where wool shoddy had been used, but with no subsequent records. **0** (0).

Juncus effusus L.   **Soft Rush**

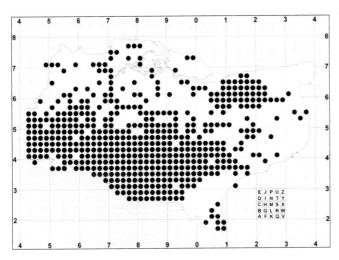

Native. By ponds, rivers and streams, and in wet fields, woodland rides, marshes and ditches. **512** (586).

Juncus aridicola L.A.S. Johnson   **Tussock Rush**

Introduced. An Australian species introduced with wool shoddy was established for a few years at Barming, but has now gone. **0** (1).

Juncus australis Hook. f.   **Austral Rush**

Introduced (neophyte). An Australian species introduced with wool shoddy was established for a few years at Barming, but has now gone. **0** (1).

Juncus distegus Edgar

Introduced (neophyte). An Australian species introduced with wool shoddy was established for a few years at Barming, but has now gone. **0** (1).

Juncus effusus x *conglomeratus*
= *J.* x *kern-reichgeltii* Jansen & Wacht. ex Reichg.

Native. In Hurst Wood TQ95W in 2000, growing with both parents, is the first record for the county. **1** (0).

Juncus procerus E. Mey.

Introduced (neophyte). An Australian species introduced with wool shoddy was established for a few years at Barming, but has now gone. **0** (1).

Juncus conglomeratus L.   **Compact Rush**

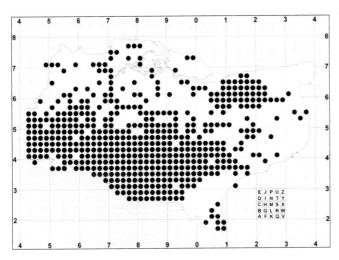

Juncus subsecundus N.A. Wakef.   **Fingered Rush**

Introduced (neophyte). An Australian species introduced with wool shoddy was established for a few years at Barming, but has now gone. **0** (1).

Juncus usitatus L.A.S. Johnson

Native. Marshes, damp pastures and woodland rides, particularly on the more acid soils. Easily confused with the similar looking (at a distance) var. *subglomeratus* of *J. effusus*. **294** (344).

Introduced (neophyte). An Australian species introduced with wool shoddy was established for a few years at Barming, but has now gone. **0** (1).

Luzula forsteri (Sm.) DC.　　Southern Wood-rush

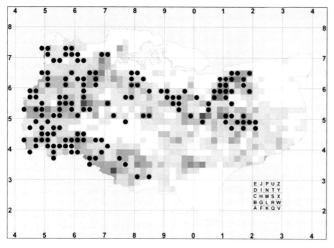

Native. In woods, hedgerows and roadside banks, usually on sandy, slightly acidic soils. **149** (168).

Luzula sylvatica (Huds.) Gaudin　　Great Wood-rush

Native. In open woods on sandy, and sometimes peaty, acidic soils. An indicator plant of long-established woodland in the county. **56** (70).

Luzula forsteri x pilosa
= *L.* x *borreri* Bromf. ex Bab.

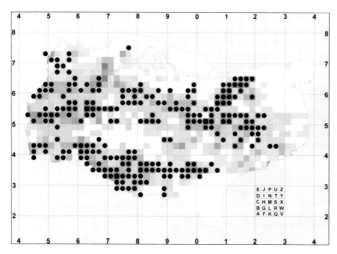

Native. In scattered localities where the two parents are found growing together. **8** (10).

Luzula campestris (L.) DC.　　Field Wood-rush

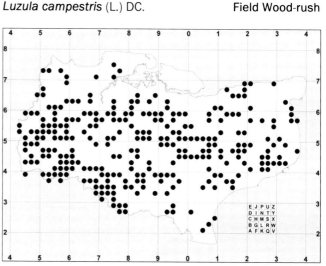

Native. In relatively infertile meadows, lawns, grassy verges and churchyards. **288** (419).

Luzula pilosa (L.) Willd.　　Hairy Wood-rush

Native. In woods, copses and shaded roadside banks. **240** (329).

Luzula multiflora (Ehrh.) Lej.　　Heath Wood-rush

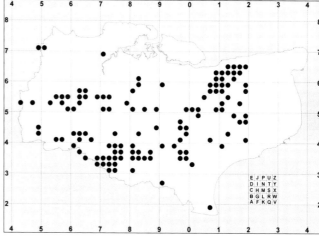

Native. On heaths and open woodland on sandy acidic soils. **123** (201).

CYPERACEAE

Eriophorum angustifolium   Common Cottongrass
Honck.

Native. In wet peaty areas, usually growing in standing water. Always a scarce plant in the county and now recorded from Hothfield Common TQ94S, Dungeness area TR01T & 01U, and Gibbin's Brook TR13E. **4** (2)

Eriophorum latifolium   Broad-leaved Cottongrass
Hoppe

Native, extinct. Not recorded since the early 19th century. **0** (0).

Eriophorum vaginatum L.   Hare's-tail Cottongrass

Native, extinct. Doubtfully recorded from the Sandwich area in the late 18th century, and positive records from near Tunbridge Wells from 1845 until the site was drained. The plant introduced to Hothfield Common in the 1950s has now, thankfully, gone. **0** (1).

Trichophorum cespitosum (L.) Hartm.   Deergrass

Native, extinct. The subsp. *germanicum* (Palla) Hegi was recorded from a few heaths and boggy areas during the 19th century, but there are no recent records of the species. **0** (0).

Eleocharis palustris   Common Spike-rush
(L.) Roem. & Schult.

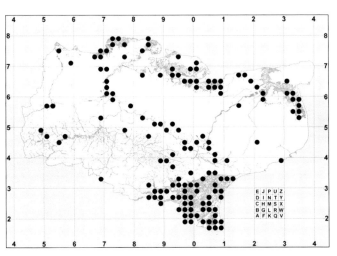

Native. In marshes and ditches, and at the margins of ponds, lakes and slow-flowing rivers. More frequent in wet areas near the coast. **145** (195).

Eleocharis uniglumis   Slender Spike-rush
(Link) Schult.

Native. A plant of wet or marshy meadows, particularly near the coast. Repeated searches in former or likely habitats have failed to find this plant during the present mapping, but it might still be present in some of the grazing meadows along the Swale or in the Lydden Valley. **0** (2).

Eleocharis multicaulis   Many-stalked Spike-rush
(Sm.) Desv.

Native. This plant has always been rare in Kent and is now only recorded from the edge of Louisa Lake in Bedgebury Forest TQ73G and from wet boggy areas on Hothfield Common TQ94S. **2** (2).

Eleocharis quinqueflora   Few-flowered Spike-rush
(Hartmann) O. Schwarz

Native, extinct. Last recorded (from Dungeness) in 1875. **0** (0).

Eleocharis acicularis   Needle Spike-rush
(L.) Roem. & Schult.

Native. Appears to have gone from its only known locality at East Peckham and could now be extinct in the county. **0** (1).

Bolboschoenus maritimus   Sea Club-rush
(L.) Palla

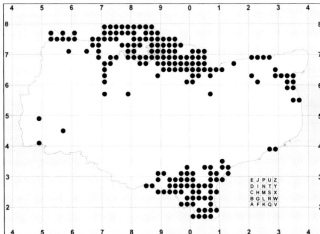

Native. At the edge of dykes, ponds and rivers on the coast, in salt-marshes, and occasionally in marshes or flooded gravel-pits inland. **199** (210).

Scirpus sylvaticus L.   Wood Club-rush

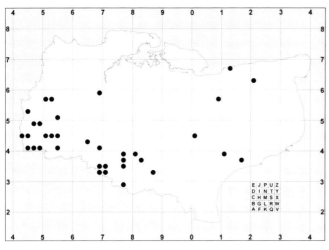

Native. In wet valley woodlands, stream-sides and marshy places. Appears to be in decline, probably through loss of habitat. **35** (86).

Wood Club-rush *Scirpus sylvaticus* © S. Poyser

Schoenoplectus tabernaemontani   Grey Club-rush
(C.C. Gmel.) Palla

Native. At the edge of dykes, ponds and rivers, usually in brackish water. **62** (89).

Schoenoplectus lacustris   Common Club-rush
(L.) Palla

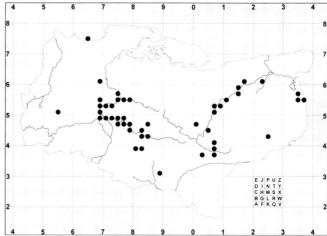

Native. At the edge lakes, ponds, slow-flowing rivers and large dykes, usually in fresh water. Most frequent along the rivers Beult and Great Stour. **46** (51).

Scirpoides holoschoenus   Round-headed Club-rush
(L.) Soják

Introduced (neophyte). In spite of several searches, the plant at Conyer has not been re-found and this club-rush is probably no longer present in Kent. **0** (1).

Schoenoplectus tabernaemontani x triqueter
= S. x kuekenthalianus (Junge) D. H. Kent

Native. Just two or three clumps remain at the edge of the River Medway at New Hythe TQ76A, all of which are in danger of being washed away as the tides gradually erode away the banks, reinforcing its national listing as 'Vulnerable'. Past records of *S. x carinatus* should almost certainly be placed here. **1** (1).

Schoenoplectus triqueter (L.) Palla   Triangular Club-rush

Native, extinct. Formerly along the River Medway in the Aylesford area where it was last recorded in 1899. **0** (0).

Isolepis setacea (L.) R. Br.   Bristle Club-rush

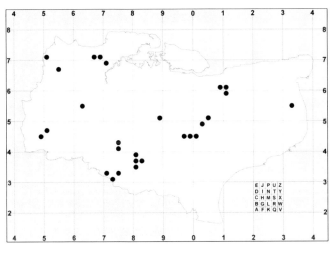

Native. On woodland rides, damp heaths and at the edge of ponds, usually on sandy soils. **27** (31).

Isolepis cernua (Vahl) Roem. & Schult.   Slender Club-rush

Native. I am informed (J. Cadbury *in litt.*) that one plant has been found at Worth Minnis TR35M. This is the first record for the county. A careful check has now been made on all the herbarium material of *I. setacea* at Maidstone Museum, including specimens from Worth Minnis, and all have proved to be correctly named. **1** (0).

Eleogiton fluitans (L.) Link   Floating Club-rush

Native. Always a rare plant in Kent, and now only recorded from the Louisa Lake area in Bedgebury Forest TQ73G. **1** (2).

Blysmus compressus (L.) Panz. ex Link   Flat-sedge

Native, extinct. A plant of marshes and calcareous flushes, last recorded from near Brook in 1955. **0** (0).

Cyperus longus L.   Galingale

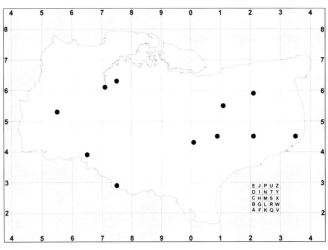

Introduced (neophyte). Scattered records of well established plants at the edge of ponds, lakes and streams. **11** (10).

Cyperus eragrostis Lam.   Pale Galingale

Introduced (neophyte). Well naturalised in Oaken Wood near Teston TQ65X, and casual plants on roadsides and waste ground at Smeeth TR03U, Ashford TR04B and Brabourne Lees TR04V. **4** (1).

Cladium mariscus (L.) Pohl   Great Fen-sedge

Native. Still in good quantity at the long known sites at Dungeness TR01U and Ham Fen TR35H. Also a few clumps in a small marshy area near Greatstone-on-Sea TR02R. Any lowering of the water table at any of these sites would threaten these plants. **3** (2).

Carex paniculata L.   Greater Tussock-sedge

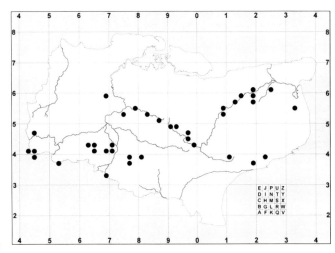

Native. In ponds, slow-running streams, bogs, fens and wet marshy areas. Usually in open areas, but will persist under tree cover where it will flower only sparsely. **37** (45).

Carex paniculata x *remota*
= *C.* x *boenninghausiana* Weihe

Native. Has been recorded very sparingly in the past, the last in 1954, and was not found during the present mapping. **0** (0).

Carex diandra Schrank　　　　Lesser Tussock-sedge

Native, presumed extinct. Recorded from Upnor, Oare, Ham Fen, Brook and Dungeness between 1839 and 1968, but with no subsequent records. **0** (0).

Carex vulpina L.　　　　　　True Fox-sedge

Native. In ponds, ditches and wet meadows. Appears to be lost from several former localities although specially searched for and is now only recorded from a marshy area near Leigh TQ54N, in a ditch near East Peckham TQ64U, and in a pond at Marden Meadow TQ74S. Listed nationally as 'Vulnerable'. **3** (9).

Carex otrubae Podp.　　　　False Fox-sedge

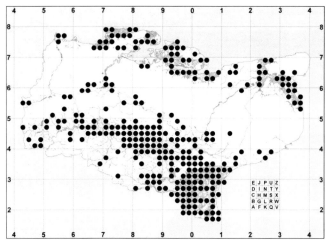

Native. At the sides of ponds and streams, and in ditches and wet meadows. **292** (363).

Carex otrubae x *remota*
= *C.* x *pseudoaxillaris* K. Richt.

Native. Found growing, together with both parents nearby, on roadside verges at Leggs Wood TQ84A, Lashenden TQ84K and Dering Wood TQ84X. **3** (8).

Carex spicata Huds.　　　　Spiked Sedge

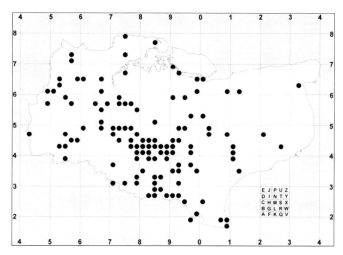

Native. On roadside banks and verges, rough grassland, open scrub and woodland rides. **121** (172).

Carex muricata L. ssp. *pairae*
(F.W. Schultz) Celak.　　　　Prickly Sedge

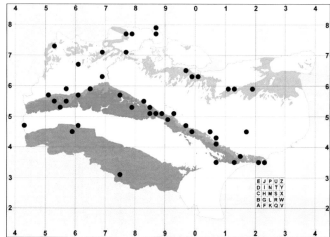

Native. On roadside banks and verges, heathland and rough grassy areas on light, usually on sandy soils. **46** (66).

Carex divulsa Stokes ssp. *divulsa*　　　Grey Sedge

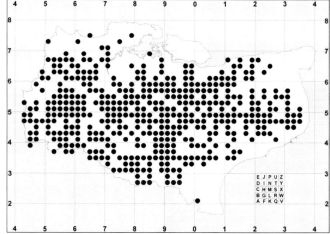

Native. Roadside banks and verges, woodland edges and scrub, usually on well-drained soils. **465** (409).

Carex divulsa Stokes   Many-leaved Sedge
ssp. *leersii* (Kneuck.) W. Koch

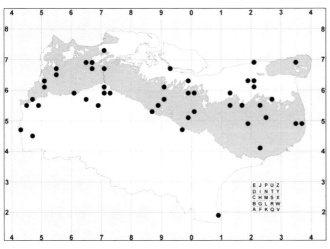

Native. On roadside banks and woodland margins on calcareous soils, particularly on the chalk. Great care has been taken to distinguish between the two subspecies and plants off the chalk or calcareous parts of the Hythe Beds have probably been originally introduced with road or railway workings. **47** (24).

Carex arenaria L.   Sand Sedge

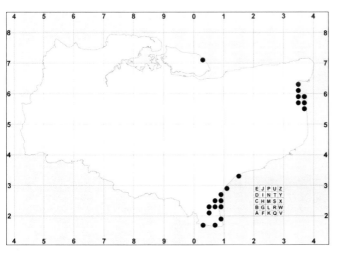

Native. In sandy habitats, particularly on fixed dunes on the coast. **20** (20).

Carex disticha Huds.   Brown Sedge

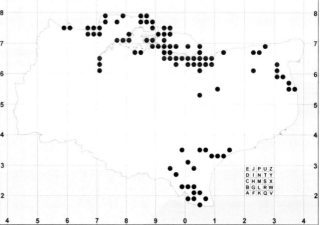

Native. In marshes, wet meadows and by ditches and streams. **15** (22).

Carex divisa Huds.   Divided Sedge

Native. At the edge of brackish dykes and in grazing meadows near the coast. Occasionally it has been found inland on roadside verges. Nationally this is a scarce plant and is noted in the Red List Category, 'Vulnerable'. However, in Kent it is often quite common in suitable habitats. **95** (113).

Divided Sedge   *Carex divisa* © L. Rooney

Carex remota L.   Remote Sedge

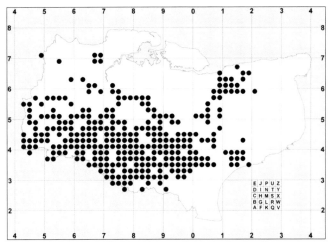

Native. In damp shady areas, either by ponds, streams or rivers, or in damp or wet woodland. **310** (311).

Carex ovalis Gooden.   Oval Sedge

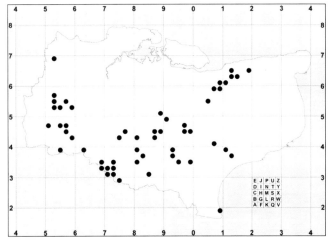

Native. In damp meadows and woodland rides. It has been lost from some former sites through land 'improvement' or development. **54** (68).

Carex echinata Murray   Star Sedge

Native. In bogs, mires and spring-flushes, usually in association with species of sphagnum moss. This is another sedge that appears to have declined through loss of habitat and is now only recorded from Brenchley Wood TQ64L, Bedgebury Forest TQ73G, Hothfield Common TQ94S & 94T, and Gibbin's Brook TR13E. **5** (11).

Carex elongata L.   Elongated Sedge

Native. A disproportionate amount of time has been spent searching for this scarce sedge during the mapping for this Flora, but it was only found in one marshy area near Leigh TQ54N. **1** (5).

Carex curta Gooden.   White Sedge

Native. Always a very scarce plant in Kent and now only recorded at the edge of some small ponds in the Orlestone Forest TQ93X. **1** (3).

Carex hirta L.   Hairy Sedge

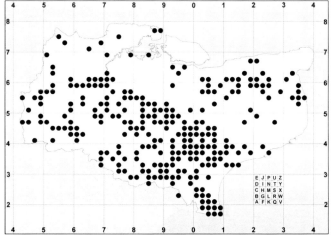

Native. Found in a wide variety of grassy habitats, including damp meadows, woodland rides, rough grassy areas and roadside verges. It has an amazing ability to push through tarmac when former sites have been developed. **271** (343).

Carex acutiformis Ehrh.   Lesser Pond-sedge

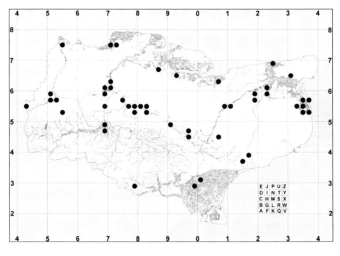

Native. At the edge of rivers, streams, dykes and ponds, and at times in wet marshy areas. **48** (81).

Carex riparia Curtis   Greater Pond-sedge

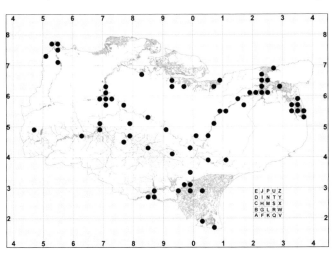

Native. At the edge of ponds, dykes and slow-flowing rivers, and in marshes. **67** (129).

Carex pseudocyperus L.   Cyperus Sedge

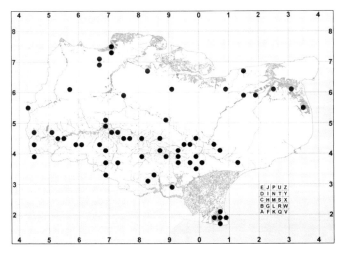

Native. By ponds, flooded gravel-pits, dykes and slow-flowing rivers. It will tolerate a certain amount of shade and at times is found by ponds and streams in woodland. **62** (85).

Carex rostrata Stokes   Bottle Sedge

Native. Another species that has been particularly searched for, but the only record is from a small area of fen at Dungeness TR01U. **1** (8).

Carex rostrata x *vesicaria*
= *C.* x *involuta* (Bab.) Syme

A 19th century record from near Cowden is the only occurrence in the county. **0** (0).

Carex vesicaria L.   Bladder-sedge

Native. Only recorded from by the River Medway at Haysden Park TQ54N; at the edge of Furnace Pond at Horsmonden TQ64V; by a pond at Marden Meadow TQ74S; and at the edge of the River Beult near Stile Bridge TQ74T. **4** (15).

Carex pendula Huds.   Pendulous Sedge

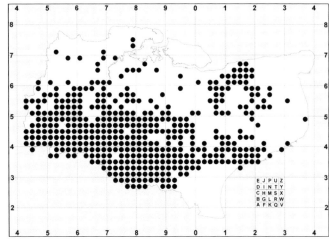

Native. In damp or wet woodlands, and by ponds and streams, usually in shaded habitats. It is commonly grown in gardens and plants away from natural habitats are likely to have escaped from cultivation. **438** (342).

Pendulous Sedge *Carex pendula* © L. Rooney

Carex sylvatica Huds.   Wood-sedge

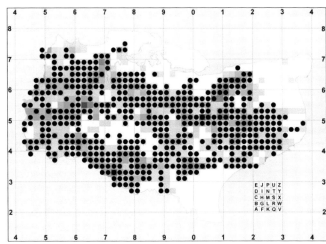

Native. In open woods and woodland rides. Very much an indicator of ancient woodland. **504** (483).

283

Carex strigosa Huds.   Thin-spiked Wood-sedge

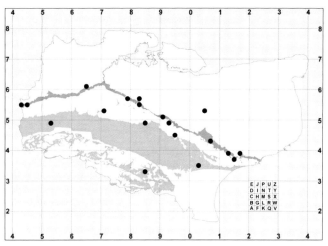

Native. In damp or wet woodland, particularly along rutted rides, and usually on clayey soils. **19** (28).

Carex laevigata Sm.   Smooth-stalked Sedge

Native. In wet woodland and marshy areas that are shaded by trees. **27** (40).

Carex binervis Sm.   Green-ribbed Sedge

Native. In heaths and in acid woodland, particularly at the edge of wide rides. **23** (37).

Carex flacca Schreb.   Glaucous Sedge

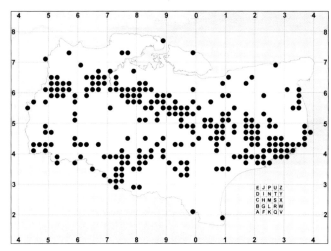

Native. In open grassland on neutral or calcareous soils. It is a common constituent of chalk downland, but also occurs in woodland rides, marshes, grassland on clays and on fixed sand-dunes. **250** (324).

Carex distans L.   Distant Sedge

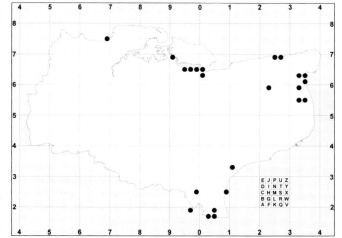

Native. At the edge of dykes, rough grassland and in damp meadows near the coast. **23** (25).

Carex panicea L.   Carnation Sedge

Native. A scarce plant of bogs and other wet, marshy, usually acid, areas. Now only recorded from near Cowden TQ44V, Chittenden Wood TQ83D, Hothfield Bog TQ94S, Gibbin's Brook TR13E and Northbourne Fen TR35L. **5** (9).

Carex extensa Gooden.   **Long-bracted Sedge**

Native.   A rare plant in Kent, but still present in its long-known locality at the mouth of the River Great Stour at Sandwich Bay TR36K & 36L.   **2** (1).

Carex viridula Michx.   **Long-stalked Yellow-sedge**
ssp. *brachyrrhyncha*
(Celak.) B. Schmid

Native.   A plant of calcareous fens and mires.   This has always been a rare sedge in Kent and is now only recorded from Etchinghill TR13U and Ham Fen TR35H.   **2** (3).

Carex viridula Michx.   **Common Yellow-sedge**
ssp. *oedocarpa* (Andersson)
B. Schmid.

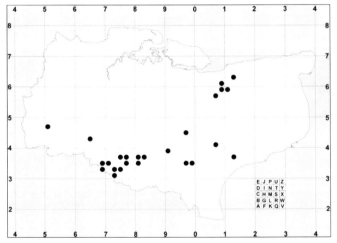

Native.   In damp woodland rides, pond margins and other wet areas, usually on the more acid soils.   **25** (33).

Carex viridula Michx.   **Small-fruited Yellow-sedge**
ssp. *viridula*

Native.   Recorded from the Dungeness area in 1947, but with no subsequent sightings.   A few other records from elsewhere in the past are almost certainly in error.   **0** (0).

Carex pallescens L.   **Pale Sedge**

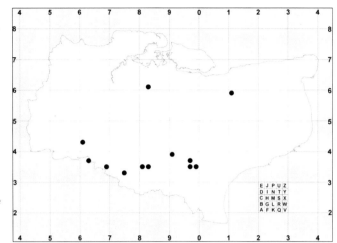

Native.   In damp meadows and woodland rides, usually on clayey and slightly acidic soils.   **12** (26).

Carex caryophyllea Latourr.   **Spring-sedge**

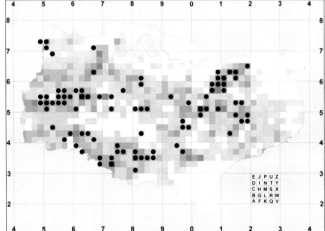

Native.   On dry open grassland and pastures, being more frequent on chalky soils.   **23** (28).

Carex pilulifera L.   **Pill Sedge**

Native.   On dry heaths and in open woodland, particularly on sandy, acidic soils.   It is most frequent in chestnut coppice woodland on sandy soils.   **87** (69).

Carex acuta L.   Slender Tufted-sedge

Native. In shallow water, or wet ground at the edge of rivers.
11 (16).

Carex nigra (L.) Reichard   Common Sedge

Native. In marshes and other wet grassy areas. This plant has
been particularly searched for in many of its former localities and
it appears that there has been a serious decline in this species.
9 (34).

Carex elata All.   Tufted-sedge

Native. At the edge of marsh dykes and ditches in the
Hacklinge/Sandwich area TR35H, 35I, 35N & 35T. Up to the end
of this survey period this was the only area in Kent where this
sedge has ever been found, and was first recorded there in 1855.
4 (4).

Carex pulicaris L.   Flea Sedge

Native. In the bogs at the K.W.T managed Hothfield L.N.R. TQ94S,
now the sole remaining site for this sedge which has always been
a rarity in Kent. **1** (1).

Yushania anceps (Mitford) W.C. Lin   Indian Fountain-bamboo

Introduced (neophyte). The only record is a small clump
naturalised at Borough Green TQ65D. **1** (1).

Sasa palmata (Burb.) E.G. Camus   Broad-leaved Bamboo

Introduced (neophyte). Naturalised clumps near Furnace Pond
TQ43P, Borough Green TQ65D and Perry Wood TR05M. **3** (2).

Sasa veitchii (Carrière) Rehder   Veitch's Bamboo

Introduced (neophyte). Recorded in the past, but not noted during
the present survey. **0** (0).

Sasaella ramosa (Makino) Makino   Hairy Bamboo

Introduced (neophyte). Recorded in the past, but not noted during
the present survey. **0** (2).

Pseudosasa japonica (Siebold & Zucc.ex Steud.) Makino ex Nakai   Arrow Bamboo

Introduced (neophyte). Often cultivated for ornament in gardens
and found naturalised at Snodland TQ66V and Maidstone TQ75T.
2(7).

Nardus stricta L.   Mat-grass

Native. This has always been a rare grass in Kent. It was re-found
on Tunbridge Wells Common TQ53U where it was first recorded in
1816, has been found in Knole Park, Sevenoaks TQ55L, and is
still in good quantity at Mersham-le-Hatch TR04Q. It now appears
to be lost from Hothfield Common, **3** (2).

Stipa neesiana Trin. & Rupr.   American Needle-grass

Introduced. Casual records in 1971 where wool shoddy had been
used, but there are no further sightings. **0** (1).

Stipa aristiglumis F. Muell.

Introduced. Past records as a casual wool shoddy alien, the last
in 1961. **0** (0).

Stipa verticillata Nees ex Spreng.

Introduced. Past casual records from wool shoddy, the last in 1960. **0** (0).

Oryzopsis miliacea   Smilo-grass
(L.) Benth. & Hook.f. ex Asch. & Schweinf.

Introduced. Casual plants on a rubbish-tip at Stone in 1977, but with no subsequent records. **0** (1).

Milium effusum L.   Wood Millet

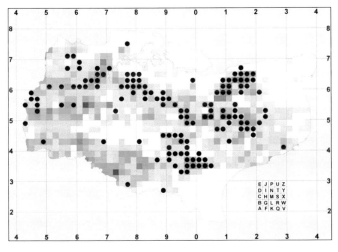

Native. In open deciduous woods, usually regarded as an indicator of ancient woodland. **136** (235).

Festuca pratensis Huds.   Meadow Fescue

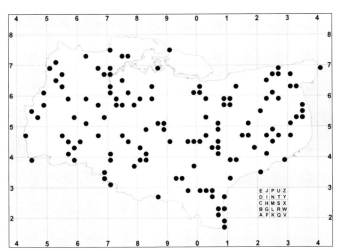

Native. In damp or wet meadows, pastures, and on grassy road-side verges, particularly along the minor roads. **129** (177).

Festuca arundinacea Schreb.   Tall Fescue

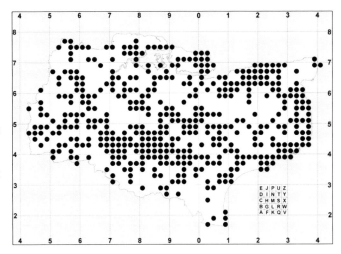

Native. In scrub, woodland margins and rough grassy areas, particularly on wide roadside verges. **465** (471).

Festuca gigantea (L.) Vill.   Giant Fescue

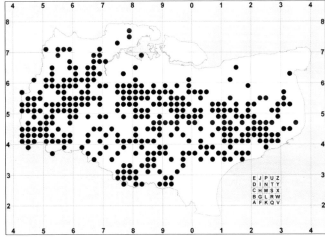

Native. In damp woodland and shaded hedge banks. **355** (428).

Festuca altissima All.   Wood Fescue

Native, extinct. Last recorded in 1852. **0** (0).

Festuca arenaria Osbeck   Rush-leaved Fescue

Native. A scarce plant of sand-dunes and recorded from Greatstone-on-Sea TR02W and Sandwich Bay TR35P & 35U. **3** (1)

Festuca rubra L.   Red Fescue

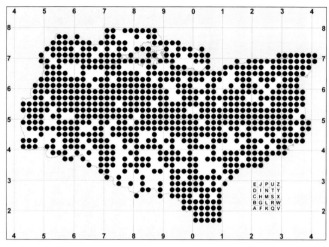

Native. A very variable plant that is found in just about every kind of grassy habitat throughout the county. Five subspecies are known for the county and these are dealt with below. The map shows the recorded distribution of the species as a whole within the county. **810** (955).

It has not been possible to map the distribution of each of the subspecies of *Festuca rubra* so as to provide meaningful distribution maps, but the following notes will give some idea of their status.

Ssp. *rubra* is common throughout the county, save perhaps for some extreme saltmarsh areas.

Ssp. *juncea* (Hack.) K. Richt. has been noted along the top of the chalk cliffs between Folkestone and Deal.

Ssp. *litoralis* (G. Mey.) Auquier has been noted quite frequently in a few brackish areas alongside the Thames and Swale in the north of the county and in the Pegwell Bay/Sandwich area.

Ssp. *commutata* Gaudin has been recorded on well drained soils at Hunton TQ74E, Sandhurst TQ72Z, Tenterden TQ83W, Kenardington TQ93R, Snargate TQ92Z and Shepherdswell TR24N. If carefully looked for, it would be expected to be found much more widely. **6** (9).

Ssp. *megastachys* Gaudin is an introduced plant recorded growing in sandy areas at Addington TQ65P, Lenham Heath TQ95F and Dungeness TR01Y. **3** (0).

Festuca ovina L.   Sheep's-fescue

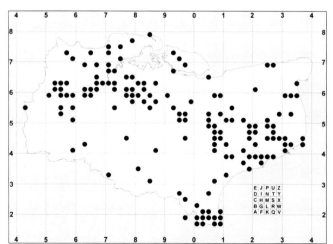

Native. On well drained soils on both sand and chalk. **153** (306).

Festuca filiformis Pourr.   Fine-leaved Sheep's-fescue

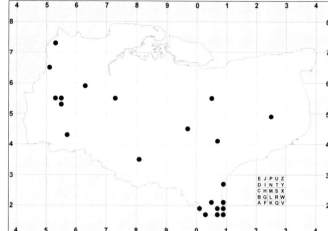

Native. On open grassy areas, usually on sandy soils. Scattered records, but it is particularly frequent on the shingle beaches in the Dungeness area. **22** (43).

Festuca brevipila R. Tracey   Hard Fescue

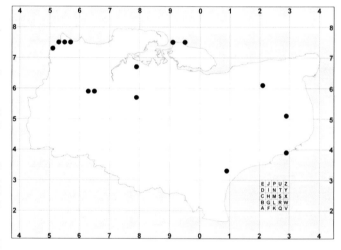

Introduced (neophyte). Now well naturalised on a few roadside verges, commons and other amenity grasslands. It occurs regularly in the grass-seed mix sown in such situations and would be expected to be found more widespread in the future. **14** (6).

Festuca pratensis x Lolium perenne   Hybrid Fescue
= X Festulolium loliaceum (Huds.) P. Fourn.

Native. In pastures, meadows and marshy grassland. Recorded from Otford TQ55J, Bearsted TQ75X, Wittersham Road TQ82U, Pluckley Thorn TQ94C, Teynham TQ96L, Stowting TR14F, Clowes Wood TR16G and Northbourne TR35I. **8** (18).

Festuca pratensis x Lolium multiflorum
= X Festulolium braunii (K. Richt.) A. Camus

Native. A plant found at Greenhithe in 1976, but there have been no further records. **0** (1).

Festuca arenaria x Vulpia fasciculata
= X Festulpia melderisii Stace & R. Cotton

Native. Has been recorded from East Kent in the past, but was not found during the present survey. **0** (0).

Festuca rubra x Vulpia fasciculata
= X Festulpia hubbardii Stace & R. Cotton

Native. Recorded from Sandwich Bay in 1954 but there are no subsequent sightings. **0** (0).

Lolium perenne L.   Perennial Rye-grass

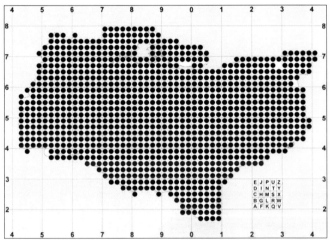

Native, but also the most commonly sown agricultural grass. In grassland throughout the county. **1025** (1036).

Lolium perenne x multiflorum
= L.x boucheanum Kunth

Introduced (neophyte). Frequently planted and recorded in the past, but not noted during the present survey. **0** (2).

Lolium multiflorum Lam.   Italian Rye-grass

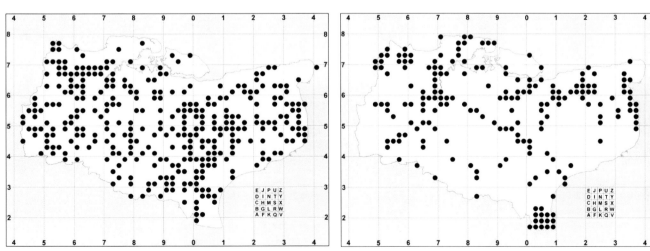

Introduced (neophyte). Widely sown in grazing meadows and now extensively naturalised in grassy areas and waste places. **335** (602).

Lolium rigidum Gaudin   Mediterranean Rye-grass

Introduced. A casual plant of rubbish-tips and found as a wool shoddy alien in the past, but not recorded during the present mapping. **0** (1).

Lolium temulentum L.   Darnel

Introduced. A casual plant of cornfields and rubbish-tips in the past, but not found during the present mapping. **0** (8).

Vulpia fasciculata (Forssk.) Fritsch   Dune Fescue

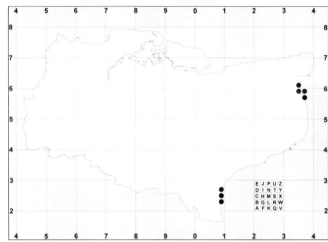

Native. A scarce plant of coastal sand-dunes. **7** (3).

Vulpia bromoides (L.) Gray   Squirreltail Fescue

Native. On open grassland, heaths and sand-dunes, and also on old walls, in quarries and dry waste areas. **196** (213).

Vulpia myuros (L.) C.C. Gmel.   Rat's-tail Fescue   *Cynosurus cristatus* L.   Crested Dog's-tail

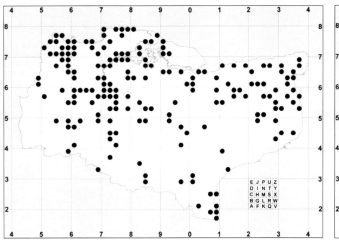

Introduced (archaeophyte). On well drained soils on roadsides, waste ground in built-up areas, in pavement cracks and on old walls, and occasionally on cultivated sandy soils. **185** (111).

Native. In most grasslands save those that are very wet or very disturbed. **629** (851).

Vulpia ciliata Dumort. **ssp. *ambigua***   Bearded Fescue   *Cynosurus echinatus* L.   Rough Dog's-tail
(LeGall) Stace & Auquier

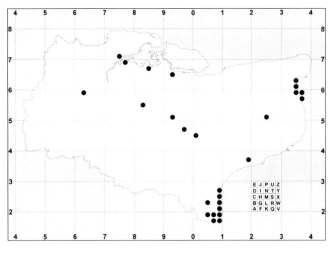
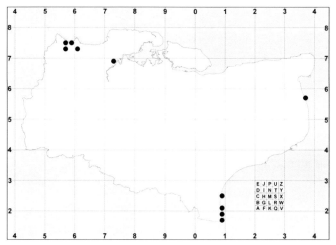

Native. A scarce plant of coastal sand-dunes and dry sandy tracks and roadside verges. **26** (23).

Introduced (neophyte). On roadside banks and disturbed waste land. **10** (8).

Vulpia muralis (Kunth) Nees

Introduced. A casual plant introduced with wool shoddy and last recorded in 1966. **0** (0).

Vulpia unilateralis (L.) Stace   Mat-grass Fescue   *Lamarckia aurea* (L.) Moench   Golden Dog's-tail

Native. A scarce, but easily over-looked grass recorded from in or adjacent to chalk quarries at Greenhithe TQ57X, Snodland TQ76B, Burham TQ76F, Cuxton TQ76I, and Rochester TQ76J. **5** (5).

Introduced. Recorded as a casual garden escape in the past, but not seen during the present mapping. **0** (1).

Puccinellia maritima   Common Saltmarsh-grass
(Huds.) Parl.

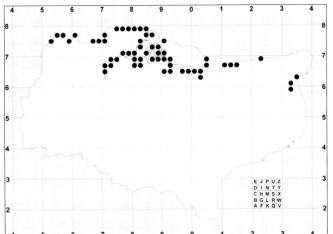

Native. In salt-marshes, tidal mud-flats and by brackish ditches. **58** (95).

Puccinellia maritima x *distans*
= *P.* x *hybrida* Holmb.

Native. Recorded from East Kent in the past, but not found during the present survey. **0** (0).

Puccinellia distans   Reflexed Saltmarsh-grass
(Jacq.) Parl.

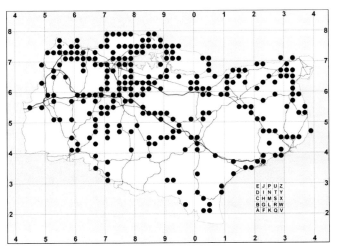

Native. On sea-walls and the upper edges of salt-marshes. From the 1970s onwards this grass has spread along the edges of motorways and other roads that are salt-treated during the winter months. **266** (163).

Puccinellia distans x *fasciculata*

Native. Plants referable to this hybrid have been found just inside the sea-wall on Dartford Marshes TQ57N, Northfleet TQ57X, and Swanscombe TQ67C. **3** (18).

Puccinellia distans x *rupestris*
= *P.* x *pannonica* (Hack.) Holmb.

Native. Recorded from Higham in 1895, but not found since. **0** (0).

Puccinellia fasciculata   Borrer's Saltmarsh-grass
(Torr.) E.P. Bicknell

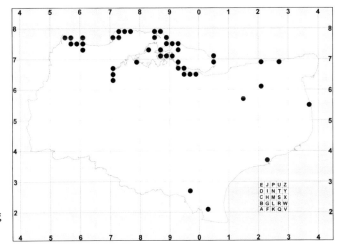

Native. On sea-walls and in coastal marshes, particularly in bare patches near gateways. It has occasionally been found inland at the edges of salt-treated roads. A scarce grass, and nationally listed as 'Vulnerable'. **45** (78).

Puccinellia rupestris   Stiff Saltmarsh-grass
(With.) Fernald & Weath.

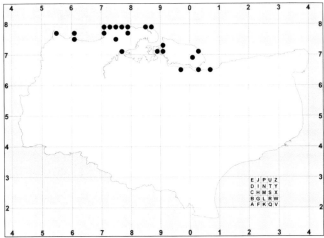

Native. On bare or sparsely vegetated patches along sea-walls and tracks over coastal marshes. Has been recorded at the edge of salt treated roads in the past but was not noted in this habitat in the present survey. Rather local and scarce. **22** (28).

Briza media L.   Quaking-grass

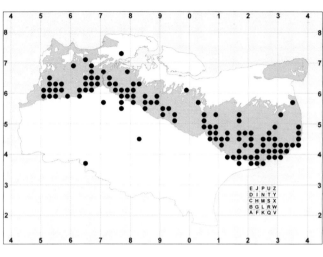

Native. On unimproved grassland on well-drained soils, particularly on the chalk. **119** (181).

Briza minor L.   Lesser Quaking-grass

Introduced. Casual records in the past, but not seen during the present mapping. **0** (1).

Briza maxima L.   Greater Quaking-grass

Introduced (neophyte). An escape from cultivation on roadside verges and waste ground. Recorded from Seal TQ55N, Cranbrook TQ73T & 73X, and Cuxton TQ76D. **4** (2).

Poa infirma Kunth   Early Meadow-grass

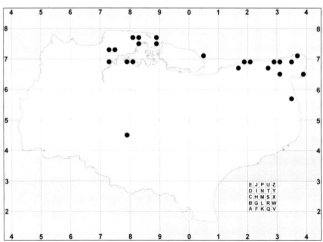

Native. Formerly restricted to the Channel Islands, Isles of Scilly and west Cornwall, this grass has been extending its range in recent years. It was first found in Kent (on the Isle of Grain) in 1999 and since then has spread along the North Kent coast and has even been found inland on a roadside verge. It occurs in bare areas where there is little or no other vegetation. **23** (0).

Poa annua L.   Annual Meadow-grass

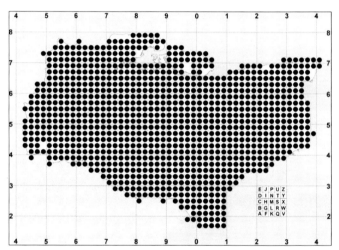

Native. On cultivated and waste ground except where crowded out by dense vegetation. Also on wall-tops, between pavement slabs and in built-up areas wherever there is the slightest bit of soil. **1033** (1035).

Poa trivialis L.   Rough Meadow-grass

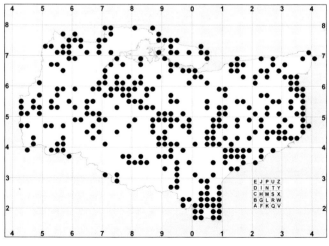

Native. In open woodland, meadows, roadside verges, cultivated and waste land. **1001** (961).

Poa humilis Ehrh. ex Hoffm.   Spreading Meadow-grass

Native. In calcareous and neutral grassland, sand-dunes, wall-tops, and particularly on road and trackside verges. **335** (90).

Poa pratensis L. Smooth Meadow-grass

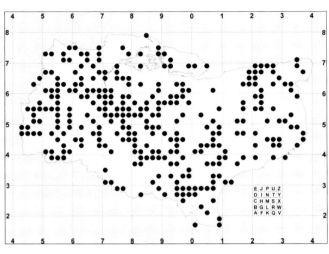

Native. In pastures, meadows and roadside verges; usually in well-drained soils of medium to high fertility. Probably over-recorded in the past because of a lack of understanding of this complex of grasses. **312** (914).

Poa compressa L. Flattened Meadow-grass

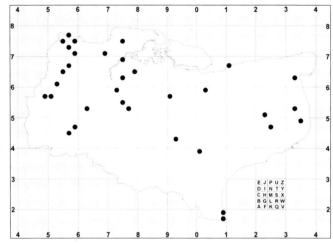

Native. On rough or stony ground, dry grassy banks, and on old walls. **33** (94).

Poa angustifolia L. Narrow-leaved Meadow-grass

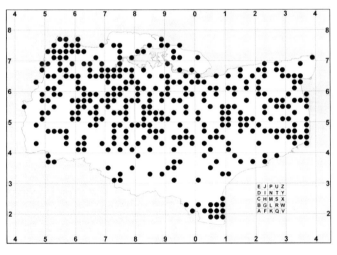

Native. On dry grassland; at the base and on the tops of walls; on railway banks, and on rough ground on relatively infertile soils. **358** (257).

Poa chaixii Vill. Broad-leaved Meadow-grass

Introduced (neophyte). A plant of cultivation recorded on occasion from West Kent but not found during the present mapping. **0** (1).

Poa palustris L. Swamp Meadow-grass

Introduced (neophyte). Appears have gone from its former site at Dungeness and is now probably extinct in the county. **0** (1).

Poa nemoralis L. Wood Meadow-grass

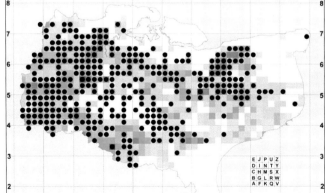

Native. In woods and shady roadside banks, and occasionally on old walls. **358** (542).

Poa bulbosa L.   Bulbous Meadow-grass

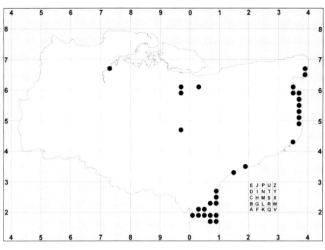

Native. On sand-dunes and stabilised shingle near the coast, and occasionally on sparsely vegetated firm sandy areas inland. **31** (21).

Dactylis glomerata L.   Cock's-foot

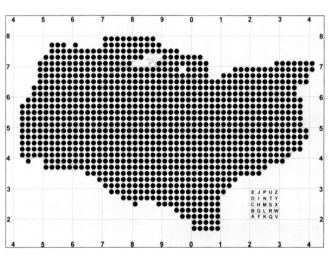

Native. A common grass of roadsides, woodland edges, meadows, rough grassland and waste ground. **1032** (1037).

Catabrosa aquatica (L.) P. Beauv.   Whorl-grass

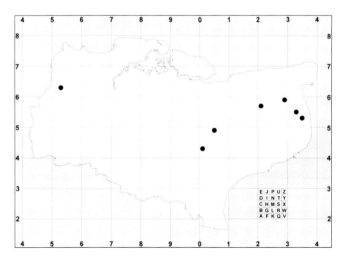

Native. A grass of muddy pond margins and at the edges of slow-flowing ditches and streams. It appears not to tolerate farm chemicals or fertilizers, and is becoming a rare plant in the county. **7** (9).

Catapodium rigidum (L.) C.E. Hubb.   Fern-grass

Native. On well-drained, poorly vegetated areas on chalk and sand, and regularly on old walls or pavement cracks. **284** (274).

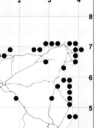

Dactylis glomerata Cock's-foot © Lee Manning

Catapodium marinum   Sea Fern-grass
(L.) C.E. Hubb.

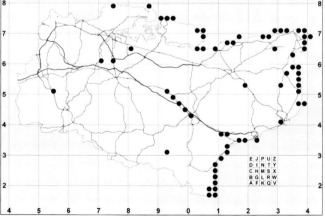

Native. On dry places by the sea such as chalk cliffs, fixed sand-dunes, and particularly in cracks in sea-walls and pavements. In recent years it has been found on bare areas at the edges of salt-treated inland roads. **65** (54).

Parapholis strigosa
(Dumort.) C.E. Hubb.

Hard-grass

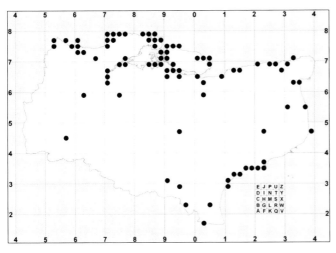

Native.   At the edge of salt-marshes and along sea-walls, and on waste ground on the coast.   In common with many other coastal plants it is now being found inland on the verges of salt-treated roads.   **85** (82).

Glyceria maxima (Hartm.) Holmb.

Reed Sweet-grass

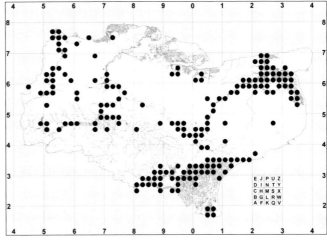

Native.   At the edge of ponds, lakes rivers, canals and streams, and in ditches and the wetter parts of marshes.   **187** (218).

Glyceria fluitans (L.) R. Br.

Floating Sweet-grass

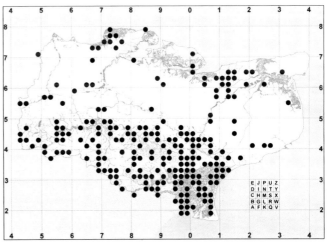

Native.   By ditches, ponds and lakes, and in marshes, margins of temporary ponds, and in other swampy areas.   **226** (389).

Parapholis incurva
(L.) C.E. Hubb.

Curved Hard-grass

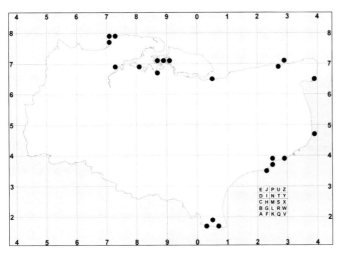

Native.   On bare places along sea-walls and on cliffs on the coast. Often found growing in a narrow band in the area reached by salt-water spray during rough weather.   **21** (24).

Glyceria fluitans x *notata*
= *G.* x *pedicellata* F. Towns.

Hybrid Sweet-grass

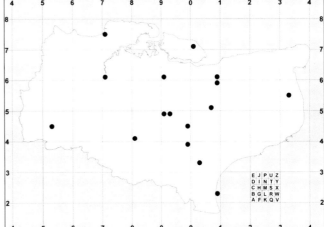

Native.   In ponds, ditches, streams and other wet marshy areas. It can be found growing with one or both parents or with neither. **16** (48).

Glyceria declinata Bréb.   Small Sweet-grass   *Melica uniflora* Retz.   Wood Melick

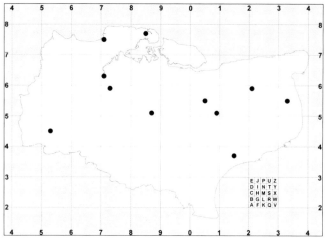

Native. By ponds and ditches, often in wooded areas or sites shaded by trees. **11** (48).

Native. In woodland margins and rides, and shaded hedgerows and roadside banks. **480** (534).

Helictotrichon pratense (L.) Besser   Meadow Oat-grass

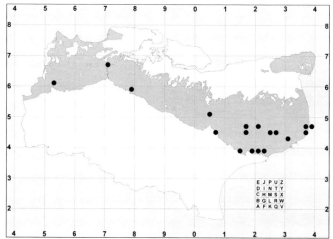

Wood Melick *Melica uniflora* © L. Rooney

Native. On grassy banks and roadside verges on the chalk. Appears to have become scarcer in recent years. **18** (58).

Glyceria notata Chevall.   Plicate Sweet-grass   *Helictotrichon pubescens* (Huds.) Pilg.   Downy Oat-grass

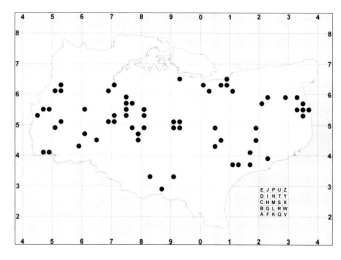

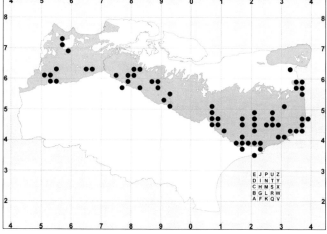

Native. In shallow ponds, streams and ditches. **63** (135).

Native. On chalk downland and on other calcareous or neutral grassland. Never abundant and rather scarce away from the chalk. **66** (101).

Arrhenatherum elatius
(L.) P. Beauv. ex J. Presl & C. Presl

False Oat-grass

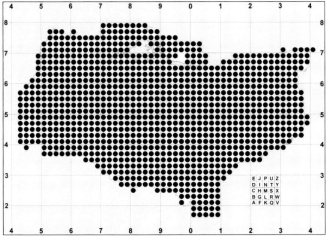

Native. A common grass of rough grassland and waste places, and it is particularly frequent on roadside verges and hedge banks. **1020** (1017).

Avena sterilis L. ssp. *ludoviciana*
(Durieu) Gillet & Magne

Winter Wild-oat

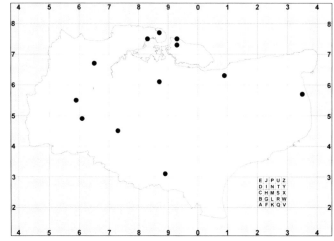

Introduced (neophyte). Although formerly cultivated, this grass is now a scarce casual in arable fields. Looking rather similar to *A. fatua*, this plant can only be satisfactorily identified when with fully mature seeds. **12** (5).

Avena strigosa Schreb.

Bristle Oat

Introduced. Formerly extensively cultivated, but now a rare casual, and last recorded in the county in the 1890s. **0** (0).

Avena sterilis L. ssp. *sterilis*

Animated Oat

Introduced (neophyte). A few plants were found on waste ground at Gravesend in 1979 but no subsequent records. **0** (1).

Avena fatua L.

Wild-oat

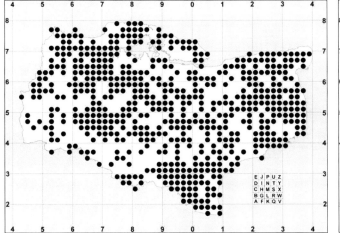

Introduced (archaeophyte). A common weed on arable land, particularly where cereals are grown, and also at times on other disturbed and waste ground. **606** (629).

Avena sativa L.

Cultivated Oat

Introduced (neophyte). A frequent relic of arable crops and occasionally on roadsides and waste ground as a relic from animal feed. **88** (150).

297

Trisetum flavescens (L.) P. Beauv.   Yellow Oat-grass

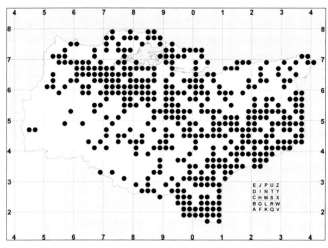

Native. In meadows, roadsides and other grassland, being more frequent in long-established hay meadows. Appears to have become less frequent in the south-west of the county where it was specifically searched for on many occasions. **452** (705).

Koeleria macrantha (Ledeb.) Schult.   Crested Hair-grass

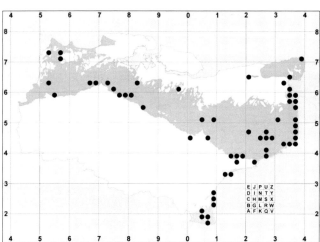

Native. On fixed sand-dunes in coastal areas, and in quarries and open grassy, or sparsely vegetated areas, on the chalk. **58** (105).

Rostraria cristata (L.) Tzvelev   Mediterranean Hair-grass

Introduced. A casual wool shoddy alien, last recorded in the county in 1960. **0** (0).

Deschampsia cespitosa (L.) P. Beauv.   Tufted Hair-grass

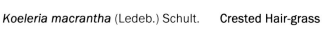

Native. In woods, marshes and meadows, usually on poorly drained soils. **470** (579).

Deschampsia flexuosa (L.) Trin.   Wavy Hair-grass

Native. On acid heaths and in woodland on otherwise poorly vegetated acid sandy soils. **118** (159).

Holcus lanatus L.   Yorkshire-fog

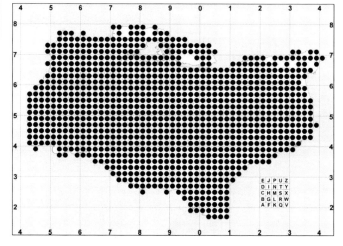

Native. In meadows, woodland, roadside verges, hedge banks and a wide range of other grassy and waste places. **1005** (1019).

Holcus mollis L.   Creeping Soft-grass

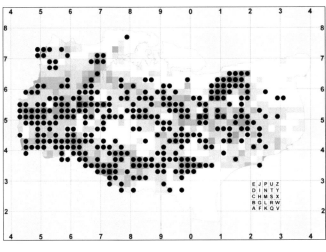

Native. In woods and on shady banks on well-drained acidic or neutral sandy soils. **337** (450).

Anthoxanthum odoratum L.   Sweet Vernal-grass

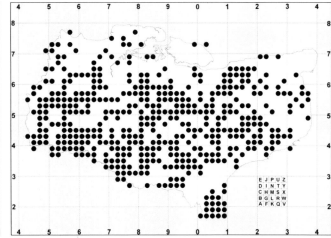

Native. On a variety of grassland habitats including old meadows, heaths, sand-dunes, being more frequent on the more acid soils. **468** (653).

Aira caryophyllea L.   Silver Hair-grass

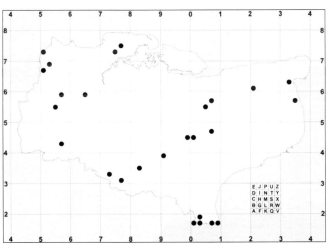

Native. On heaths, commons and fixed sand-dunes on well-drained sandy or gravelly soils. **26** (78).

Phalaris arundinacea L.   Reed Canary-grass

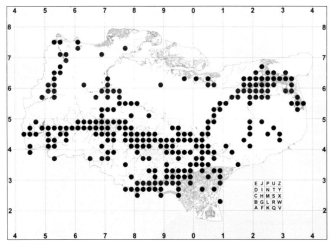

Native. At the edge of rivers, lakes, ponds, ditches, and in other wet marshy areas, particularly where there is some fluctuation in the water level. **260** (327).

Aira praecox L.   Early Hair-grass

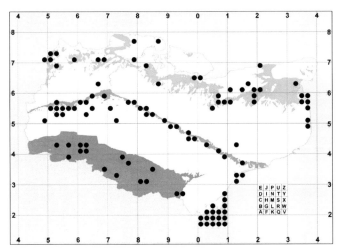

Native. On fixed sand-dunes and gravel on the coast, and on heaths, commons and other open areas on thinly vegetated sandy soils. It is occasionally found on old walls. **108** (132).

Phalaris arundinacea L. var. *picta* L.   Gardener's Garters

Introduced (neophyte). A garden throw-out noted as established on waste ground at Bough Beech TQ44Y, Seal TQ55N, New Ash Green TQ66C and Greatstone-on-Sea TR02R. **4** (0).

Phalaris aquatica L.   Bulbous Canary-grass

Introduced (neophyte). On field-borders, woodland rides and waste ground, probably as a relic from game bird food. Recorded from Dartford marshes TQ57N, near Meopham TQ66I, Istead Rise TQ67F and Cooling TQ77T. **4** (2).

Phalaris canariensis L.   Canary-grass   *Agrostis capillaris* L.   Common Bent

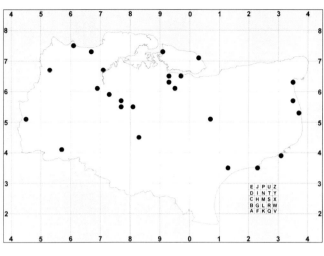
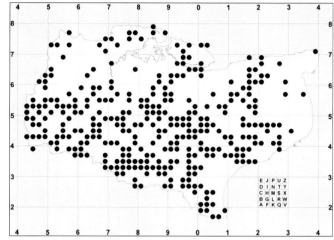

Introduced (neophyte). On rubbish-tips, gardens and roadside verges as a relic from bird seed. It is also occasionally found in arable fields. Appears to have declined in recent years as other seed species are more favoured in the bird seed mixes. **25** (90).

Native. A common plant of grassland on neutral to moderately acid soils. Widely distributed and under-recorded on the present map. **333** (644).

Phalaris brachystachys Link   Confused Canary-grass   *Agrostis capillaris* x *stolonifera* = *A.* x *murbeckii* Fouill.

Introduced. A casual wool shoddy alien, recorded from East Kent in 1960, but not since. **0** (0).

Native. Recorded from West Kent in the past, but not found during the present mapping. **0** (4).

Phalaris minor Retz.   Lesser Canary-grass   *Agrostis gigantea* Roth   Black Bent

Introduced. A casual plant on rubbish-tips. arable fields and waste ground. The only recent record is of a few plants in an arable field at Naccolt TR04M. **1** (0).

Phalaris paradoxa L.   Awned Canary-grass

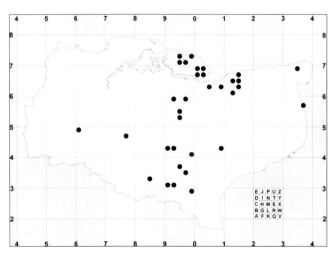

Introduced (archaeophyte). In cornfields, neglected arable land, hedgerows, and occasionally in gardens and waste ground. **343** (521).

Agrostis castellana Boiss. & Reut.   Highland Bent

Introduced (neophyte). An increasing species, now well established as an arable weed in fields and roadside verges in parts of the county. **33** (4).

Introduced (neophyte). Recorded from How Green in West Kent in 1978 and would be expected to be found elsewhere in the county. **0** (0).

Agrostis stolonifera L.   Creeping Bent

Agrostis scabra Willd.   Rough Bent

Introduced. Recorded as a casual on a rubbish-tip at Stone in 1980 but with no subsequent records. **0** (1).

Agrostis stolonifera x **Polypogon monspeliensis**
= X **Agropogon littoralis** (Sm.) C.E. Hubb.

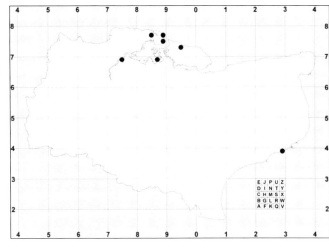

Native. On roadsides, marshy ground, rough grassland, and cultivated and waste ground. Generally common throughout the county. **974** (1007).

Native. On vehicle or cattle disturbed soils on or near the coast, usually with both parents nearby. **7** (2).

Agrostis avenacea J.F. Gmel.   Blown-grass

Introduced. A casual wool shoddy alien in East and West Kent and last recorded in 1960. **0** (0).

Agrostis canina L.   Velvet Bent

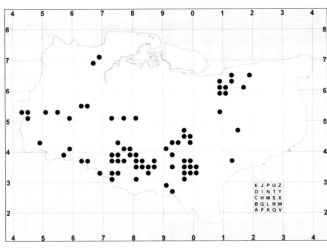

Native. Heaths, commons and open woodland on acidic sandy or peaty soils. **73** (138, total combined with *A. vinealis*).

Calamagrostis epigejos (L.) Roth   Wood Small-reed

Native. In damp woodland, chalk quarries and scrub, and rough grassy areas. **11** (18).

Agrostis vinealis Schreb.   Brown Bent

Native. On dry or free-draining sandy or peaty soils. Only presently recorded from Sundridge TQ45X, Dartford Heath TQ57B & 57G, near Stansted TQ65A and the Orlestone Forest TQ93X.
5 (138, total combined with *A. canina*).

Calamagrostis canescens   Purple Small-reed
(F.H. Wigg.) Roth

Native. In marshes and fen-meadows. Last recorded in 1959 and now perhaps extinct in the county. **0** (0).

Ammophila arenaria (L.) Link   Marram

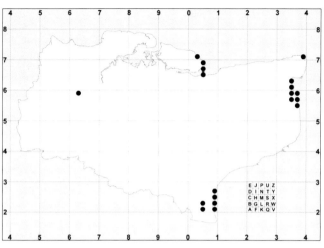

Polypogon monspeliensis (L.) Desf.   Annual Beard-grass

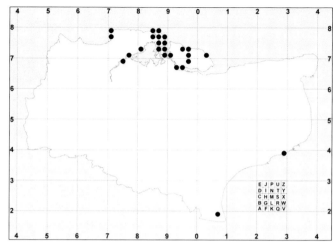

Native. On coastal sand-dunes although perhaps originally introduced at some sites to help stabilise the sand. Has persisted for over twenty five years on a roadside sand bank at Wrotham TQ65J. **19** (21).

Native. In damp places by the sea, particularly in cattle-trodden grazing marshes, and in dried-up brackish pools and ditches. **25** (17).

Gastridium ventricosum   Nit-grass
(Gouan) Schinz & Thell.

Native. First recorded in Britain from near Tunbridge Wells in 1690 but has always been a rare grass in Kent and with the last record from Chattenden Wood in 1954. During the present mapping it was re-found at what is probably the same locality alongside Chattenden Wood at TQ77L. **1** (0).

Polypogon viridis (Gouan) Breistr.   Water Bent

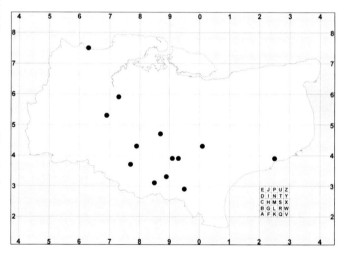

Lagurus ovatus L.   Hare's-tail

Introduced (neophyte). Well established on sand-dunes, sandy banks and roadside verges in the Dungeness to Greatstone-on-Sea area TR01U, 01Y, 02V & 02W. **4** (5).

Introduced (neophyte). Formerly as a casual wool shoddy alien, but in recent years it has become a weed in garden nurseries. From this source it is now occasionally found in gardens and as a street weed in built-up areas. **13** (0).

Apera spica-venti (L.) P. Beauv.   Loose Silky-bent

Introduced (neophyte). A casual on neglected ground at Stone TQ57X, and in arable fields at Luddesdown TQ66T. **2** (4).

Apera intermedia Hack.

Introduced. A casual where wool shoddy had been used in East Kent, and last recorded in 1960. **0** (0).

Polypogon maritimus Willd.

Introduced. A casual wool shoddy alien last recorded in 1960. **0** (0).

Alopecurus pratensis L. Meadow Foxtail

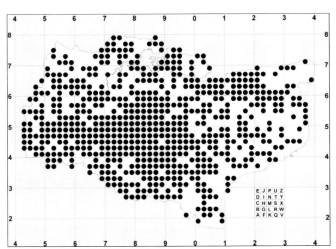

Native. In meadows, roadside verges and damp grassy areas. **649** (873).

Meadow Foxtail *Alopecurus pratensis* © L. Rooney

Alopecurus geniculatus x bulbosus = A. x plettkei Mattf.

Native. First recorded from the Higham Marshes in 1987 but although looked for, could not be re-found there. However it was found at a new site in 1994 on the Snodland Marshes TQ76B. **1** (0).

Alopecurus bulbosus Gouan Bulbous Foxtail

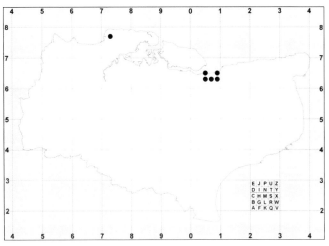

Native. A rare plant of coastal grazing marshes that have periodically been flooded by the sea. **6** (1).

Alopecurus aequalis Sobol. Orange Foxtail

Native. A scarce plant that occurs at the edges of ponds and ditches. Recorded from Shorne TQ67V, Goudhurst TQ73I, Riverside Country Park TQ86E and Gibbin's Brook TR13E. **4** (1).

Alopecurus geniculatus L. Marsh Foxtail

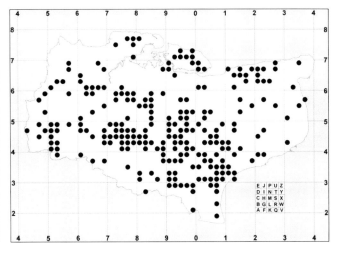

Native. In wet meadows and at the edge of ponds and ditches, particularly in ditches in grazing meadows that dry up during the summer months. **188** (326).

Alopecurus myosuroides Huds. Black-grass

Introduced (archaeophyte). A long-established annual weed of arable fields, which also occurs on disturbed roadside verges and neglected ground. **243** (194).

Phleum pratense L.   Timothy

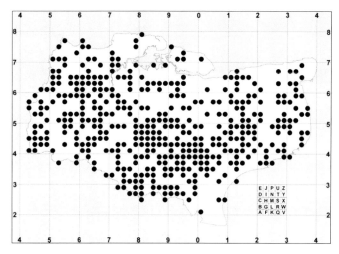

Native. In meadows, pastures and rough grassy areas. It is regularly sown in grassland and some records will be due to these introductions. **441** (700).

Phleum bertolonii DC.   Smaller Cat's-tail

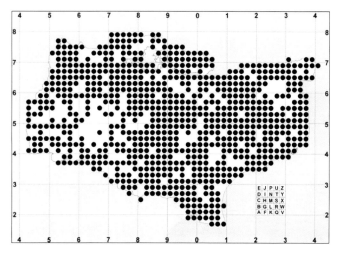

Native. In meadows, pastures, and on downland, roadside banks and waste grassy areas, particularly on well-drained sandy or chalky soils. **814** (952).

Phleum arenarium L.   Sand Cat's-tail

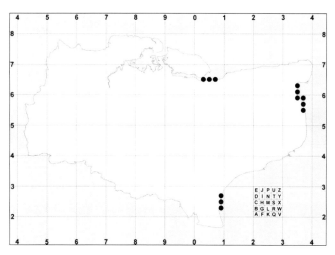

Native. A scarce plant of coastal sand-dunes and sandy shingle. **12** (17).

Bromus arvensis L.   Field Brome

Introduced. A casual plant of arable and cultivated fields. The only record is from a field at Adisham TR24G. **1** (1)

Bromus racemosus L.   Meadow Brome

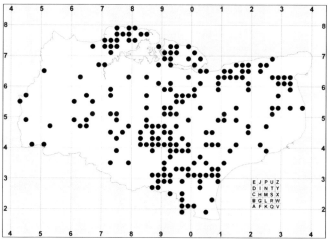

Native. *Bromus commutatus* and *B. racemosus* were mapped separately, but it was found that there was a complete gradation between the largest *commutatus* down to the smallest *racemosus* and with many plants that could be referred to either species. It is now the opinion of many botanists that there is only one species, and that is the opinion that is taken here. As *racemosus* is the earlier name, that is the one that must now be used. Typically found in damp unimproved meadows, but also in waysides, roadside verges and at the margins of cultivated fields. This grass appears have become more frequent in recent years. **194** (46).

Bromus hordeaceus L.   Common Soft-brome
ssp. *hordeaceus*

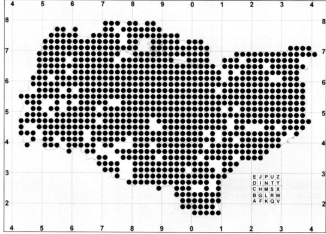

Native. A common grass in meadows, roadsides and waste ground, but not where it is heavily grazed nor in very wet or acid localities. **910** (894).

Note. The various subspecies of *hordeaceus* are not recognized by all authorities and are thought by some just to be variants depending upon the habitat. However, they are recognizable and are mapped here.

Bromus hordeaceus ssp. divaricatus
(Bonnier & Layens) Kerguélen

Introduced (neophyte). Reported in the past in association with wool shoddy, but with no recent records. **0** (0).

Bromus hordeaceus L. ssp. thominei   Sand Soft-brome
(Hardouin) Braun-Blanq

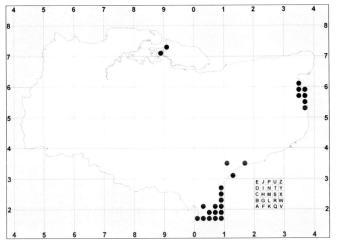

Native. A small, usually prostrate grass, that is found on fixed sand-dunes and other sandy places on or near the coast. **26** (34).

Bromus hordeaceus ssp. longipedicellatus Spalton

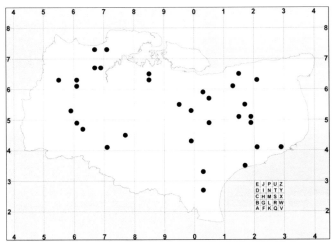

Native. Although not recognized and formally described until 2001, there are Kent herbarium species dating back to 1930. It is now a frequent weed at the edge of cultivated fields and occasionally in disturbed waste places. **33** (0).

(Note, some authorities might refer this taxon to a form of **B. racemosus**).

Bromus hordeaceus x lepidus   Lesser Soft-brome
= B. x pseudothominei P.M. Sm.

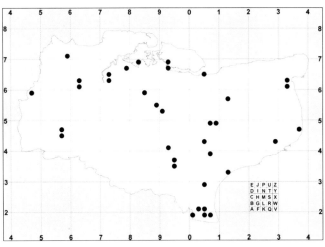

Introduced (neophyte). Sometimes difficult to distinguish from the parents and only plants clearly intermediate have been mapped. In sown grassland and occasionally in arable fields and waste land. **35** (125).

Bromus lepidus Holmb.   Slender Soft-brome

Introduced. The only recent record is from a sheep-grazed meadow at Petham TR15F. **1** (9).

Bromus interruptus (Hack.) Druce   Interrupted Brome

This grass is not known outside Britain and is usually classed as an introduction (neophyte) but could have claims to being native. It was first collected from Preston in East Kent in 1890 and last recorded from Upper Halling in West Kent in 1936. There are no subsequent records and it is probably now extinct in the county and in the country as a whole. **0** (0).

Bromus secalinus L.   Rye Brome

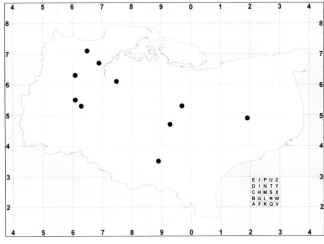

Introduced (archaeophyte). A casual plant of arable fields. **10** (1).

Bromopsis ramosa (Huds.) Holub   Hairy-brome

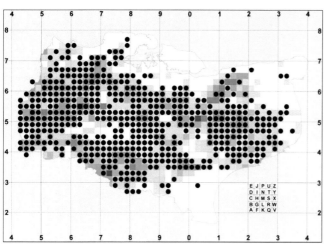

Native. In woodlands, hedgerows and other tree-shaded habitats.
514 (615).

Bromopsis inermis (Leyss.) Holub   Hungarian Brome

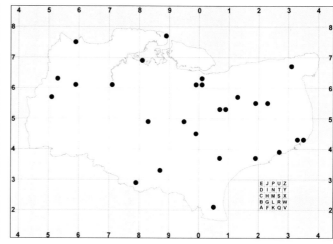

Introduced (neophyte). On roadside verges, field margins and
rough grassy places. Appears to be spreading, but only slowly.
All specimens checked have proved to be subspecies *inermis*, but
subspecies *pumpelliana* (Scribn.) W.A. Weber has been recorded
from West Kent in the past. **27** (19).

Bromopsis benekenii   Lesser Hairy-brome
(Lange) Holub

Native. Recorded at Shoreham in 1973, but not re-found there,
or at any other locality, although specifically searched for.
0 (1).

Anisantha diandra   Great Brome
(Roth) Tutin ex Tzvelev

Bromopsis erecta (Huds.) Fourr.   Upright Brome

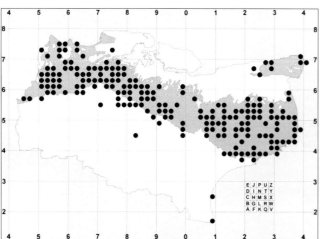

Introduced (neophyte). On roadside verges, arable fields and
disturbed waste ground, usually on well-drained soil. Has become
more frequent in recent years. **34** (16).

Native. A common plant of rough grassland on the chalk, and
occasionally on calcareous sand-dunes, or other calcareous soils.
201 (251).

Anisantha rigida (Roth) Hyl.   Ripgut Brome

Introduced (neophyte). Casual plants recorded at Greenhithe
TQ57S and Snodland TQ76A. **2** (2).

Anisantha sterilis (L.) Nevski   Barren Brome   *Ceratochloa cathartica* (Vahl) Herter   Rescue Brome

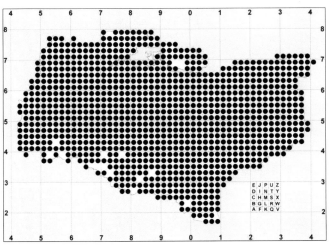
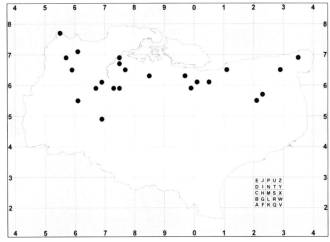

Introduced (archaeophyte). Now completely naturalised and widespread throughout the county on roadside verges, hedge banks, cultivated fields and gardens, and on waste ground. **1000** (973).

Introduced (neophyte). On roadside verges, field borders and waste ground. Although known as a casual or wool shoddy alien since 1884, it is only in recent years that this grass has become established and is now spreading quite steadily and often forming large patches. **23** (5).

Anisantha tectorum (L.) Nevski   Drooping Brome

Introduced. A casual grass of roadside verges and waste ground and only recorded from Otham TQ75W during the present survey. **1** (4).

Anisantha madritensis (L.) Nevski   Compact Brome

Introduced. A few casual plants at Rainham TQ86D, but well established and spreading at Pegwell Bay TR36L & 36M. **3** (4).

Anisantha rubens (L.) Nevski   Foxtail Brome

Introduced. The only record for this rare casual is of a few plants on the sea-wall at Gillingham Country Park TQ86E. **1** (0).

Brachypodium pinnatum (L.) P. Beauv.   **Tor-grass**

Ceratochloa carinata   California Brome
(Hook. & Arn.) Tutin

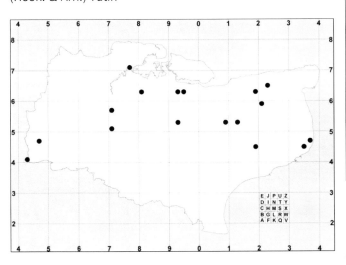

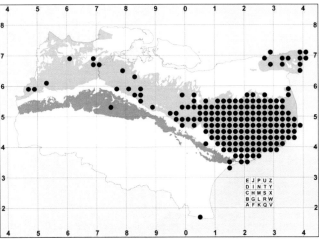

Native. On dry, relatively infertile grassland on the chalk, in chalk quarries, and occasionally on well-drained calcareous soils elsewhere. It can become rather dominant where it does occur and it is considered as a troublesome weed on nature reserves on the chalk as it suppresses the finer chalk plants.

Introduced (neophyte). The first Kent record was from Hoo in 1972 (specimen in **MNE**, originally identified as *C. cathartica*) and it is now increasingly found on roadside verges and field borders. **17** (0).

Note: some, or all of the records here might refer to *Brachypodium rupestre* (Host) Roem. & Schult., the taxonomy of which has still to be resolved. **190** (199).

Brachypodium sylvaticum   False Brome
(Huds.) P. Beauv.

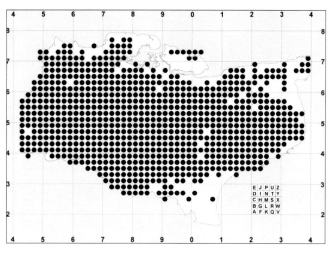

Native. A plant of woodland, hedgerows and shady roadside banks. **815** (837).

Brachypodium distachyon (L.) P. Beauv.   Stiff Brome

Introduced. Recorded as a garden casual, introduced with wild bird seed, at Tunbridge Wells in 1976, but with no subsequent records. **0** (0).

Elymus caninus (L.) L.   Bearded Couch

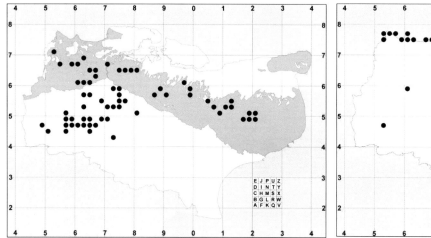

Native. In shaded, free-draining banks by rivers and streams, and on shaded roadside and track sides on the chalk. **64** (86).

Elytrigia repens   Common Couch
(L.) Desv. ex Nevski

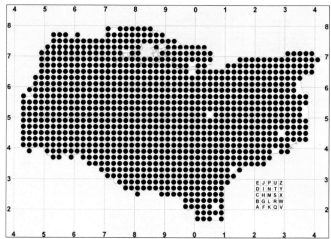

Native. In disturbed soils on roadsides, hedgerows, sand-dunes, arable fields and gardens. A difficult weed to eradicate from cultivated ground, but does not occur in deep woodland or heavily grazed pastures. **1005** (1015).

Elytrigia repens x *atherica* = *E.* x *drucei* Stace

Native. Recorded from the Swanscombe Marshes TQ67C and Littlestone-on-Sea TR02X, but easily over-looked and would be expected to be found in further localities where both parents grow together. **2** (5).

Elytrigia repens x *juncea* = *E.* x *laxa* (Fr.) Kerguélen

Native. Has been recorded from East Kent in the past, but was not noted during the present survey. **0** (0).

Elytrigia atherica (Link) Kerguélen   Sea Couch

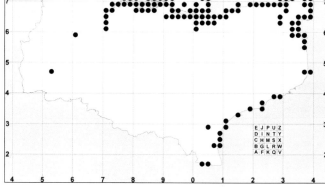

Native. On the margins of tidal river and brackish creeks, in saltmarshes, sand-dunes, shingle banks, tops of coastal cliffs, and along sea-walls. In recent years there has been the occasional patch established on roadsides well away from the coast. **148** (160).

Elytrigia atherica x *juncea*
= *E.* x *acuta* (DC.) Tzvelev

Native. Recorded from Isle of Grain TQ87Y and the Sandwich Bay area TR35S, 35T & TR36K. **4** (0).

Elytrigia juncea (L.) Nevski   Sand Couch

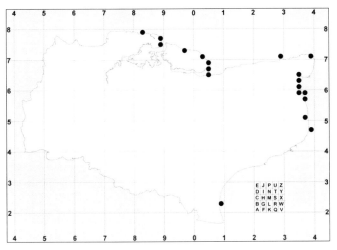

Native. On young sand-dunes and sandy beaches just above the high-tide line. **19** (29).

Leymus arenarius (L.) Hochst.   Lyme-grass

Native, although perhaps originally planted. Still persists at Sandwich Bay TR36K where it was first recorded in 1962. **1** (1).

Hordelymus europaeus (L.) Jess. ex Harz   Wood Barley

Native. Not found during the present survey although searched for at Riverhill where it was last recorded in 1956. Perhaps now extinct in the county. **0** (0).

Hordeum vulgare L.   Six-rowed Barley

Introduced. A casual relic from former cultivation. Not found during the present survey and many past records probably refer to *H. distichon*. **0** (20).

Hordeum distichon L.   Two-rowed Barley

Introduced. Casual relics from cultivation or animal feed noted growing on roadside verges or waste land at Dartford TQ57L, Swanscombe TQ67C, Maidstone TQ75N, Snodland TQ76A, Harrietsham TQ85S, Little Chart TQ94N, Charing TQ95K and Birchington TR26U. **8** (55).

Hordeum murinum L. ssp. *murinum*   Wall Barley

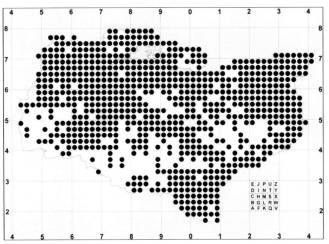

Introduced (archaeophyte). A long established plant of roadside verges, railway banks, rough grassland and other disturbed ground. **777** (834).

Hordeum murinum L. ssp. *leporinum* (Link) Arcang.

Introduced. A casual wool shoddy alien during the period 1960-1980, but with no recent records. **0** (1).

Hordeum murinum L. ssp. *glaucum* (Steudel) Tzvelev

Introduced. Casual plants 1960-1980 as a relic from wool shoddy, but with no recent records. **0** (1).

Hordeum pusillum Nutt.   Little Barley

Introduced. A casual wool shoddy plant, last recorded in 1960. **0** (0).

Hordeum jubatum L.   Foxtail Barley

Introduced. Casual plants noted on disturbed ground on Dartford Marshes TQ57N, on the banks of Milton Creek TQ96C, and on a roadside verge at Whitstable TR16C. **3** (8).

Hordeum pubiflorum Hook. f.   Antarctic Barley

Introduced. Established for a few years in the 1970s in an orchard where wool shoddy had been used. The site has now been destroyed and no further plants have been found. **0** (1).

Hordeum secalinum Schreb.   Meadow Barley

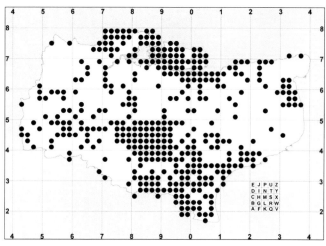

Native. In meadows, grazing marshes and roadside verges, particularly on clay soils. **414** (530).

Triticum aestivum L.   Bread Wheat

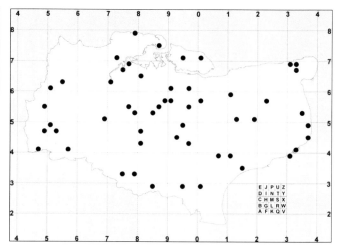

Introduced. Casual plants on roadside verges and field edges as escapes from cultivation or from animal feed. **53** (75).

Triticum turgidum L.   Rivet Wheat

Introduced. Casual record in the past but not seen during the present mapping. **0** (25).

Hordeum marinum Huds.   Sea Barley

Aegilops cylindrica Host.

Introduced. Casual plants from wool shoddy in 1976, but with no recent records. **0** (1).

Aegilops geniculata Roth

Introduced. Casual plants from wool shoddy in 1976, but with no recent records. **0** (1).

Native. On barely vegetated patches on sea walls and coastal tracks, and on trampled margins of dried-up coastal pools and ditches. Nationally a scarce plant and listed as 'Vulnerable'. **48** (60).

Danthonia decumbens (L.) DC.   Heath-grass

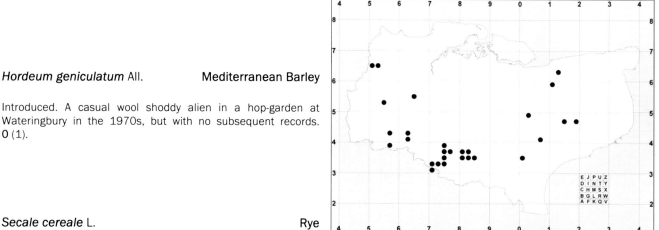

Hordeum geniculatum All.   Mediterranean Barley

Introduced. A casual wool shoddy alien in a hop-garden at Wateringbury in the 1970s, but with no subsequent records. **0** (1).

Secale cereale L.   Rye

Introduced. Casual plants on a roadside verge at Newington TQ86M. **1** (8).

Native. On heaths, rough pastures and woodland rides on mildly acidic soils. **28** (45).

Rytidosperma penicillatum (Labill.) Connor & Edgar

Introduced. A casual wool shoddy alien recorded from near Sandwich in 1960. **0** (0).

Cortaderia selloana   Pampas-grass
(Schult. & Schult. f.) Asch. & Graebn.

Introduced. A garden plant found as a relic or established on waste ground at Snodland TQ76A, Cliffe TQ77D, Isle of Grain TQ87X, Greatstone-on-Sea TR02W, Ashford TR04B, Dover TR34G and Cliffs End TR36M. **7** (2).

Molinia caerulea (L.) Moench   Purple Moor-grass

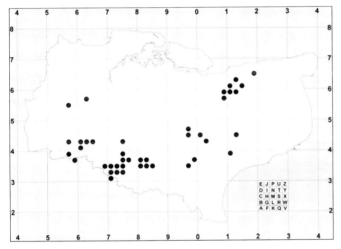

Native. On heaths, bogs and open woodland on sandy, often acidic, soils. **42** (47).

Phragmites australis   Common Reed
(Cav.) Trin. ex Steud.

Native. In shallow water at the edge of rivers, streams, lakes and ponds, and in swamps and fens. At times it can persist on motorway verges and other developed lands where the original wet habitat has been destroyed. **343** (346).

Schmidtia kalihariensis Stent

Introduced. A casual wool shoddy alien, last recorded in 1960. **0** (0).

Leptochloa fusca (L.) Kunth   Brown Beetle-grass

Introduced. A casual wool shoddy alien last recorded in 1960. **0** (0).

Leptochloa uninervia (J. Presl) Hitchc. & Chase

Introduced. A casual wool shoddy alien last recorded in 1980. **0** (1).

Eragrostis curvula (Schrad.) Nees   African Love-grass

Introduced. A casual wool shoddy alien last recorded in 1960. **0** (0).

Eragrostis cilianensis   Stink-grass
(All.) Vignolo ex Janch.

Introduced. A casual wool shoddy or grain alien last recorded in 1980. **0** (2).

Eragrostis parviflora   Weeping Love-grass
(R. Br.) Trin.

Introduced. A few casual plants with wool shoddy from near Sandwich in 1971 are the only record. **0** (0).

Eragrostis neomexicana Vasey ex L.H. Dewey

Introduced. Noted in the 1970s in a disused quarry where soya waste had been dumped, but no subsequent records. **0** (1).

Eleusine indica (L.) Gaertn. **ssp.** *indica*   Yard-grass

Introduced. A casual oil-milling adventive last recorded in 1976. **0** (2).

Eleusine indica (L.) Gaertn. **ssp. africana**
(Kenn.-O'Byrne) S.M. Phillips

Introduced. A casual wool shoddy alien last recorded in 1960.
0 (0).

Dactyloctenium radulans   Button-grass
(R. Br.) P. Beauv.

Introduced (neophyte). A wool shoddy alien last recorded in 1970.
0 (0).

Chloris truncata R. Br.   Windmill-grass

Introduced. A casual wool shoddy alien recorded from near
Sandwich in 1959, but no other records. 0 (0).

Chloris virgata Sw.   Feathery Rhodes-grass

Introduced. A casual wool shoddy alien, last recorded in 1960.
0 (0).

Cynodon dactylon (L.) Pers.   Bermuda-grass

Introduced (neophyte). A wool shoddy alien which often persisted
for several years where it did occur. However, it was not found
during the present mapping, the last recorded occurrence being
in 1982. 0 (2).

Cynodon incompletus Nees   African Bermuda-grass

Introduced. A casual wool shoddy alien last recorded in 1985.
0 (1).

Spartina maritima (Curtis) Fernald   Small Cord-grass

Native. A rare plant of tidal mud-flats and now listed nationally as
'Endangered'. Although specifically looked for, it could not be
found in any of its previous known localities during the present
mapping. Always a scarce plant, it has been slowly decreasing for
many years now, being last recorded in the county in 1988, and
might now well be extinct. 0 (1).

Spartina anglica C.E. Hubb.   Common Cord-grass

Native. On tidal mud-flats and in saltmarshes. 80 (84).

Tragus racemosus (L.) All.   European Bur-grass

Introduced. A casual wool shoddy alien last recorded in 1970.
0 (0).

Tragus australianus S.T. Blake   Australian Bur-grass

Introduced. A wool shoddy alien that persisted for a few years at
East Malling where it was last seen in 1980. There are no further
records. 0 (1).

Panicum schinzii Hack. ex Schinz   Transvaal Millet

Introduced. Casual plants on a rubbish-tip at Stone in the 1970s,
but with no subsequent records. 0 (1).

Panicum dichotomiflorum Michx.   Autumn Millet

Introduced. On various sites in the Dartford area where oil-seed
waste had been tipped 1973-1976, but with no subsequent
records. 0 (3).

Panicum capillare L.   Witch-grass

Introduced. On disturbed waste ground at Plaxtol TQ65B and
Northfleet TQ67F. 2 (2).

Panicum miliaceum L.   Common Millet

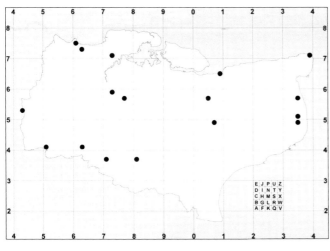

Introduced. Casual plants on road verges, field borders and waste ground, usually as a relic from wild bird or game bird seed. **16** (27).

Echinochloa colona (L.) Link   Shama Millet

Introduced. A few casual plants on a rubbish-tip at Stone TQ57S. **1** (5).

Echinochloa frumentacea Link   White Millet

Introduced. Casual plants on rubbish-tips and waste ground at Dartford TQ57M, Stone TQ57S and Swanscombe TQ67C. **3** (0).

Paspalum dilatatum Poir.   Dallis-grass

Introduced. A casual wool shoddy alien last recorded in 1973. **0** (1).

Panicum subalbidum Kunth

Introduced. Casual plants on a rubbish-tip at Stone in 1973, but with no further records. **0** (1).

Setaria parviflora   Knotroot Bristle-grass
(Poir.) Kerguélen

Introduced. Casual past records from rubbish-tips, the last in 1973. **0** (2).

Echinochloa crus-galli (L.) P. Beauv.   Cockspur

Setaria pumila   Yellow Bristle-grass
(Poir.) Roem. & Schult.

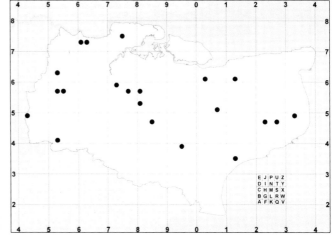

Introduced. Casual plants on roadside verges, cultivated and waste land. Sometimes sown as food for game birds. **17** (19).

Introduced (neophyte). Cultivated and waste land, roadsides and gardens. Seed of this grass is regularly used in wild bird food and is also found in the mix that is sown for game birds. **21** (9).

Echinochloa esculenta   Japanese Millet
(A. Braun) H. Scholz

Introduced. Casual plants on rubbish-tips and waste ground at Dartford TQ57M, Stone TQ57S and Swanscombe TQ67C, and on a field margin near Godmersham TR05Q. **4** (17).

Setaria verticillata (L.) P. Beauv.   Rough Bristle-grass

Introduced. Casual records in cultivated fields from wool shoddy and also on rubbish-tips in the past; last recorded in 1978. **0** (4).

313

Setaria viridis (L.) P. Beauv.   Green Bristle-grass

Introduced. Casual plants on roadside verges at Shoreham TQ56G and Swanscombe TQ67C. **2** (22).

Setaria faberi Herrm.   Nodding Bristle-grass

Introduced. Occasional plants in the Dartford area 1973-1976 in places where oil-seed waste had been dumped. There are no recent records. **0** (3).

Setaria italica (L.) P. Beauv.   Foxtail Bristle-grass

Introduced. Regularly sold as food for cage birds and surprisingly the only record is of a few plants growing on waste land at Swanscombe TQ67C. **1** (13).

Digitaria ischaemum   Smooth Finger-grass
(Schreb. ex Schweigg.) Muhl.

Introduced. A casual plant in arable fields and rubbish-tips from bird seed or wool shoddy, last recorded in 1976. **0** (0).

Digitaria sanguinalis (L.) Scop.   Hairy Finger-grass

Introduced (neophyte). A pavement weed at Sutton-at-Hone TQ56P, on a roadside verge at Hextable TQ57A, a persistent garden weed at Aylesford TQ75J, and on waste ground near Leeds TQ85B. **4** (4).

Digitaria ciliaris (Retz.) Koeler   Tropical Finger-grass

Introduced. Casual records from the Dartford area where oil-seed waste had been dumped 1973–76, but with no subsequent sightings. **0** (3).

Digitaria didactyla Willd.   Blue Couch

Introduced. A few casual plants with wool shoddy in the Hextable area in 1948, but with no subsequent records. **0** (0).

Pennisetum clandestinum   Kikuyu-grass
Hochst. ex Chiov.

Introduced. Casual plants on waste ground at East Malling in the 1970s, but with no subsequent records. **0** (1).

Cenchrus echinatus L.   Spiny Sandbur

Introduced. Casual plants on a rubbish-tip at Dartford in 1976 but with no other records. **0** (1).

Sorghum halepense (L.) Pers.   Johnson-grass

Introduced. Casual records in the past and with the only recent record being from a churchyard at Thurnham TQ85D. **1** (7).

Sorghum bicolor (L.) Moench   Great Millet

Introduced. On a field margin near Godmersham TR05Q, perhaps derived from game bird food. **1** (4).

Zea mays L.   Maize

Introduced. Casual plants noted on waste ground at Hextable TQ57A and at Swanscombe TQ67C. **2** (11).

SPARGANIACEAE

Sparganium erectum L.   Branched Bur-reed

Native. An emergent plant found in shallow waters at the edge of rivers, canals, lakes, ponds, streams and wet ditches. The subspecies can only be separated when in fruit and have not been mapped separately; subsp. *neglectum* is the most frequent, closely followed by subsp. *erectum*. Subsp. *microcarpum* and subsp. *oocarpum* also occur on occasion. **353** (324).

Sparganium emersum Rehmann   Unbranched Bur-reed

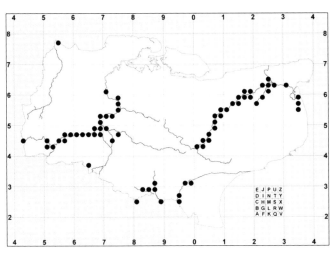

Native.   In slow-flowing rivers, deep streams, marsh dykes and canals.   **67** (45).

Typha latifolia x *angustifolia* = *T.* x *glauca* Godr.

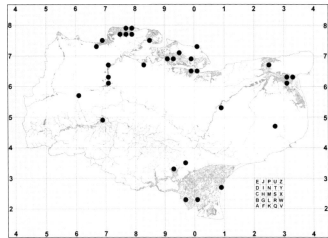

Native.   In shallow water at the edge of lakes, flooded gravel pits, canals and marsh dykes, sometimes in the absence of one or both parents.   **32** (0).

Sparganium natans L.   Least Bur-reed

Native.   Still present in marsh dykes about Worth Minnis TR35M where it has been known since at least 1829.   **1** (1).

TYPHACEAE

Typha latifolia L.   Bulrush

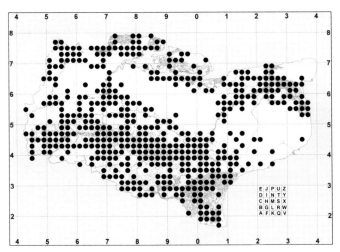

Native.   An emergent plant in shallow water or exposed mud at the edge of lakes, ponds, canals, rivers and wide marsh dykes. **484** (483).

Typha angustifolia L.   Lesser Bulrush

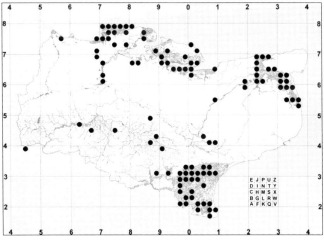

Native.   At the edge of lakes, ponds, canals, flooded gravel-pits and marsh dykes, being more frequent in areas near the coast. **107** (180).

LILIACEAE

Narthecium ossifragum (L.) Huds.   Bog Asphodel

Native.   A plant of wet heaths and bogs which has always had a very restricted range in Kent.   Now only recorded from Hothfield Common TQ94S.   **1** (3).

Hemerocallis fulva (L.) L.   Orange Day-lily

Introduced (neophyte). A common garden plant and found naturalised on wide roadside verges near Woodchurch TQ93G and near Sellindge TR03Z. **2** (7).

Kniphofia uvaria (L.) Oken   Red-hot-poker

Introduced (neophyte). Well established garden outcasts recorded at Dartford TQ57H, St. Mary's Bay TR02Y, Warden TR07B, Leysdown-on-Sea TR07F, Kingsdown TR34U and Sandwich Bay TR35T. **7** (1).

Colchicum autumnale L.   Meadow Saffron

Perhaps originally native, but had become extinct sometime before 1899. Now only known as a casual escape from cultivation and noted on waste ground at Upper Halling TQ66X and Milton Regis TQ86X. **2** (0)

Gagea lutea (L.) Ker Gawl.   Yellow Star-of-Bethlehem

Native, but now extinct. Recorded from the Dartford area at some time before 1899, but not since. **0** (0).

Tulipa sylvestris L.   Wild Tulip

Introduced (neophyte). Has been known for about a hundred years in small quantity from some parkland at West Malling and still present, although the area has recently been brought into more formal cultivation. **1** (1).

Tulipa gesneriana L.   Garden Tulip

Introduced. A common garden plant and found growing on roadsides and waste ground as a garden relic or where garden refuse or soil from developments had been dumped. Casual plants noted from near Five Oak Green TQ64N; at Horsmonden TQ64V; Cobham TQ66U, Gravesend Marshes TQ67S; near Tenterden TQ93C; Hothfield TQ94S; St. Mary's Bay TR02Y; Faversham TR06B; West Blean Wood TR16R, and at Sandwich Bay TR35T & 35U. **11** (12).

Fritillaria meleagris L.   Fritillary

Introduced. Frequently cultivated in gardens and has occasionally been found as a casual in damp meadows. The only record during the present mapping was of two or three plants alongside the River Len at Maidstone TQ75S. **1** (1).

Lilium martagon L.   Martagon Lily

Introduced (neophyte). A strong, and long-established colony in a wood near Ridley TQ66B; several plants at a long-established site at Putt Wood TQ95U; and a few plants at a woodland edge near Wootton TR24I. **3** (1).

Lilium candidum L.   Madonna Lily

Introduced. A casual garden escape seen flowering on a roadside verge near Lydd TR02F in 1996. **1** (0).

Convallaria majalis L.   Lily-of-the-valley

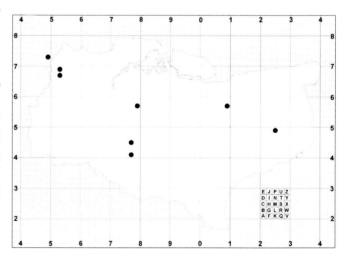

Native. Woodlands, wood-borders and hedgerows. Although this plant usually does very well under cultivation in gardens, as a wild plant its steady decline appears to continue. It has definitely gone from several former sites through development or change in management. **14** (49).

Polygonatum multiflorum (L.) All.   Solomon's-seal

Native. A scarce, and declining, plant of deciduous woodland. **8** (36).

Polygonatum multiflorum x *odoratum*   Garden
= *P.* x *hybridum* Brügger   Solomon's-seal

Introduced (neophyte). A garden outcast found growing in woodland, hedgerows and roadside verges. Recorded from Knockholt TQ45T; Kilndown TQ63X; Offham TQ65N; Yalding TQ65V; Meopham TQ66N; Old Park Wood TQ73P; Maidstone TQ75T and Tyler Hill TR16K. It was also noted freshly planted in a private woodland nature reserve! **8** (5).

Polygonatum odoratum
(Mill.) Druce

Angular Solomon's-seal

A native British plant, but almost certainly introduced in Kent. Recorded from Joyden's Wood in 1821, but with no further records. **0** (0).

Paris quadrifolia L.

Herb-Paris

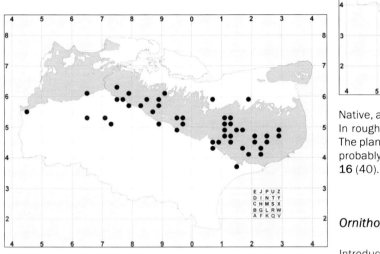

Native. In moist, calcareous, usually ancient woodland. **47** (57).

Ornithogalum angustifolium Boreau

Star-of-Bethlehem

Native, although most records probably refer to introduced plants. In rough grassy areas and open woodland where it looks native. The plants on roadside verges, shingle beaches and waste ground probably refer to escapes or throw-outs from cultivation. **16** (40).

Ornithogalum nutans L.

Drooping Star-of-Bethlehem

Introduced. A few casual records of this garden plant in the past, but not noted during the present mapping. **0** (1).

Herb-Paris *Paris quadrifolia* © J. Shorter

Scilla bifolia L.   Alpine Squill

Introduced (neophyte). A garden plant recorded from a roadside at Benenden (where it had probably been planted) in the 1970s, but with no subsequent sightings. **0** (1).

Scilla siberica Haw.   Siberian Squill

Introduced (neophyte). Persisted for a few years on Dartford Heath in the 1970s, but with no recent records. **0** (1).

Scilla autumnalis L.   Autumn Squill

Native, extinct. Last recorded at Shorne Warren in 1829. **0** (0).

Hyacinthoides non-scripta   Bluebell
(L.) Chouard ex Rothm.

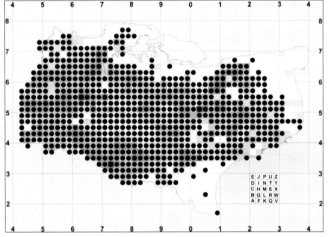

Native. In woodlands, hedgerows and shady banks. **712** (755).

Hyacinthoides non-scripta x hispanica
= *H.* x *massartiana* Geerinck

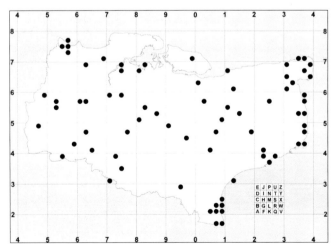

Introduced (neophyte). Hedgerows, woodland edges, churchyards, rough ground and waste places. Sometimes as a natural hybrid where the two species occur together and sometimes spreading out from where this hybrid bulb had been planted. A considerable increase in records in recent years, although some of this may be due to a better understanding of this group. **74** (4).

Hyacinthoides hispanica (Mill.)   Spanish Bluebell

Introduced (neophyte). A plant of cultivation that readily spreads out from gardens, and all too frequently planted out in wild situation in mistake for the native *H. non-scripta*. In copses, woodland edges, roadside verges and waste ground, being particularly frequent in some coastal areas. **59** (44).

Hyacinthus orientalis L.   Hyacinth

Introduced (neophyte). On roadside verges and banks, either as a discard, or deliberately planted, from garden stock. Noted well established at Lamberhurst Quarter TQ63U, Brenzett TR02D and Dover TR34G. **3** (3).

Muscari armeniacum   Garden Grape-hyacinth
Leichtlin ex Baker

Introduced (neophyte). Roadside verges, railway banks, woodland edges and waste ground. Odd bulbs discarded with garden refuse soon grow and multiply, and most records are from this source, although occasionally bulbs are planted out in wild areas. Because of the rate of spread, the Garden Grape-hyacinth is likely to become much more frequent in the future. Past records of *M. neglectum* almost certainly belong here. **45** (21).

Allium schoenoprasum L.   Chives

Introduced. A casual escape from cultivation noted growing wild on rough ground at Staple TR25T. **1** (1).

Allium cepa L.   Onion

Introduced. Casual records in the past and only noted growing on the upper beach at Allhallows TQ87P during the present survey. **1** (5).

Allium uniflorum Kellogg   American Garlic

Introduced (neophyte). A garden escape recorded from West Kent in the past, but not seen during the present mapping. **0** (0).

Allium roseum L.   Rosy Garlic

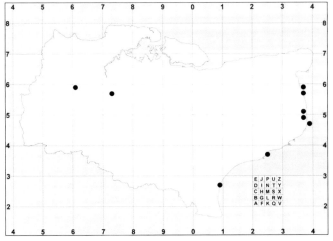

Introduced (neophyte). A garden plant now well established on sand-dunes and rough ground in some coastal sites, and as a casual roadside plant inland. **9** (4).

Allium neopolitanum Cirillo   Neopolitan Garlic

Introduced (neophyte). Well established at the edges of footpaths and rough ground at or near Ash TR25Y, St. Margaret's at Cliffe TR34S, and at Pegwell Bay TR36M & 36S. **4** (0).

Allium subhirsutum L.   Hairy Garlic

Introduced. Has been recorded in the county, but not during the present survey. There is a chance that some records of *A. neopolitanum* should have been placed here. **0** (0).

Allium moly L.   Yellow Garlic

Introduced (neophyte). A garden plant naturalised in a small copse at Borstal TQ76I. **1** (0).

Allium triquetrum L.   Three-cornered Garlic

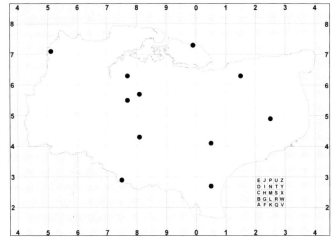

Introduced (neophyte). An escape from cultivation, or from dumped garden rubbish, and now well established, and spreading, in woods, woodland edges and roadside verges. **11** (1).

Allium paradoxum   Few-flowered Garlic
(M. Bieb.) G. Don

Introduced. A garden escape with a few casual records from West Kent in the past, but not noted during the present survey. **0** (0).

Allium ursinum L.   Ramsons

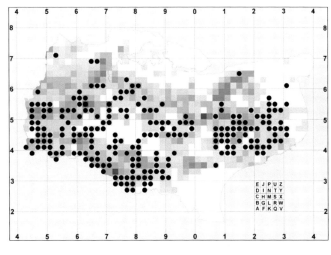

Native. In damp woods, stream-sides and shady hedge banks. **230** (229).

Allium oleraceum L.   Field Garlic

Native. At the edge of footpaths and on roadside verges at Offham TQ65N, Maidstone TQ75T and Borstal TQ76I. Noted in the Red List as 'Vulnerable'. **3** (1).

Allium ampeloprasum L.   Wild Leek

Introduced (archaeophyte). A few casual records in the past, the last being in 1954. **0** (0).

Allium vineale L.   Crow Garlic

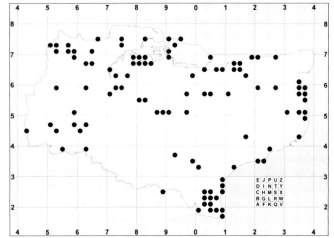

Native. On roadside verges, hedgerows, cultivated and rough ground, and on fixed sand-dunes on the coast. **103** (107).

Nothoscordum borbonicum Kunth   Honeybells

Introduced. A casual record of this garden plant in the 1970s, but none since. **0** (1).

Agapanthus praecox Willd.   African Lily

Introduced. A casual record from a rubbish-tip in the 1970s, but none since. **0** (1).

Tristagma uniflorum (Lindl.) Traub   Spring Starflower

Introduced (neophyte). A garden plant found established on roadside verges or waste ground at Joyden's Wood TQ57A, Rochester TQ76P, near Hartlip TQ86G, Warden TR07F, Covert Wood TR14Z and Ramsgate TR36Y. **6** (1).

Leucojum aestivum L.   Summer Snowflake

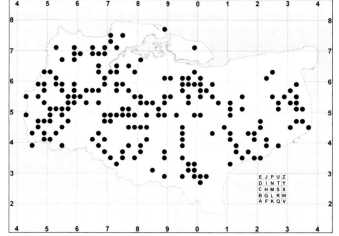

Introduced (neophyte). A garden plant, sometimes escaping or dumped with garden refuse, but often deliberately planted on roadside verges and woodland edges, and now well established. All plants checked have proved to be subsp. *pulchellum* (Salisb.) Briq. **16** (12).

Leucojum vernum L.   Spring Snowflake

Introduced. A sprawling clump, on rough ground at Hythe TR13M, was almost certainly a relic of cultivation. **1** (1).

Galanthus nivalis L.   Snowdrop

Introduced (neophyte). A common garden plant and often planted out in the wide countryside. It soon establishes itself and spreads and is now a frequent plant of lanesides, woodland, copses and churchyards. **196** (93).

Galanthus elwesii Hook. f.   Greater Snowdrop

Introduced (neophyte). Noted as established and spreading in the churchyard at Selling TR05I. **1** (1).

Narcissus pseudonarcissus L.   Wild Daffodil
ssp. pseudonarcissus

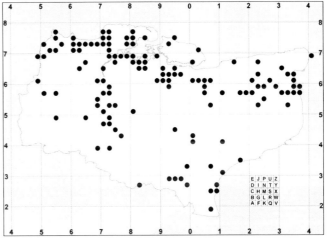

Native. In damp deciduous woods and damp meadows. The true native Wild Daffodil is in danger of extermination through hybridizing with the various forms of cultivated daffodils that are being planted out in the countryside. **15** (17).

Narcissus agg.   Cultivated Daffodil

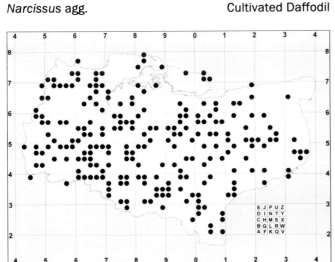

Introduced (neophyte). A very common garden plant regularly found as a relic from cultivation, or growing from tipped soil that has been removed with building developments. Also there is a growing tendency by local authorities and well-meaning citizens to plant out daffodils along roadside verges and woodland edges and rides. The source of most of these bulbs is from bulk lots supplied by nurserymen. These nurserymen (and nursery-women) are continually hybridizing various species, forms and cultivars in the search for even better plants for the show-bench and garden. Each year many thousands of these hybrid bulbs are grown on, the best new varieties are selected for breeding on; and the rest, which will contain a selection of un-named varieties which can vary from wonderful to terrible, are then sold on to the public. So the bulk of all these daffodils that are now naturalised all over our countryside cannot be named to species or variety and have just been recorded as *Narcissus* agg. **229** (32).

Narcissus tazetta x poeticus   Primrose-peerless
= N. medioluteus Mill.

Introduced (neophyte). Recorded before 1899, but with no recent sightings. **0** (0).

Narcissus poeticus L.   Pheasant's-eye Daffodil
ssp. poeticus

Introduced (neophyte). Noted on waste ground near Swanscombe TQ67A & 67B, and on a roadside at Hothfield TQ94S. **3** (3).

Narcissus cyclamineus DC.   Cyclamen-flowered Daffodil

Introduced (neophyte). Established in thousands in a wood at Hocker Edge TQ73U. **1** (0).

Asparagus officinalis L.   Garden Asparagus

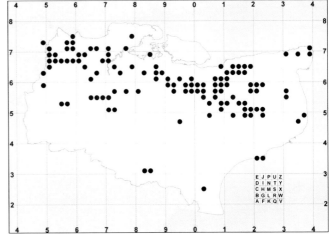

Introduced (archaeophyte). On roadside verges and waste grassy areas, particularly on sandy soils; in orchards; and on fixed sand-dunes in coastal areas. **132** (142).

Ruscus aculeatus L.   Butcher's-broom

Native. In woods, copses and hedgerows on well-drained chalky or sandy soils. **119** (152).

Alstroemeria aurea Graham   Peruvian Lily

Introduced. Casual records of this garden plant noted from the Dartford area in the 1970s, but with no subsequent records. **0** (2).

IRIDACEAE

Sisyrinchium bermudiana L. — Blue-eyed-grass

Introduced. Casual plants have been noted from West Kent in the past, but there are no recent records. **0** (0).

Sisyrinchium striatum Sm. — Pale Yellow-eyed-grass

Introduced. Casual plants noted on waste ground by roadsides at Stone Hill TR03Z, Palmarsh TR13G and Hacklinge TR35M. **3** (0).

Iris germanica L. — Bearded Iris

Introduced (neophyte). Casual plants noted established on waste ground at Snodland TQ76A, Lydd TR01P, Lydd-on-Sea TR01Z and Kingsdown TR34T. **4** (29).

Iris sibirica L. — Siberian Iris

Introduced (neophyte). A garden escape found naturalised at Otford TQ55J. **1** (0).

Iris pseudacorus L. — Yellow Iris

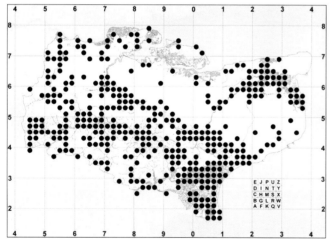

Native. At the margins of lakes, ponds and dykes, and in marshes and wet ditches. **390** (404).

Iris ensata Thunb. — Beaked Iris

Introduced (neophyte). A garden escape recorded from Dartford Heath in the past, but not noted during the present mapping. **0** (0).

Iris spuria L. — Blue Iris

Introduced (neophyte). In wet meadows at Northfleet TQ67C. **1** (0).

Iris orientalis Mill. — Turkish Iris

Introduced (neophyte). Has become well naturalised on roadside banks, and on waste grassy areas on the coast in a few scattered localities during recent years. **10** (0).

Iris foetidissima L. — Stinking Iris

Native. In hedge banks, coastal cliffs, scrub, open woodland and gardens. The Stinking Iris appears to have become much more frequent in recent years. **310** (153).

Iris latifolia (Mill.) Voss — English Iris

Introduced (neophyte). A garden escape noted from Fawkham in the 1970s, but with no subsequent records. **0** (1).

Iris xiphium L. — Spanish Iris

Introduced (neophyte). A garden escape noted growing with *I. latifolia* in the 1970s, but not recorded since. **0** (1).

Crocus vernus (L.) Hill   Spring Crocus

Introduced. Much planted in parks and gardens, and in recent years on many roadside verges. Plants considered to have escaped and growing wild were recorded at Horton Kirby TQ56T, Hextable TQ57A, Yalding TQ64Z, Offham TQ65N and Hoad's Wood TQ94L. **5** (2).

Crocus tommasinianus Herb.   Early Crocus

Introduced (neophyte). Commonly planted in gardens where it can become very invasive, and is likely to be found in the wild more frequently in the future as a result of spread from discarded garden rubbish. Recorded growing 'wild' at Crockham Hill TQ44K, West Peckham TQ65G, Collier Street TQ74D, Maidstone TQ75T, Lenham TQ95A, Whitfield TR34C and Martin Mill TR34N. **7** (0).

Crocus speciosus M. Bieb.   Bieberstein's Crocus

Introduced (neophyte), A garden plant, recorded in the past, but not seen growing wild during the present mapping. **0** (0).

Crocus ancyrensis (Herb.) Maw   Ankara Crocus

Introduced (neophyte). Reported from a roadside verge in the past where it had probably been planted, but not seen growing wild during the present mapping. **0** (0).

Crocus flavus x angustifolius   Yellow Crocus
= **C. x stellaris** Haw.

Introduced (neophyte). Past records of *C. flavus* almost certainly belong here. This is the common yellow crocus of gardens, parks and now frequently planted on roadside verges. Escaped plants growing 'wild' were noted near Five Oak Green TQ64N, West Peckham TQ65G, near Bethersden TQ94K and Sandgate TR13X. **4** (1).

Gladiolus communis L.   Eastern Gladiolus

Introduced. Casual plants noted on roadside verges or rough ground alongside roads at Maidstone TQ75P, Littlestone-on-Sea TR02X, Folkestone TR23J, Kingsdown TR34T, Walmer TR34Z and Richborough TR36G. Our plant is subsp. *byzantinus* (Mill.) D.C.V. Douin. **6** (2).

Gladiolus x colvillei Sweet   Garden Gladiolus

Introduced. A casual garden outcast noted from Dartford in the 1970s, but with no subsequent records. **0** (2).

Crocosmia pottsii x aurea   Montbretia
= **C. x crocosmiiflora** (Lemoine) N.E. Br.

Introduced (neophyte). On roadside verges, waste ground, and particularly in woodland margins, most often from discarded garden plants. **37** (53).

AGAVACEAE

Yucca recurvifolia Salisb.   Curved-leaved Spanish-dagger

Introduced. Well established on sand-dunes at Greatstone-on-Sea TR02W and a beach area at Kingsdown TR34U. **2** (0).

Phormium tenax   New Zealand Flax
J.R. Forst. & G. Forst.

Introduced. Casual records from West Kent in the past, but not noted during the present survey. **0** (0).

DIOSCOREACEAE

Tamus communis L.   Black Bryony

Native. In hedgerows, scrub and wood-margins. **681** (773).

ORCHIDACEAE

Cephalanthera damasonium (Mill.) Druce — White Helleborine

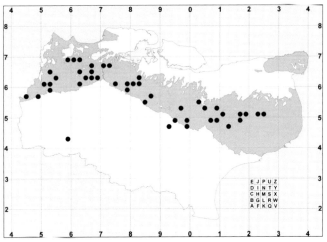

Native. In woodland on the chalk, especially under beech trees. It is listed nationally as 'Vulnerable'. **45** (84).

Cephalanthera longifolia (L.) Fritsch — Narrow-leaved Helleborine

Native. Always a rare plant in Kent and not found during the present mapping. **0** (1).

Epipactis palustris (L.) Crantz — Marsh Helleborine

Native. In a chalk-pit at Swanscombe TQ67C and scattered colonies on fixed sand-dunes in the Sandwich Bay area TR35N, 35P & 35T. **4** (4).

Epipactis purpurata Sm. — Violet Helleborine

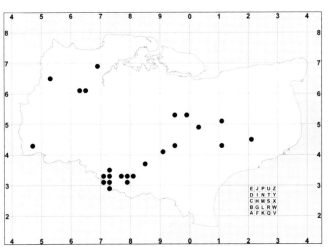

Native. In woods and shady roadside banks on well-drained soils. Appears to have gone from several former localities, but is easily over-looked and does not show every year. **24** (61).

Epipactis purpurata x helleborine = E. x schulzei P. Fourn.

Native. Was recorded from the Upper Hardres area in 1955, but there are no subsequent records. **0** (0).

Epipactis helleborine (L.) Crantz — Broad-leaved Helleborine

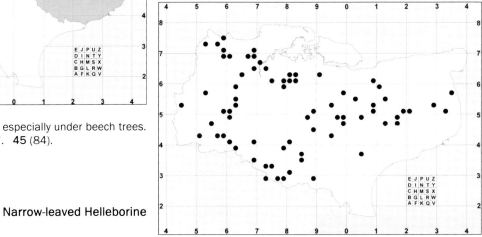

Native. In woods, hedgerows, shady banks and roadside verges, and occasionally on fixed sand-dunes. **73** (107).

Epipactis leptochila (Godfery) Godfery — Narrow-lipped Helleborine

Native. Past records from a few localities in East Kent, but repeated searches in all the previous known localities have failed to re-find this plant during the present mapping. **0** (3).

Epipactis phyllanthes G.E. Sm. — Green-flowered Helleborine

Native. Still to be found in a plantation belt at Eynsford TQ56H, at the site where it was first discovered in Kent in 1956. The numbers appear to vary each year but 58 flowering spikes were counted in 2004. It has also been found in disused quarries and on waste chalky ground in the Stone/Greenhithe/ Swanscombe area TQ57S, 57X & 67C in sites that are likely to be lost to development in the near future. **4** (3).

Neottia nidus-avis (L.) Rich.　　　　Birds-nest Orchid

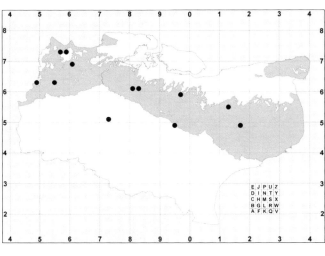

Native. In shady woods and copses, particularly under beech trees. This orchid appears have declined quite seriously in recent years. The present national status is 'Near Threatened'. **12** (44).

Listera ovata (L.) R. Br.　　　　Common Twayblade

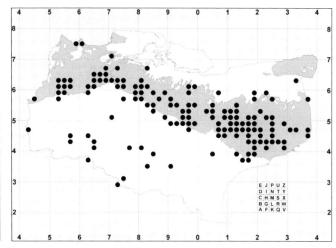

Native. In woods and copses, and occasionally in more open grassy areas. Most frequent in woods on the chalk. **145** (114).

Autumn Lady's-tresses　*Spiranthes spiralis*　© S. Smith

Spiranthes spiralis (L.) Chevall.　　**Autumn Lady's-tresses**

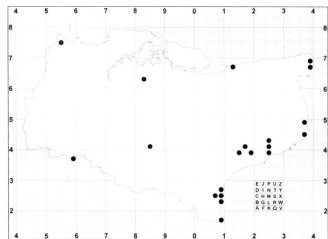

Native. In grassy areas on chalk downland, damp meadows, roadside verges, coastal dunes, and other grassy areas such as tennis courts. The number of plants showing each year is very variable and much dependent on how much rainfall there has been earlier in the year. Also, the sites where this plant grows are often those that are regularly mowed, which tends to make recording very difficult, and the real distribution is likely to be wider that that shown on the map. In the Red List, it is categorised as 'Near Threatened'. **20** (31).

Liparis loeselii (L.) Rich.　　　　Fen Orchid

Native, extinct. Past records from the Ham Fen area, the last in 1802. **0** (0).

Hammarbya paludosa (L.) Kuntze   Bog Orchid

Native. Doubtfully recorded in the county between 1640-1778, but if correct, this plant is certainly long extinct in the county. **0** (0).

Herminium monorchis (L.) R.Br.   Musk Orchid

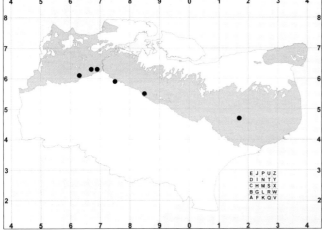

Native. In short turf on the chalk, usually on steep slopes. Appears to have gone from some former localities, and is listed nationally as 'Vulnerable'. **6** (12).

Platanthera chlorantha   Greater Butterfly-orchid
(Custer) Rchb.

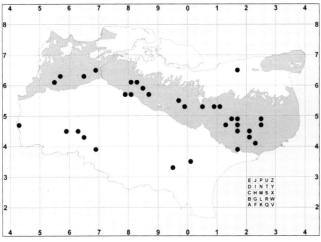

Native. In woods and grassy banks, particularly on the chalk. Usually in small numbers and easily over-looked. In the Red List Category, 'Near Threatened'. **34** (50).

Platanthera bifolia (L.) Rich.   Lesser Butterfly-orchid

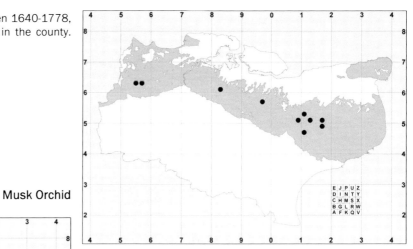

Native. Open scrub and woodland on the chalk. Scattered records of small colonies or of single plants. Becoming less frequent and noted in the Red List Category as 'Vulnerable'. **10** (10).

Greater Butterfly-orchid *Platanthera chlorantha* © S. Smith

Anacamptis pyramidalis (L.) Rich.   Pyramidal Orchid

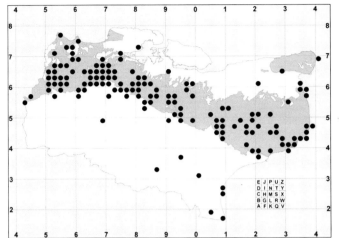

Native. On open grassland, roadside verges and fixed sand-dunes, always on well-drained soils and particularly on the chalk. **145** (147).

Pseudorchis albida   Small-white Orchid
(L.) Á. Löve & D. Löve

Native, extinct. Recorded from near Lyminge at some time before 1873, but with no subsequent sightings. **0** (0).

Gymnadenia conopsea (L.) R. Br.   Fragrant Orchid

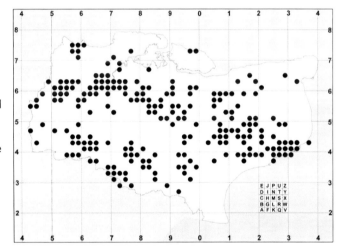

Native. On open downland and light scrub on the chalk. No attempt has been made to map the different subspecies, but *conopsea* is the usual form and *densiflora* has been noted on occasion. **53** (87).

Gymnadenia conopsea x *Dactylorhiza fuchsii*
= X *Dactylodenia st-quintinii* (Godfery) J. Duvign.

Native. This hybrid has been recorded in the past, but there are no recent records. **0** (0).

Coeloglossum viride (L.) Hartm.   Frog Orchid

Native. Always a rare plant in Kent, and with the last small colony being discovered near Dover in 1943. This colony could be found most years up until 1988, but repeated searches during the present mapping have failed to find this plant, and it could now be lost to the county. **0** (2).

Dactylorhiza fuchsii   Common Spotted-orchid
(Druce) Soó

Native. On chalk downland, woodland rides, grassy banks and damp meadows, and often in abandoned gravel-pits and quarries. Probably the most frequent orchid noted by members of the general public. **225** (337).

Dactylorhiza fuchsii x *maculata*
= *D.* x *transiens* (Druce) Soó

Native. A single plant at the edge of Bedgebury Forest is the only record. **1** (0).

Dactylorhiza fuchsii x *praetermissa*
= *D.* x *grandis* (Druce) P.F. Hunt

Native. Noted growing together with both parents nearby at Sevenoaks TQ55D & 55I, Leybourne TQ65Z, and at Snodland TQ76A & 76B. **5** (8).

Dactylorhiza maculata (L.) Soó Heath Spotted-orchid

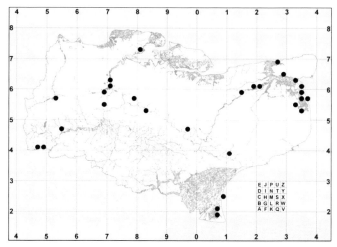

Native. On heaths, bogs and flushes in wet acid soils. Our plant is ssp. *ericetorum* (E.F. Linton) P.F. Hunt & Summerh. **6** (9).

Dactylorhiza maculata x *praetermissa*
= *D.* x *hallii* (Druce) Soó

Native. Found growing together with both parents on Hothfield Common TQ94T and Gibbins's Brook TR13E. **2** (2).

Dactylorhiza incarnata (L.) Soó Early Marsh-orchid

Native. In wet meadows and marshes. The Early Marsh-orchid has always been rare in Kent and is now only recorded from the Snodland marshes TQ76A & 76B, a wet meadow at Leeds TQ85H, and a marshy area near Wickhambreaux TR25J. Our plant is subsp. *incarnata*. **4** (5).

Dactylorhiza incarnata x *praetermissa*
= *D.* x *wintoni* (A. Camus) P.F. Hunt

Native. A few plants present on the Snodland marshes during the early 1980s, but not found there, or anywhere else, during the present mapping. **0** (0).

Dactylorhiza praetermissa Southern Marsh-orchid
(Druce) Soó

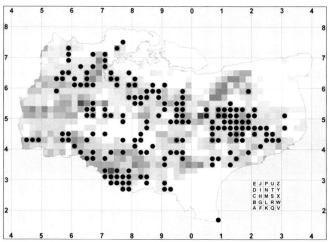

Native. In marshes, fens and wet meadows. This orchid has turned up at some new sites in wet areas on the floor of quarries, but has disappeared from other natural sites through land drainage. The variety *junialis* (Vermuel.) Vermuel. has been noted near Leigh TQ54N, East Malling Heath TQ65X, Detling TQ75Y, Snodland TQ76A, and Northbourne Fen TR35L. **28** (38).

Orchis mascula (L.) L. Early-purple Orchid

Native. In woods, copses and shady roadside banks, and with a strong colony on a fixed shingle beach at Dungeness. **181** (211).

Orchis mascula Early-purple orchid © L. Manning

Orchis morio L.   Green-winged Orchid

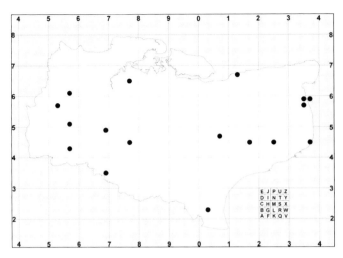

Native. On chalk grassland, damp meadows, roadside verges and churchyards. Has gone from some former sites through land drainage and ploughing, and the Red List places it in the 'Near Threatened' category. **17** (24).

Orchis ustulata L.   Burnt Orchid

Native. Now a very rare plant in Kent (as well as being nationally listed as 'Endangered') and only known in small numbers from Wye Crown TR04T and in two areas near Lydden TR24M & 24S. **3** (4).

Lady Orchid *Orchis purpurea* © R. Moyse

Orchis purpurea Huds.   Lady Orchid

Native. In open woods and scrub, and occasionally roadside banks, on the chalk. Although quite numerous in a few woods in Kent, it is a rare plant outside the county and is listed as 'Endangered'. **44** (48).

[Orchis militaris L.   Military Orchid

The Military Orchid has been claimed from the county in the past, but all herbarium specimens that the writer has checked have proved to be forms of *O. purpurea*, or are records of plants in cultivation in gardens. **0** (0).]

Orchis simia Lam.   Monkey Orchid

Native. With a few scattered old records this plant was re-discovered near Ospringe in 1955 (see Wilks, 1960). It still persists in small numbers in the Ospringe area TQ96Q & 96V. Seed from this site was introduced to the Kent Wildlife Trust reserve at Park Gate Down where, under management, it has spread extensively over the reserve in TR14S & 14T. In the Red List Category, 'Vulnerable'. **4** (3).

Orchis purpurea x Aceras anthropophorum
= Orchiaceras x meilscheimeri (Rouy) P. Fourn.

Native. This hybrid was recorded from somewhere in Kent (see Rose, 1998), but there is a suspicion that this could be the progeny from a deliberate cross by hand pollination.

Orchis simia x Aceras anthropophorum
= X Orchiaceras bergonii (De Nant.) E.G Camus

Native. First discovered at the *Orchis simia* site TQ96Q in 1985, there were two plants present in 1992. **1** (0).

329

Aceras anthropophorum (L.) W.T. Aiton   Man Orchid

Ophrys insectifera L.   Fly Orchid

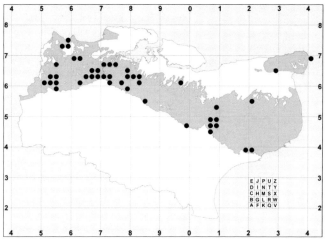

Native. In hedgerows, wood margins, rough grassland, quarries and roadside verges, usually on the chalk. The Man Orchid has disappeared from some former sites through ploughing, spray drift or inappropriate management, reinforcing its national listing as 'Endangered'. **45** (65).

Native. In open woodland, scrub, shaded grassland and quarries on the chalk. In line with the national trend, this plant appears to be in steady decline and is now listed as 'Vulnerable'. **33** (57).

Ophrys insectifera x *sphegodes*
= *O.* x *hybrida* Pokorny

Native. Was recorded growing with both parents on Winchcombe Downs in 1957, but there are no subsequent sightings. **0** (0).

Himantoglossum hircinum (L.) Spreng.   Lizard Orchid

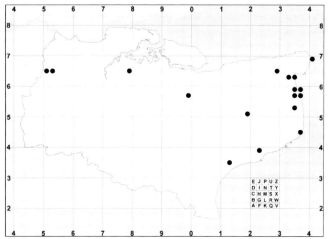

Ophrys sphegodes Mill.   Early Spider-orchid

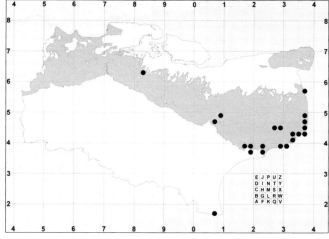

Native. A rare plant that has shown some fluctuation in numbers and distribution in the past. At present it is in very good numbers in the Sandwich Bay area and has appeared in several new localities, so that the present population is probably the highest ever known in the county, although nationally it is listed as 'Near Threatened'. **17** (6).

Native. On open grassland on the chalk, particularly near the coast. **21** (16).

Serapias cordigera L.   Heart-flowered Orchid

Status uncertain. One fine plant in flower at Monkton chalk pit nature reserve TR26X in 1997. The plant had certainly not been introduced, and the chance of seed from any local plants in cultivation is very unlikely. So this was probably from a stray seed blown in from southern Europe, but the plant has now disappeared. **1** (0).

Ophrys sphegodes x *fuciflora* = *O.* x *obscura* Beck

Native. Recorded from a site in East Kent in 1828 where the two parents still grow, but not found during the present survey. **0** (0).

Ophrys apifera Huds. Bee Orchid   *Ophrys fuciflora* (Crantz) Moench   Late Spider-orchid

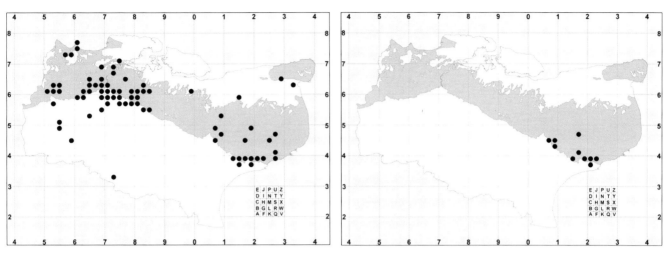

Native. Grassy banks, hedgerows, roadside verges, lawns and coastal dunes on well-drained habitats. Mainly on the chalk, but occasionally on other soils. **75** (101).

Native. Within the British Isles this orchid occurs only in East Kent. It is restricted to a few sites on species-rich short chalk grassland. The population appears fairly stable at present but is listed nationally as 'Vulnerable'. **10** (9).

Ophrys apifera x *fuciflora*
= *O.* x *albertiana* E.G. Camus

Native. Past records from two sites in East Kent, but not seen during the present survey. **0** (0).

Early Spider-orchid *Ophrys sphegodes* © L. Manning

331

Acknowledgements

That completes the account of the flora of Kent together with maps or lists of those plants recorded by the author over the period 1991-2005.   Some plants have been missed through lack of time to get back to every known or reported locality, but it is felt that an even coverage has been obtained over the whole county and the distribution maps do give a reasonable assessment of the present distribution of each species within the county.

All this would not have been possible without the help from many people, and my thanks are due to all of these.   Jim Bevan, Mervyn Brown, Doug Grant, Peter Heathcote and Brian Woodhams have been regular companions throughout the whole of the mapping and have been of great help and wonderful company.   Alec Bull has made regular trips each summer and without this help then an account of the brambles would not have been possible.   Jim Bevan has been of great assistance with the hawkweeds, both in the field and at the end of the mapping in checking herbarium material. Geoffrey Kitchener has accompanied me on at least one excursion each year and has provided great help with the identification of hybrids, particularly within docks and willowherbs. Thanks are also due to Bob Harvey and Bob Tuthill for boat assistance to record in parts of the Medway estuary not reachable by foot. Many other people have accompanied me on several trips or just the odd occasion, and many observers have sent me details of scarce or elusive plants that I have been able to follow up.

My thanks are due again to Geoffrey Kitchener for carefully reading my draft account and making useful suggestions and correcting many typographical errors. Finally my thanks also go to all the staff, past and present, at the Kent and Medway Biological Records Centre, particularly to Steve Smith who convinced me that I should publish this second Atlas, to Lee Manning for constant help throughout with computer problems and particularly to Judith Church for checking my records, producing the maps, the page layout and seeing the atlas through to publication.

Thanks are due to The Wild Flower Society for financial assistance towards the cost of this publication.

List of helpers

Acock, P.J.
Austen-Price, Mrs. G.
Ayers, Mrs. H.
Badmin, J.
Banks, B.
Bevan, J.
Booth, F.
Broad, Mrs. A.
Broughton, D.
Brook, J & G.
Brooks, R.
Brown, M.
Buckingham, Mrs. S.
Bull, A.L.
Cadbury, Dr. C.J.
Cannell, Mrs. B.
Carder, D.
Chambers, D.
Church, Miss J.
Clement, E.J.
Cope, Dr. T.A.

Croft, A.
Dale, J.
Davies, M.
Dowling, C.
Draper, Mrs. J.
Easterbrook, M.
Easterwood, L.
Ferry, Dr. B.W.
FitzGerald, Lady R.
Fray, A.
Fox, K.
Gay, P.H.
Godfrey, Mrs. M.
Grant, D.W.
Green, Prof. B.
Green, P.R.
Griffiths, M.
Harmes, P.A.
Harvey, R.C.
Heathcote, P. & Mrs. P.
Hodd, D.

Holland, D.A. & Mrs. L.K.
Ingram, Prof. G.I.C.
Johnson, D.G.
Joyce, Dr. G.S.
Kersey, Mrs. K.
Kirby, P.
Kitchener, G.D.
Knapp, Dr. A.G.
Knott, Mrs.
Laney, B.
Lang, D.C.
Langton, Mrs. J.M.
Manning, L.
McClintock. D.
Melville, Dr. S.L.
Mills, Miss D.
Morgan, G.H.
Morris, T.
Moyse, R.I.
Page, Mrs M.
Palmer, J.R.

Parker. A.
Parker, S.J.
Pavis, Mrs. R.
Pearman, D.A.
Pitt, Mrs. J.
Powis, Mrs. R.
Poyser, Mrs. S.
Puckett, Dr. J.
Randall, R.D.
Rich, Dr. T.C.G.
Ruck, T.
Rule, Miss L.
Russell, J.
Smith, Mrs. N.
Smith, S.
Southam, M.J.
Spalton, L.M.
Stace, Prof. C.A.
Taplin, J.
Tuthill, R.
Woodhams, B.

References

Bentham, G. & Hooker, J.D. (1924). *Handbook of the British Flora,* edn. vii revised by A.B. Rendle. London: L. Reeve & Co. Ltd.

Burton, R.M. (1983). *Flora of the London area.* London: London Natural History Society.

Cheffings, C.M. & Farrell, L. eds. (2005). The Vascular Plant Red Data List for Great Britain. *Species Status* 7: 1-116. Peterborough: Joint Nature Conservation Committee.

Clapham, A.R., Tutin, T.G. & Warburg, E.F. (1962). *Flora of the British Isles,* edn. 2. Cambridge: Cambridge University Press.

Clement, E.J. (1980). Aliens and Adventives. *B.S.B.I. News* 25: 10.

Clement, E.J. & Foster, M.C. (1994). *Alien Plants of the British Isles.* London: Botanical Society of the British Isles.

Edgington, J. (2008). *Asplenium septentrionale* in Kent - native or alien? *B.S.B.I. News. 107: 16-18.*

Green, B. H. (2008). *Natural Kent: an introduction to the habitats, wildlife and wild places of the county.* Seaford: SB Publications.

Hanbury, F.J. & Marshall, E.S. (1899). *Flora of Kent.* London.

Kent, D.H. (1992). *List of Vascular Plants of the British Isles.* London: Botanical Society of the British Isles.

Kent Habitat Survey. 2003. Kent County Council.

Kitchener, G. (1996). Some recent Kentish Botanical Records. *Bulletin of the Kent Field Club* 41: 41.

Lousley, J.E. (1964). Plant notes. *Proc. B.S.B.I.* 5 (4): 338-341.

McVeigh, A., Carey, J.E. & Rich, T.C.G. (2005). Chiltern Gentian, *Gentianella germanica* (Willd.) Börner (Gentianaceae) in Britain: distribution and current status. *Watsonia* 25: 339-367.

Palmer, J.R. (1977). Oil-milling Adventive Plants in North-west Kent 1973-6. *Transactions of the Kent Field Club* 6 (2): 85-90.

Palmer, J.R. (1981). *Ziziphora capitata* L. – new to the British Isles. *B.S.B.I. News* 28: 25.

Palmer, J.R. (1989). Field meeting report, Kent - October 1st and 2nd [1988]. *Wild Flower Magazine* 414: 13-14.

Philp, E.G. (1982). *Atlas of the Kent Flora.* Maidstone: Kent Field Club.

Preston, C.D., Pearman, D.A. & Dines, T.D. eds. (2002). *New Atlas of the British and Irish Flora.* Oxford: OUP.

Pugsley, H.W. (1948). A prodromus of the British *Hieracia. Journal of the Linnean Society of London (Botany)* 54: 1-356.

Rickard, M. (1994). Ferns – a case history, in Perry, A.R. & Ellis, R.G. eds. *The Common Ground of Wild & Cultivated Plants.* Cardiff: National Museum of Wales.

Rose, F. (1998). A new orchid hybrid for Britain – X *Orchiaceras meilsheimeri (Aceras anthropophora* x *Orchis purpurea). B.S.B.I. News* 79: 19-20.

Rumsey, F.J. (2007). An early specimen of *Cystopteris diaphana* (Bory) Blasdell supports its native status. *Watsonia* 26: 489-490.

Sell, P. & Murrell, G. (2006). *Flora of Great Britain and Ireland, 4, Campanulaceae – Asteraceae.* Cambridge: Cambridge University Press.

Sell. P.D. & West, C. (1965). Key to the *Hieracia* Recorded from Kent (Vice Counties 15 and 16*). Transactions of the Kent Field Club* 3 (1): 50-54.

Stace, C.A. ed. (1975). *Hybridization and the flora of the British Isles.* London: Academic Press.

Stace, C.A. (1991). *New Flora of the British Isles.* Cambridge: Cambridge University Press.

Stace, C.A. (1997). *New Flora of the British Isles,* edn. 2. Cambridge: Cambridge University Press.

Stace, C.A., Ellis, R.G., Kent, D.H. & McCosh, D.J. (2003). *Vice-county Census Catalogue of the Vascular Plants of Great Britain.* London: Botanical Society of the British Isles.

Wilks, H.M. (1960). The re-discovery of *Orchis simia* Lam. in Kent. *Transactions of the Kent Field Club* 1 (2): 50-55.

Index

337